SUCH
A
LIFE

by EDITH La ZEBNIK

G.K.HALL &CO.
Boston, Massachusetts
1979

Library of Congress Cataloging in Publication Data

LaZebnik, Edith.
  Such a life.

  Large print ed.
  1. LaZebnik, Edith. 2. Jews in Russia--Biography.
3. Russia--Biography. 4. Large type books.
I. Title.
[DS135.R95L265 1979] 947'.004'924 [B] 78-26782
  ISBN 0-8161-6662-5

Published in Large Print by arrangement with William Morrow
and Company, Inc.

Set in Compugraphic 18 pt English Times

My daughter worked her fingers to help us make the English: Jeanette Bernhard, her husband a doctor.

And I also want to thank my son Jack for being so smart and so helpful.

1

Who can tell what life will bring? My children, six I have, God bless them in good health, they tell me I am seventy-two years old, a mistake, because Sam I married when I was sixteen, and you figure it out, he is eight years older than me, so I am sixty-six. But I don't want to argue. Why should I wear my heart out with seventy-two, sixty-six, who knows? Except for one or two, I am the only family left from the Eisenbergs.

My father, ah, my father, how he fell in love, such an alter kluger he was, nobody can know now but me. A gentleman! He lived to a hundred and ten years old. I'm telling you the truth! To the end, he was a handsome man, a long white beard he combed every day and washed, it shouldn't turn yellow. I was his favorite from fourteen children, eight girls and six sons. David Eisenberg. Dauvidel they called him—little David. Nu, he wasn't so tall.

From the beginning in Minsker Gubernya, my father was a man even when he was a boy. The oldest from ten children, he worked with *his* father, Gershon Eisenberg. They used to travel to Kiev with Gentiles who would drive the barge, and they would buy many things— flour, sugar, yeast, cereals, salt—to bring home to sell in the stores. They would stay two months and then travel again to Kiev and bring back the same things. My father would always come with nice presents. My grandfather would buy him something every time. He loved him very much because my father always obeyed him. Is that a son?

My grandfather and my father used to go to Minsk or Odessa, and that's the way their life went. My grandmother was very pretty and always liked to dress and fix her hair in the latest styles. She didn't do like the orthodox, chop her hair short and put on a plain wig so she shouldn't appeal to men, strangers. You see, she was modern, such a pretty woman, sometimes a ribbon in her hair, even a red ribbon, a yellow, naturally in the house. Outside, a babushka. Her name was Leah. My grandfather loved her very much. When he used to come from Kiev, he always brought her something to wear. "Leah!" he would say, standing with a surprise in the front door. "My pretty one!" She would come to him with the wooden bowl in her arm, still chopping the liver. "I saw you in the market. Yes, you were there, in this blouse."

"Never," she said, but she laughed with her eyes.

"Don't you dare," he said to her. "You see? I bought you." And the blouse he held up for her, a white blouse, light like a feather, with a design in the little beads, red, blue, with such a nice tiny lace collar, you should see, it would make soft your heart. They were happy people!

Finally, my father was thirteen, very handsome, a prince, bluish-green eyes, such curly hair! And very good, a good boy, and he looked older. Like a man, the way he held himself straight, and he

3

would smile like a man, with life behind him. Already, the people started to call him David, no longer Dauvidel.

In another town, not far from Minsk, lived a rich Jew. His name was Shmuel. He used to come to my grandfather's to buy things for his grocery store. This Shmuel had five children, three sons and two daughters. His oldest daughter was a very sickly girl. At that time she was nineteen. Like a stick with shoulders, her dress hanging from her neck, and her skin yellow. Yes! Maybe she had a sickness. Who knows? Maybe now the doctors would find something. But at that time anybody could be a doctor. Nu? She was dying.

When Shmuel saw my father for the first time, aha, something maybe, a hope. "How long since he is Bar Mitzvah?" Shmuel asked.

My grandfather laughed. "Not yet!"

"Not yet?" Shmuel with his big eyebrows on top of his head. "What are you telling me?"

Grandfather raised a shoulder. "Why should I lie to you?"

Shmuel, like a man a little bit crazy in his head, did a tiny dance in front of David. "By me, he looks older, nineteen, twenty. A grown man! With such red hair—a mensch!" And he danced in front of David, who looked to one side, a good boy, yes, a beauty, a nice head of red hair a girl should have, curls he could hardly comb, but always he combed his hair neatly and was nicely dressed. Very clean. My grandfather always bought him the best clothes. My father always listened to him. Whatever my grandfather told him to do, he would do it, and that's the reason he would always buy him the best.

So, Shmuel said to my grandfather, "Do you know, Gershon, your son appeals to me."

"He's a good boy. I am proud," Grandfather said. "You will honor us by his Bar Mitzvah."

"My pleasure. I will come with my wife and my oldest daughter."

"In two weeks."

"In two weeks." He nodded at David like a wise old man, like he thought it's good, and he ran out in a hurry to tell his wife.

Shmuel's daughter was always sick, from the time she was born. Now, she was worse from day to day (What can you do when God wants it?) and Shmuel brought a big doctor from Germany. He examined her and called her father and told him she was very sick. "What can I do? I can do nothing for her."

"What do you mean nothing?" Shmuel yelled at him. "Don't I pay you? What do I pay you for? From Germany yet."

"If maybe she has a different life," the doctor said.

"How can she have a different life? Where can we go?"

In Russia then the Jews had to stay in one place. The Pale of Settlement was like another land in the middle of the country, like an island by itself, no one should go out. And this is where the Jews had to live.

"Maybe," said the doctor, "if she should get married, maybe this would help. I can do nothing for her."

So Shmuel thought of Gershon's son. So, she was a little older. It didn't matter.

The main thing was to save her. He stood there thinking, and he called his wife, "Hannah, I have a match making. Somebody from the highest window, a prize, a diamond, a boy like gold. Gershon's son. His name is David, and we are invited to his Bar Mitzvah. We will take our daughter Elke."

So they dressed her in the best clothes, with a coat with fur inside. That's the way they dressed in Russia many years ago. She had big eyes, hollow, a skeleton. Like a piece of yellow wood, she looked as though somebody pulled from it the bark, shiny, hard, skin over bone. She couldn't smile by herself. Always they had to talk her into it.

David didn't know what was going on; my grandfather and Shmuel talked. My grandmother, what did she know? She saw on the day of the Bar Mitzvah they came in a fancy carriage with four beautiful black horses and a driver. My grandparents took them into the house, where there was a great tumult from all the children. But it was not a big party. In Russia they didn't make such big Bar Mitzvahs like here in America.

The whole family went to shul, the synagogue. Like always, the men downstairs, the women upstairs, the men with the yarmulkes, the women with empty heads. They prayed, they went through the whole business, but, when the rabbi took out the Torah, David went to the altar, put the Torah on his shoulder, took it to the table, and there he opened up the scroll and sang the portion perfectly.

When they came back home there was wine, vodka, and cake, and David and the girl sat down at the head of the table — David, yes, because it was his day, but he couldn't understand why the girl. He was not bashful, and so he could smile at her, but the girl did not know what to do with her hands. She sat with her chin touching her chest, a long chin, such a bone for a chest.

"Mazel tov! Mazel tov!" the fathers called, and everybody raised their glasses and drank to David, the new man. Now, you see, he was part of the community. Now he could sit with the alter kluger in the synagogue, even sometimes by the east wall, and now he could make from a minyan, he could hold the Torah and read. So he bowed a little bit to everybody, he raised his glass, he drank to himself.

"Business!" Grandfather cried out. He ran behind his chair and pushed everybody else's chair to the table, except David and the girl. "Business, business! Everybody!" And he raised his arms. "Go to the other room. Never mind, go, go." Like sheep he pushed them, and he ran back to David and the girl and held his hands against them. "Not you. No, sit. David." No more Dauvidel. "Sit with Elke. Talk, talk things over, everything should be all right."

So they were sitting alone. She sat like a doll with her neck broken. He sat hitting his fingernails against the glass. What's going on? He didn't care to look at her. And neither one spoke a word to the other. Maybe she would like to say something, but she was crying a little bit, one drop from her eye. David? He couldn't understand. He was thinking. What's happening? Does it

9

mean something?

In the other room sat Shmuel with Grandmother and Grandfather and Elke's mother. They drank wine and said mazel tov to each other and should be with luck. But that was not all. Grandfather said to Shmuel, "Now that we have drunk L'chayim, what is with the dowry?" Grandfather knew that Shmuel was a wealthy man.

Shmuel said, "I will give a couple hundred rubles and two years' room and board." That meant David didn't have to do anything, just eat and sit and learn the Torah.

Grandfather Gershon said, "That won't go, brother. Your daughter is nineteen years old and my son is thirteen. I want a thousand rubles." What could Shmuel do when his oldest child was so sick and the doctor said maybe she should marry? He had to give in to Grandfather. They wrote the engagement, broke a dish, and even danced.

So they agreed that the wedding should be the Shabbos after Shevuoth, and they said good-bye to everyone. Grandfather came inside the room. "Nu?" he said to David. "What do you think?" David didn't say anything. What could he say? "This beautiful young lady is a pride to her family," Grandfather said, and the hand he put on the back of her head almost covered it. Like he was touching a flower to see if it's got a bee in it, he shook her head a little bit, gently. "She's all right. She's all right. She'll be all right. She'll make a fine one, you'll see. She'll be better than anybody knows."

But the bride-to-be never said a word and David did not know what happened. Then they got into their droshky with the four black horses and the driver and they all went back to their home in Minsk.

Came the day of the wedding, Grandfather told David he should put on his nicest clothes. "For what?" David asked. "It's the middle of the week."

Grandfather gave such a shout, "Do what your father tells you. You must have respect for your father!" So David did what his father told him. That was what David always did. He never argued.

The whole family traveled to the

wedding. When they got to Shmuel's house they saw so many people that they wondered how they could all fit inside. He was a wealthy man. But Shmuel took them straight to the synagogue, and when David saw the canopy with the flowers over it and the silk covers and the rabbi waiting, he looked for the wedding couple. "Who — ?" He saw everybody looking at him and he saw Elke. Her face was covered with a veil. "What's going on?" David asked.

"Today is your wedding," his father said.

David's face was like a sheet. His eyes, oy, they were like two pieces stone. He opened his mouth, but nothing would come out, like he was choking to death, all the blood went from his head. His father got mad. "Don't ask!" Such a face, red like a beet. "Do what we tell you to do!" David tried to hold back but he started to cry like a child.

"Dauvidel," his mother said, "it's for your happiness. You must be the scholar for the family. Dauvidel, my son, trust in God. It's for the best." But with her eyes she threw knives at her husband and she hissed at him like a goose. "You see? Secrets you keep."

Grandfather didn't say anything.

David was broken, and when his parents took him to the canopy, the rabbis waiting in their robes, the people waiting in their seats, he was shaking and he didn't see where he was going. He stood under the canopy, and then Elke's parents brought her, like a ghost, next to David. Then the first rabbi read, and the cantor sang from the book, such a voice, like an angel, and the fathers read. Nu, you know, it's a song, baruch atoh adenoy, not like you read from a newspaper, but happiness. But David was deaf in both ears and Elke was shaking like a leaf, so weak, and the rabbi gave the glass wine to David. But he could hardly drink, it was like vinegar to him. And then to Elke, who raised her veil to drink and showed a face like it had no eyes and no cheeks, like today the skinny ones with the dresses, the models. So, they waited and the rabbi said to David, "Nu? Break it." Grandfather grabbed the glass and put it under the heel of David's foot,

and he gave David such a push, such a
hold on his leg, and the glass broke.
Mazel tov. Mazel tov. Everybody shouting
and crying and David, he felt like a baby
in the forest, lost at nighttime, owls
making *hoo! hoo!* and the wolves
laughing, crickets like violins in the house,
everybody climbing on him. Mazel tov!

Finally, they all went to Shmuel's house
for the reception. The tables, loaded with
the best — vodka, wines, fish, hot challeh,
meatballs, beet horseradish, black bread,
anything you can think of. David and
Elke sat on chairs next to each other but a
hundred miles apart; both looking at
nothing, at the floor. The people laughed
and danced the way they did in the old
country. Did you see me dance? Oh, how
I danced! Hands over the head, clap clap,
and the feet like guns, so fast you can't
see them, the heels on the wooden floor
like ten men with hammers. Round and
round, the men and women, the boys and
girls, then line up, side to side, back and
forth they all go, grabbing hands, spinning
around, letting go, grabbing again — oy!
A dance!

But David and Elke, they sat like stones. Finally, the party was over, everybody stopped for mazel tov, to shake the hand. "A catch, a catch, my boy!" And they all went, all except the parents and their children. Both mothers came to David and Elke. "Now," Grandmother said to him. "Go." They took them by the hand to a small room with two little beds. A little push inside. For a minute Grandmother looked at David, tears in her eyes. "Dauvidel," she said. He looked at her with tears, too, big ones, the eyes, like he was calling to her, begging her. But she closed the door.

David didn't look at Elke. He just sat on one little bed. In a little while she sat on the other bed. They looked at their hands in their laps. The moon looked like a teardrop in the window, shining, shaking in the sky. They sat. Neither one said a word. Finally, when the moon was gone from the window, Elke gave a jump, a shake. She woke up. But after a while her head went down more and more, and she very slowly went to one side, to the fancy cover on the bed, and fell asleep. When

David noticed what she had done, he also lay down and went to sleep.

In the morning both mothers came to the door. Elke's mother gave a tiny push, it opened, they peeked inside. Grandmother Leah wanted to see if the daughter was healthy — to see if she was kosher. You understand? What did they see? Both David and Elke still sleeping in their clothes, each one on a different bed.

"Ah!" Elke's mother gave a cry like she stuck herself with a needle. Quick, she ran to tell her husband. Grandmother looked at David a little, and then at Elke, and, shaking her head, she laughed a little bit, silently. "Dauvidel," she said. Then she went to tell her husband.

The two men came to see the way the children were sleeping in their clothes on separate beds. Grandfather, who was a very smart man, said, "If not today, tomorrow. What's the hurry? You will see. They will bring us a lot of grandchildren." But Elke's parents knew that their child did not have long to live.

The young couple was living at Shmuel's house, and every day David went to the yeshiva. One summer day when he returned to the house he came straight into the living room. The sun was coming through the windows on the west side; it was very, very still, dust in the windows, in the air, the fine dust you see only in the sun. So quiet he could hear a little dog far away. It was like everybody was sleeping, nobody in the house. But Elke was on the sofa where they brought her so she could rest and watch, and they could feed her so she shouldn't be so lonely. Elke was by herself in the living room with her face looking up. Maybe she was watching the dust in the sunlight, but she didn't blink. "Elke?" David said. "I'm home." She didn't answer. "How do you feel?" He was polite. But they were never man and wife. He never forced her. "Elke?" But she was quiet. He went to her and he saw she was dead. Where was everybody? What to do? He went to the kitchen, where Elke's mother was cooking.

"David," she said to him with a nice smile. "Your favorite I am making — kreplach. A taste maybe?" She held up a spoon to his mouth. "Taste a little. Maybe it needs something." She touched his lips with the spoon filled with kreplach.

"Elke," he said.

"What, Elke?" She was smiling, but all of a sudden she looked at him and dropped the spoon on the floor. "Elke!" She put her hand to her face, a clap! It left a mark on her cheek. "Elke!" Screaming, she ran into the living room. David didn't know what to do. Pretty soon he heard the mother crying my God, my God, and running, somebody coming, and the neighbors, and then he heard the father like a lion call out, "Elke!" and the father crying oy! oy! like he was mad at God. David was very frightened.

He went to his room and put his things in a cardboard suitcase, only what he brought with him to the house, and then he went outside to the street, walked toward the east, out of town, and into the country. All night he walked. His mind was not working, like it was asleep, so he couldn't see how he was going. Then the morning came, people on the road, carts with horses, drivers yelling he should get out of the way.

Finally, in the afternoon, very thin, sick, and hungry, he came to his village, went inside his house, and collapsed. His mother asked, "What? What? Dauvidel! What is?" On her knees, she took his head in her lap and held him, rocked him in her arms like a baby. "What did they do to you?" Then Grandfather came in from the other room. "Dauvidel, Dauvidel," Leah was crying. Grandfather said nothing. He picked him up and carried him to the bedroom. "He's dying," Grandmother Leah said, but Grandfather brought tea from the samovar, gave David a sip, two sips, and put a cube sugar in David's mouth and then more tea.

"He's all right," Grandfather said. "Nu?" he asked David. "What happened?" David couldn't speak.

"They threw him out," Grandmother said. "They threw him out from the house."

"Why should they do that?"

"Who knows why? You should tell me why. You, who put him in there like a piece of merchandise."

"Don't decide before you know what's going on."

"My son is dying in bed and you don't decide!" She ran outside without even a babushka or a shawl and grabbed a wagon and a horse from the stable and jumped on by herself. She gave the horse a good whip and drove as fast as the horse could go. Grandfather yelled after her but she heard nothing. Like a madwoman she drove the horse toward the west. No one could stand in her way. Other wagons had to fall off the road and the people had to watch out or she would knock them down. Like a wind she drove to the in-laws. By the time she got there the poor horse was shaking, his breath like smoke, as if he were on fire.

She ran into the house, noises already coming from her mouth, her arms over her head. Into the living room she came, and then she stopped. The whole family was sitting. "What are you doing?" she cried. "God!" Because she saw something had happened. Elke was lying in the wooden coffin already with the holes made for the worms to come, and everybody was crying, rocking this way and that way, covered over with shawls, the men with the lapels ripped, the women knocking their heads with their fists, and they were saying prayers, singing them in low voices.

Elke's mother told Grandmother Leah the whole story. "Why didn't you tell us before?" Grandmother asked. "Before we took our handsome son and mixed his head? Now he is so sick. Oh, vey's mir, what have I done with my dearest boy? He didn't even know how to be with a woman." She started to cry bitterly. No, she couldn't listen anymore, she couldn't look at Elke, she had to go back home, broken. Slowly she went home, with the horse walking like he was going to fall down, so slow, so tired.

Grandfather Gershon was waiting for her. She told him everything. He went to the bed and said to David, "Forgive me, my son. I sold you for a thousand rubles." And he cried.

David lay very sick for six months. From hunger and from sitting in the yeshiva learning the Gemara. It was very damp there and he had become chilled. He used to eat once a day when he came from the yeshiva, only to find Elke in bed. He was so young, and he did not understand why he had to be there with her.

2

From day to day he was beginning to feel better, and he was getting out of bed thinking what to do. In those days people got older faster. Why? Because they had to, because they were supposed to. At thirteen a boy was a man and at fourteen he was already making a living. Or he was a scholar in the yeshiva or the synagogue, in the basement where all the scholars study and think. Also because they didn't have as much as nowadays — to be poor is a lesson, too. A poor boy is a little old man. So, when David was thinking what to do, it meant how he should work, how he should support himself and help his family — they needed his help, not the other way around. Today, well, times change. Who can help it? The world doesn't stand still. You have to live.

Finally, he turned fourteen. Then his father asked him, "Do you want to go with me on the barge?"

"It's been so long since I last went," David said. "Yes, I would like to."

Grandfather told him he was going to Kiev to buy supplies to sell to the retailers in our town. By us were only Jewish stores. From the villages the Gentiles came on Sundays to buy in the Jewish stores that made a good living. When a Gentile didn't have enough money, he would bring eggs, potatoes, a chicken, sometimes even a little calf. That's the way the Jewish people were living with the Gentile people, very good. And that's the way time went, and David and his father kept on going together.

Grandfather Gershon and Grandmother Leah, they did not mention getting married to their son. When did he see girls? On the street, like a good Jew, he kept his head down so he shouldn't notice or think of them. He was walking to shul, saying the prayers, his hands behind his back like a mensch, a scholar. And everybody was walking to one side so they shouldn't bump him, because he was saying God's words and they shouldn't insult God. To tell the truth, he didn't see a girl who appealed to him. His father and mother started to worry: Was he going to be an old man without a wife and children? A good Jew is not a single man.

When David was eighteen he said to his father, "Pa, why should two of us go to Warsaw on the train? We are paying for two tickets and expenses. One should be enough. I will go by myself." He was looking at his father for him to say yes — never would David force him.

"Why not?" Grandfather said.

David was very happy he was going alone for the first time. That day he even woke up before his mother and said his prayers. Oh, prayers, when he was waking, before he washed himself, after, even when he was going to the bathroom — you should forgive the expression. And prayers before breakfast. In the end he was ready. A wet kiss from his mother. His father gave a nod — a nod yes, but a little bit no, too — and David was leaving, walking to the train station. Soon the train was giving a whistle, very high, and black smoke was coming, a mountain. When it stopped, the doors went to one side, sliding.

David stepped in the train. He gave the wicker seat a blow from his mouth so it should be clean, and he sat down. The whistle, the conductor yelling, a little bell from the engine ding-donging, like a teakettle bubbling, and the train was leaving.

Not far from him sat a young girl with red hair like his, with two long braids, and a face, my, my, a peach, peaches and cream, a beauty! She appealed to him. He couldn't take his eyes off from her and she was blushing. She looked outside, with her eyes turning toward him, and she blushed every time. Finally, from his suitcase David took out two apples. With one hand he held out an apple for the girl. He nodded, "Take. It's all right, I've got two. Take, take. It won't poison you." He could smile, such white teeth, sparkles, like stars, and a little red mustache he now had. How could she refuse?

Both were eating the red apples, juicy

little apples, not big and dry like today. When you eat with someone, it's very close. Didn't they look at each other when they were biting? Pretty soon they began to laugh and a little piece fell from David's mouth. She had white teeth, too, tiny red lips, and two pretty dimples. In the old country a woman should have two dimples, shows she's healthy, not skinny. Finally, David was sitting next to her.

"Where are you going?"

"To Warsaw," she said.

"Fine! Me, too. For my father, on business. We are buying different things — cloth, leather, buttons, needles, everything you can think of — to bring back to sell to the stores. We don't get rich, but it's a living. I'm a partner with my father. He does the business at home."

"My father has a cloth store in Moozer," she said. "Always he goes to Warsaw to buy materials, but he is sick in bed. His leg bothers him, we don't know what, a cramp, a soreness. The doctor gives medicine, pills even, but it doesn't help. The only thing helps is staying in bed. After a few days he is all right again.

But now he needs cloth. The holidays are coming, people are making clothes. Mama can't go, she's got little ones. It's up to me. They don't know what to do but I say what's to worry? I am sixteen, I can take care of myself. Plenty of times I went with Pa."

"You are a very brave girl," David said.

Again she was blushing. "They wouldn't like it, they should see me now." She laughed like a bell, and like a bell her head was swinging, too. "They made me promise I wouldn't talk to strangers."

"I wouldn't harm you," David said. "I would die first."

She looked at him, close, but shy.

Warsaw came. They hardly noticed until they saw more houses, bigger ones, apartments, stores, and more people, everybody in a hurry, horses and buggies, soldiers and policemen, and they both pressed their noses against the windowpane like they were never there before. The train stopped and the people all grabbed their suitcases and bumped into each other. David stood by the girl but somebody shoved in between. "Oy," David said, and they were separated. "Do you see?" he tried to say, but she couldn't hear him. She thought he was behind her and she went off from the train. The people were pushing and running, like in a fire. Everybody was going in different directions, such a tumult! David looked for her. My goodness, he didn't even know her name! What was she, how could he find her, what could he holler to anybody? Why didn't they tell each other their names? Foolish! They were talking too close, he was looking at her like in a dream, and she talked, how she lived in Moozer in Minsker Gubernya with her parents, and she was working in the store, fine goods, clothes, all kinds materials. But they didn't tell each other their names. Oy, God, he thought, I lost her!

He turned around like a Chasid — a Jew who dances, out of his mind to dance to God — and he bumped someone — red hair, teeth, stars, eyes looking at his. Yes, it was! Oy, so happy he was, he grabbed her and gave her such a hug! "How can we talk," he asked her, "and not even know who is who?'' He held her shoulders so he could see her face. ''I am David Eisenberg.''

''I am Tzeepeh Shimin.''

So close they were, eyes staring at eyes, laughing, how it is when you feel so happy you are laughing for no reason. Let them laugh. They could find out later when to cry.

David held her by the hand so this time they would stay together. They knew from before what to do. To save money they walked to the hotel, the same when his father was there with him, and she, too. The Jewish traveling people came together. Inside they didn't hold hands, and both were blushing like fire when they went to sign the paper for the rooms. One room for David, one room for Tzeepeh, singles, not even the same floor. Who cared? The clerk from the hotel? Why should he care? But they were shy people, behaving. Nobody had to worry then.

They both went out together to eat, and when she had to buy, David went with her, and when he had to buy, she went with him. It's a big city, Warsaw, with the buildings that make you look up, it gives you a kvitch in the back. But what were they looking at? At one the other. In the streets, beggars with no legs, little children holding shoeshine boxes, and all kinds pushcarts, the old men with the long beards down to the chest full of grease and dirt, and they're yelling right in your ear: "Vegetables! Good, nice vegetables! Melons!" Comes a man with glass for windows on his back, carrying it in a frame bigger than himself. "Glass man! Glass man! Glass!" Who else? Everybody by himself a business — shoes, pins and needles, pots with pans, fish, chickens, ducks, a goose, the whole business in the hands. What was this to the young boy and girl when they only saw each other? Music, beautiful paintings, ballerinas, such a wonderful world, happiness!

Finally, they had to leave. Now, on the train, they sat close together, hand in hand. They looked, they smiled, but what could they say? They talked about writing letters to each other. David had to get out from the train first. A long time he held her hand, and he looked and she looked, with tears in her eyes, but happy, sad, too. That's how it was. "I will write," David said, and the train was already huffing so he had to jump off. She couldn't get the window open. So she waved to him and he waved and yelled to her, and it was over.

At home he showed his father what he had bought — good materials, good things for the stores. Grandfather was pleased. His son, a mensch! The mother worried so much she hadn't slept. "Didn't you eat anything?" she asked. "What did you eat? Come. Come." She wouldn't leave him alone. He had to eat so she would be satisfied.

Right away he wrote a letter:

Dear Tzeepeh,
How are you? I am fine except my thoughts will not go away from you and the way we walked down to the river where the trees went up over us like God's arms and his fingers let little birds fly over to say hello to us. Now I walk by our little stream all by myself and the crows stay in the

branches, cawing insults at me. "Crazy boy, wearing out your shoes kicking stones!" What are you doing now? Yesterday I picked delicious apples from the tree. Must I go so far to give one to you? Now it is your turn to write me. With prayers for your good health, may God go with you.

David Eisenberg

To him she wrote, too:

Dear David Eisenberg,
I am well, thank you, and hope the same for you. I am working very hard at my father's store as usual. Sometimes he lets me go free for an hour or two, and I run to the river. Thank God it is not too far away. But it is not a large one either, so pretty soon it bores me. In our town everything is like dead, God forbid. There is nothing to do. I wish my father would send me to the city again to buy. If he does, I will write you and hope your father will send

you, too. May God help us in our dreams. I will write you again if you will write me again. God be with you.
Tzeepeh Shimin

David felt lonesome for her. He got very nice letters from Tzeepeh and he wrote nice letters back, and that's the way time went by. There was plenty to do each day. Work with his father, study — he didn't give that up — prayers, shul. He had to argue over the Talmud with the scholars. What means this? What means that? "Thou shalt not cast stones in a blind man's way." And who owns the ox when another ox puts a horn inside? Questions, questions. His mind was with his heart, so sometimes he was far away when somebody asked, and they laughed at him: "His head is in the clouds. Dauvidel. Maybe an angel is carrying you to heaven for a personal talk with God? Tell us when the Messiah will come. What does he say?" But he didn't care. What he thought was better than their words. That's how much he was in love.

Two more times his father let him go to

Warsaw. He met Tzeepeh, they sat together, they spent as much time as they could with one another. The best thing they liked was finding a beautiful park with statues, all kinds flowers, and big ponds, like lakes almost. They would sit on the benches, with no one to bother them, watching the children push the little boats in the water. When two people are in love, all of a sudden they see children; they dream of how they will be married and have children, how wonderful the little girl says "Papa," and how the little boy holds his mama's hand. Thank God they don't know yet the heartaches and the hard work in having children. If they knew, the world would be without people.

A year passed. One Friday night, at the table with his parents and all his brothers and sisters, when Grandfather made Kiddush, cut the challeh, and gave each child a piece to make a prayer, David stood up but could hardly speak with his full mouth or swallow as he said to everyone, "I beg you to be quiet." Everyone was looking at him to see what he would say. It was hard for him. He was swallowing and swallowing. Finally, "I have a girl. Very pretty girl with red hair." And he told his parents how they became acquainted.

His father was pulling on his beard. "Child, my son, you don't know her parents. Maybe they are common people."

Soft, quiet, David answered, "She is educated, intelligent."

David was more modern, his father was thinking. God changes things; he doesn't like to sit in one place. All right, if God wants.

Then Leah said to her son, "My child, we want to see if she's healthy. Let her stay with us, and then we'll see."

So David wrote a letter: Come, his parents want to meet her. She wrote to him: All right, she'll come with her mother. Her mother's name is Basha, and her father's is Moishe. She had three sisters and one brother.

Two weeks later, on a warm day, David waited at the little depot. He walked, he couldn't sit still. How would it be? How would he say hello, how are you? Was that all? The train was late. Nu, that's

36

how it is. Like a little old man he walked, his hands behind his back. He bent his head, he rocked this way, and that way, like he's davening — praying — back and forth, back and forth. Ah! The whistle! This time is screamed like a woman. So! So! The train, black smoke, a cloud. Maybe they were not coming. Maybe he had the wrong day.

But they hopped from the wagon car, Tzeepeh and her mother, a pretty woman with a sheitel — a wig, religious, so men shouldn't look at her and she shouldn't appeal to them. It was the mother who talked; David and Tzeepeh didn't know what to say, only to smile so hard it hurt their faces, and they blushed, both, and everything made them laugh a little bit — a tree, a dog, the horse going too slow, too fast.

"So it's David," the mother said. "By me, you look like a nice boy. By Tzeepeh, I should expect maybe an angel, you're so perfect. Go in good health, God be blessed. We had to be sure. An ordinary girl, it doesn't matter; but with Tzeepeh, she is very sensitive, very particular. We raised her to the best, everything the hand can hold. I didn't want to come. The boy should bring his parents to visit the girl. But Tzeepeh got it in her head she had to come, so all right."

When they came by the house, Grandmother Leah saw right away Tzeepeh's mother was religious, and Grandfather was blessing, thank God, it's good. And everybody was how-do-you-doing, how's by you, God be blessed, come have a cup tea. The house was spotless, not one drop dust, the best things on the table, the cloth so white you couldn't look at it, everything shining. They sat and drank and talked. About what? The relatives, who was who, and Leah was bragging about David, what a good boy he was, a scholar, never complaining, a hard worker and a thinker. "Oy, he thinks!" she said. "I don't know from what, the deepest. He studies the Talmud every day, he doesn't miss, such a kluger! From all the rest, he is the smartest."

"My Tzeepeh, God be praised, if she wasn't a girl, she could be a boy, so intelligent, so much education she's got. Nothing but the best. Tzeepeh, show. Read something. Even the Gemara she can read. Maybe it's too much for a girl to read, but we want for her nothing but the best. Tzeepeh!" The poor girl had tears in her eyes, she was so embarrassed; she ran out to the kitchen. David went after her.

"Don't cry," he said, and he put his arms around her. She laid her head on his chest. "You don't have to read."

"I can!" She pushed him away, like she was mad all of a sudden. "I know how to read even the Gemara. I learned better than my brother. You shouldn't say I don't read."

"I didn't say, I didn't say." David held out his hands. "I believe you. What's wrong? Did I do something?"

"It's terrible. In front of everybody she tells me. Show, show, Tzeepeh, how you can read, like I'm a child and everybody is watching so they can say, look how she is, without a brain in her head, like a stupid girl. What do they expect?"

"They like you," David said. "They love you. Tzeepeh, you have nothing to worry about. Who cares you should read or not read? It doesn't matter."

"I can so read!" she yelled. And she cried. Who can figure? She was nervous, she worried what kind impression she'd make on the parents. Maybe she thought she wasn't good enough. At least David was thinking maybe that's the reason. So he pulled her to himself, even when she tried to turn away, even putting her arms in front of her. He pulled her and held her and pretty soon she stopped. Before you knew it, she held him, too, and both pressed their lips to cheeks.

Of course, they stayed over Shabbos. The religious Jews don't travel on the Sabbath. It's forbidden. They went to the synagogue all day, no work, nothing, not even to make the meals. You know how it is. Friday, before sundown, the mother and the daughters cook everything. Then, a Gentile comes in, for pay, on Shabbos to warm the food and serve the meals.

All the time Grandmother Leah couldn't take her eyes off Tzeepeh. She didn't appeal to her. But she remained quiet, afraid to say a word to her son. After the second Shabbos David was traveling with his mother to Moozer, and they, too, were staying over the Shabbos.

The girl's father, a Jew with a long beard and long payess, that means sideburns, very orthodox, said that David appealed to him, and he listened to David read the Gemara. "Ah! It's a pleasure to hear. How did it happen you should meet all by yourselves? God wants it. There's no question. Look, I'm saving. I don't even have to pay the matchmaker." He laughed, a good joke. He had enough money, he didn't have to worry. "So, now we must write the engagement. We won't put it off. Not a second." He sat and wrote David's father he should come right away.

He came as soon as possible. The two fathers greeted each other. "Nu?" said Moishe. "They arranged for themselves, God be willing. You see how the children are these days? Do they need us? Are we good for something?" That night they sat and made the engagement agreement — one year room and board with five hundred rubles dowry. Grandmother Leah took off the watch on her neck and put it on Tzeepeh's with a pin to the dress. They broke a dish, drank vodka, and wished mazel tov. That's the way the evening passed. It looked like David was very happy.

So, again the canopy in the synagogue, the rabbis saying the prayers, the cantor singing, only this time David took the wine and drank. It tasted good, and he broke the glass with his foot so everybody should hear it, and they were married.

They went to live with her parents. Nice, plenty to eat, with a room to themselves. Tzeepeh still helped in her father's store. She got up before David and wanted to fix his breakfast. She jumped from the bed and the cold floor made her laugh on her toes. David liked to sleep late; in the early morning he especially liked to be in the bed alone, underneath the big fluffy blanket with feathers, puffed up like a cloud and soft and warm. But one thing he didn't like: Tzeepeh was whistling from happiness. Why not? But David said, "Don't whistle! It brings bad luck. You should know better."

"Are you so religious?" she asked.

"Religion has nothing to do with it. In the house you don't whistle, the same way you don't open an umbrella."

"Foolishness!" she said, and she whistled. He didn't like it. "Come, breakfast," she said. "Come!"

"I'm not hungry."

"I made it. It's on the table already. You can't go to shul hungry. You have to eat."

"Who knows? Maybe today I'm not going to shul."

"What are you saying? Don't let Pa hear such things from you."

"Let him hear. I don't want to go to the yeshiva all my life. I want to do something in my life."

"To study is not doing? What does Pa ask from you? He wants the best for you. Why are you complaining, it should give a knife in my heart? In your place a thousand boys would be fighting to be like you. You eat, you study, you sleep. Everything is ready for you — a prince!"

43

"Prince. At least a prince has to look out for his country. Me, one day is another."

Tzeepeh was busy putting her hair in braids on top her head. "So, what can you do?"

He sat on the bed. "Maybe I can go to Warsaw."

"To buy for Pa? He wouldn't let you. He made a dowry for a scholar, not for a buyer."

"A bargain." He hadn't noticed before that she had a mole behind her neck.

After a while, in the yeshiva, he was sitting in the big room with the others, some like him, young, little beards growing, you could count how many hairs, some old with yellow beards. And they all sat to daven, and study. Such a tumult! Each had to sing, to talk out loud, to learn in his bones, and they bent like trees in the wind. By now, David was talking, but at the same time he was thinking. What to do? What to do? He felt like it was a tiny locked room, but it's not locked, like he couldn't move, like the town was a shrinking wool blanket, like the whole Pale of Settlement was shrinking, and pretty soon everybody would push him, and the world was laughing. "Dauvidel! What are you doing?"

It was Heimie talking in his ear. A skinny boy with green cheeks, yes, like moss grows on the tree, and big green eyes. His hair even looked like grass. He always bothered David in the yeshiva. "Dauvidel! What are you doing? I have to ask you a question. In Proverbs it says, 'The spirit of man is the lamp of the Lord, searching all the inward parts.' Tell me, how far is it we go, the inward parts? The good parts, yes, but bad parts we got also. Maybe it means we have to look on the forbidden parts also? How can we be forbidden when we got to look?"

"Oy," said David.

"What, oy? It's a question? All the inward parts. All, it says. You see? Here. Am I wrong? We look at the same time we shouldn't look."

"Ask the rabbi."

"You think I didn't. 'It means,' he said, 'the parts of the Talmud.' Is that an answer? The Talmud has inward parts? What's inward? Don't we see what we see?''

"You see the words. But the words tell you more than you can see. Is that the fault of the words? It's your own eye you have to light up.''

"Such a kluger!'' Heimie says. "No, I don't see. Do you shine a light in my eyes so I can see? No, you shine the light on the words. The eye is a window, glass.''

'' 'And those who look out of the windows be darkened.' If a window is dirty, you don't see.''

"Don't tell me from windows. Glass I know. My father has a store. He sells glass. Some kinds you see. Some kinds he makes you can't see. There are different kinds. So, some eyes see better than others. Is that the fault of the eyes?''

"It's a good business, glass?'' David asked.

"Glass? It's a business. It keeps me here.''

"From where does your father get glass?''

"Where else?'' Heimie said. "From the

glass factory.''

''Where is it, the glass factory?'' David asked.

''Where else? In the Leeteh.''

In bed that night David said to Tzeepeh, ''I want to go to a different town.''

''What're you saying?'' She lay on her side, away from him. She wanted to go to sleep.

''I want to move away to a different place.''

She was quiet. But finally she asked, ''What place?''

''In the Leeteh,'' he said, ''is a small town where they make glass, a factory.''

''In the Leeteh? Who is in the Leeteh?'' Tzeepeh asked.

''What do you mean, who? People. A small town.''

''There are no people here? What do we want, strangers?''

''You don't understand.'' David heard how she lay on her back and looked at the ceiling. Now she couldn't get to sleep. Like a board she lay, and when he touched her she didn't move. Finally, he felt her cheeks, wet from the tears, and he said, "Tzeepeh." And what did she do? She let out a cry, the whole house should hear. So he took her, he held her, and she cried on his shoulder, in his arms. What could he do?

The next morning he got up before Tzeepeh. It was dark, the roosters weren't crowing yet, but some birds knew and were singing a new day. A little shop, David was thinking, with a sign that said "Glass," and behind, or maybe on top, would be the house, a nice living room, a kitchen, a bedroom, and only the two of them. And when the children came, he could build more rooms. People need glass. Don't they have windows? He thought and dressed himself. He thought so much he forgot the prayers. He said some, but not all. He started a prayer, but in the middle he was thinking about glass.

Pretty soon he heard the father, Moishe, saying "Oy, oy." He was getting up and making noise and scratching himself. He prayed like he was in the last breath, coughing up phlegm, he spit, and he prayed. The light from the sun was coming like wine creeping on the tablecloth, and David stood at the window in the living room; he heard the girls start to talk in bed and the mother pulling on the sheets, the brother pounding his feet on the floor to get his shoes on, and Tzeepeh called, "David?"

Moishe looked into the living room like he was afraid. "David? You're up? What's the matter, she don't let you sleep? Nu, what can you do? She's like her mother, God bless her. But she respects you, believe me. A scholar? She's proud, we're all proud. Go, go, study. An old man like me, I didn't have the chance. Wait, she'll have children, she'll let you alone."

"I got something to tell you," David said. They looked at each other for a minute. Moishe waited. David's heart was pounding, a hammer, his hands behind his back.

"Nu?"

"Maybe you won't like it."

"How do you know? Maybe I will like it. Can it be so bad?"

Then Tzeepeh came into the living room. Her hair was not in braids yet; it hung like a veil on her shoulders.

"Mine daughter," Moishe said, "it's not nice you should come where men are talking." He looked at her like he had never seen her before. "Still the long hair, like a shikseh? You're a married woman now. It's a shame to let men look at you with the hair. You must cut it and put on a wig like your mother. Where do you get such ideas?"

"I told her," David said.

Moishe opened his mouth but nothing came out. Finally, "This is what you have to tell me? Nu, she's your wife now. I have nothing to say. What can I do? A scholar, a holy man maybe, he knows more than me."

Now the mother was coming. "Oy," she said, a hand on her chest. "I got a feeling."

"What?" Moishe was scared.

"A hot flash maybe. Like a warning, yey's mir." She knocked her knuckles on the table. Everybody was listening.

Finally David said, "I got an idea I want to go into a business."

"Business?" Moishe looked like he

was losing something. "A business?" He looked at his wife. "A business?" He looked at Tzeepeh. "You put into his head a business?"

"I'm tired of doing nothing," David said. "I want to go to another city. In the Leeteh is a small town. A glass factory is there. I figured I can fix a little store, a shop with glass, and make a living."

"To study is nothing?" Moishe asked. "To learn the Gemara is nothing? To be a holy man is nothing?"

"For me, I don't have enough interest."

Moishe clapped his hand on his head. "Interest! He doesn't have enough interest! To pray to God isn't enough?" He poked a finger. "For what did I pay a dowry of five hundred rubles? So you should have interest? For what did I marry my daughter to you? Interest, sminterest, I don't care! You got to do what you got to do. Study!"

David made fists behind his back. "I'll go to the Leeteh."

"First," Moishe yelled, "I'll kill myself!"

"Oy," the mother said. "Oy."

Moishe threw his hands into the air and looked toward the ceiling. "What have I done to deserve this? Do I eat pig? Do I curse so I am cursed? No," he said to David. "No, we are happy, things are going regular, everything is good. You'll stay here and study and make children, our grandchildren, God be willing —"

"I made up my mind," David said.

"All right, go, go!" he said like thunder. "But you'll go alone." He breathed like a horse. Finally he said, more quiet, "So go. Go and see what you'll do. Then, you'll see, you'll do, and you'll find out what's what — and you'll come home. Tzeepeh will wait for you here."

"Oy," the mother said.

David looked at Tzeepeh. She couldn't look at him. Her eyes faced the floor, with her hands and fingers laced up in front. "Tzeepeh," he said. He waited. Everybody was looking at her. She didn't move. "Tzeepeh," David said, "if you don't come with me, I'll go home and be back with my father in business."

"She's not going," Moishe said.

"It's a scandal," the mother said.

David shook his head and ran to the bedroom, pulled a suitcase from under the bed, and took out from the top bureau drawer the socks that Tzeepeh rolled in nice little balls, from the middle one the shirts folded nice, from the bottom one long underwear. He put everything inside the suitcase. From the doorway Tzeepeh watched, crying.

"Why?" she asked. "Why, all of a sudden? Did I know how you'd be? If I knew, I wouldn't have married you. What do you want from me? I have to help my parents. My father can't do it alone. He's got to have me. Can't you go into business here? Maybe my father will say all right, you can go in with him. So you won't be a scholar, so you'll make business. He'll be satisfied."

David put the straps on the suitcase. He carried it to the door. "Pardon me," he said.

"Where are you going?"

"I'm going either to the Leeteh or home to my father. Which place?" he asked. "Which place do I go?"

"Oy," she said. "Oy, you're asking me?"

"So make a decision," he told her.

"You have no feelings!" she yelled at him. But when he started to push by the door, she held onto him. She cried and ran to the bureau, took her clothes, and pretty soon everybody was yelling and crying. Moishe threw a lamp at the wall. *Smash!* The mother sat on a kitchen chair crying, her face in her hands. "Mein kind, mein kind." And Tzeepeh yelled at David, "Are you satisfied? Do you see what you do? Is that a thing to do, to raise a tumult on everybody? Does it give you satisfaction?" All the time she was running after him, with the suitcase and bags, to the depot.

When they came to the small town, David left Tzeepeh by the inn to wait while he went to look for a place to stay. Luckily he found a small store with a tiny room behind it. That was it. When Tzeepeh saw where he was bringing her, she sat on a suitcase and clapped a hand to her mouth. "Here? A place to live? A room? My father would keep dirty rags in such a room. I'm giving up my nice home for a shack?''

"Later we'll make better," David told her.

Finally he went to the glass factory. He had the five hundred rubles from Tzeepeh's dowry. He bought a lot of glass and made for himself a business. And it was good.

So, now, he sat in the store, sold pieces of glass, and talked to the people like an owner. "Yes, it's twisting in my heart how the times are going. It's bad for business when there's trouble in the world. What can you do? Always, we are the ones who have to suffer. What is the Jew for? God says let the world know what is a faith. Make the world bad for the Jews so people can understand it's no use — you can't turn them away. As long as the Jews live, God lives.'' He started to smoke cigarettes. He looked out the window for this one and that one who goes by. A piece glass he sold, it's a living. It was not a bad life.

For Tzeepeh such a living was not a living. "I'm going crazy," she told him.

"This is how I married? A boy I'm meeting on the train to Warsaw. He takes me to the big city. A lover! Look at him now. He sits in a tiny shack filling up with glass. Life is going by and he sits. How much can I clean one room? Is this a life? We don't do anything, we don't know anyone — strangers! You've got to take me home. That's all, that's the end, finished. Didn't I come to see what's what? In one minute I saw everything. I have to go far away from my parents to see four walls? What do you want, we should live like peasants?"

David watched from the window with the cigarette on his lips. Now he grew a nice little beard, too. Red on his chin like a nobleman, a prince. Tzeepeh got mad at him, she went into their room and slammed the door. For spite only she cut off her beautiful hair and put on a wig. Nu, she wanted attention. David smiled and said to her, "Now a man won't look at you. Jealous I'm not."

Finally, she couldn't stand it. She woke up like always, David still in bed, and she got out the suitcases. She'll go, it was all settled. But all of a sudden such a hotness came to her, such a tumble in the stomach, she thought she would throw up. She lay down again and cried like she was dying.

"What's the matter?" David asked.

"I don't feel good."

"You got a pain?"

"Oy, don't touch me. I feel I have to vomit."

"What did you eat yesterday?" David asked. "I'm not surprised. All day you were eating shmaltz on bread. What can you expect? All day she eats shmaltz on a piece bread — plain fat. No wonder you have to vomit."

So she didn't say when she'd go home. She thought tomorrow she'd do it. Why should I stay? He'll get mad and make trouble. I'll go, I'll go. But next morning, when she got up, it was the same thing. Her stomach wouldn't let her alone. She had to lay down and hold her head. "Oy, oy."

"Again?" David asked. "Didn't you learn something? What did you eat?"

"A cup of chicken soup, a piece bread.

Nothing. Oy, I'm dying. What's going to happen? So far from home and I have to die in a strange place. Oy, oy."

This time David got scared, maybe he's got bad luck. Another dying wife? So he dressed himself and ran quickly for the doctor — a Gentile, old, but a good man, plenty of experience. In those days, well, the doctor came to the house. He examined her, he couldn't find anything. As soon as he came she felt better already. The doctor asked David, "How long are you married?"

"Almost a year."

"Aha." To Tzeepeh he said, "When was your period?"

"Period?" She didn't know what he meant.

"The period, the monthly."

"When you are unclean," David said, "and you go to the mikva to submerge in the bath."

"In this place there is no mikva," she said. "I have to make my own in the washtub. Didn't I tell you before? What's here for a Jewish woman? A washtub."

"How long since?" the doctor asked.

She couldn't look at him. She started to blush, he should say such things.

"Two months?" he asked. No. "Three?" Her eyebrows were on top of her head. She raised a shoulder. Maybe. The doctor closed his bag. "Be happy," he said to David. "You'll be a papa next."

David grabbed the doctor's hand like the handle of a pump, so grateful was he. "God is good. God is good. You see?" he said to Tzeepeh. "It's a blessing."

"A blessing?" and she looked around the room. "Here, it's got to be a curse."

"Don't say such things. My God, it's not right." And he started to pray.

Tzeepeh wanted to go to her father's house for the baby but David wouldn't listen — she belonged here, in her own house. He had a little more money now, so he found a nice house in town and arranged things with the doctor. A Jew can't buy himself a house, so the doctor buys for him, and he then pays the doctor back. They moved into the small new house. Tzeepeh was beside herself, so happy with a house to themselves. Soon she fixed it up nice with tables, chairs, curtains, and rugs. Their neighbors, naturally, were Jews, and they came, got acquainted with Tzeepeh and David, and brought nice presents. Finally, David was going to the little synagogue again for minyan and was getting up early. All day long Tzeepeh drank tea with the neighbors, mostly older housewives who didn't care how they looked. One was two or three years older than Tzeepeh, fat, and always eating David out of house and home, too. She used to come and sit all day, drinking tea and eating challeh. But she and Tzeepeh were close friends. As long as David didn't see the neighbors, it was all right. He left early for synagogue, went to the shop, and returned late to the synagogue. When he went home it was already dark and he was tired like a dog. He could hardly eat, and so he went to bed. Tzeepeh didn't mind. Herself, she ate too much — oy, did she get fat. Pretty soon David slept on the couch.

The baby came. In the middle of the night — how else? — David ran for the midwife. In those times the doctor didn't bring the babies. Tzeepeh screamed for three hours as if she were dying, but it came out all right, and the midwife — an old woman with no teeth — showed him a baby girl. Well, thank God, both were all right. A girl? It was a disappointment. But if God sends a girl, he sends a girl. What can you do? David saw she was like him. She had red hair.

That's how they lived in the little town. Tzeepeh was getting happier each day, but David grew unhappy. Because Tzeepeh and the neighbors expected it, David went to the synagogue twice a day, and even more on holidays. And also, he had to keep up the business. What was he wanting from life? Aggravation? How was it better now than before? He came home tired, he could hardly walk, and right away Tzeepeh said, "The baby cried all day, it kills me, and I'm washing, cooking, baking, sewing, cleaning — what pleasure do I get from my life? You had to bring me to a strange place, away from my family —"

"You don't like it?" David asked one day. "All right, we'll go back."

"Go back?" she asked. "You build up a business, we make a house and settle down for a change, and now you say go back? Go back to what, a bedroom, and that's all?"

"You said you want to go home."

"Home? Here is home, God be willing. What can I do? I am here with my child in my house."

David sat and looked at the floor. "Tzeepeh," he said, "I'm not satisfied."

She pushed the baby toward him and stirred a pot soup on the stove. "It's almost ready."

"Tzeepeh," he said, "I came to this place so I could be a man, by myself. All right, maybe I'm still too young. Your father was forcing me. A scholar I didn't want to be. But a loafer, a beggar — that I didn't want either. All right, maybe I'm not a businessman by myself. Maybe I should go home. Together with my father in the business I can make something out of myself."

"Home?" She stirred the soup. "This is home."

The baby pulled on David's little beard,

so he held her hands. "I'm not satisfied."

"Listen to him. He's not satisfied. He's got a business, it's not good enough. He's got a wife who works her fingers to the bone for him, it's not good enough. He's got a place in the shul, they respect him, he reads from the Torah, he stands with the rabbi at the services, it's not good enough. Did I ask you to bring me here? What kind of life is it for me, hah? I had to go away from my family. It broke my heart, but do I complain now? Do I sit and cry all day? I work. I do what I have to do. And he's not satisfied." She threw a bowl soup on the table and said, "Eat. Eat. And don't bother me anymore."

"I'll go to my father and talk it over with him," David said.

"Oy. Such a man! He has to go to his father to find out what to do. And me? What should I do? All day long I sit by myself, a fine life. What pleasure do I get from it?"

"Tzeepeh," and he shook his head sadly. He gave her the baby and went to the pantry for an apple.

"I get nothing but heartaches," she

said, as she bounced the baby on her knee. "So don't tell me you're going. Home, he says! A home he's got, but he's going home."

"Tzeepeh," David said, and he held out an apple and smiled. She looked at him, at the apple, at his face. Now he was crazy. "Go, take," he said. "It's all right."

"What's the matter with you?" she yelled, and she picked up the baby.

"An apple. Take an apple." His face was turning to fire. "Don't you see? An apple!" He put it before her nose. But with her left hand she knocked it to the floor. As she looked at him, she couldn't recognize who he was. He shook his head once. "Good health to you," he said. "May the days be long for you. I'll go to my father."

Finally, she watched him go to the bedroom and take out the suitcase underneath the bed. "Where am I?" she asked. "Your wife and your child? Should we starve and freeze? While you go on a visit, what should I do?"

"Stay in the store," he said.

"And who will take care of the house?"

"Hire somebody."

"Hire? Just like that? All of a sudden we're rich?"

"You won't starve." He looked at her. "It's steady now, the business. From the factory you get glass. People are buying from you. Now they know the store. There's nothing to it."

"You won't go!" she yelled. "You won't leave me alone! How dare you spit on your wife!" He reached toward her. "Don't touch me!" she shouted. "Get out! I don't want to look at you! A man? He's worse than a child! Get away from me!"

"You can have the business," he said. "You can be alone."

So once again David was on the train, on his way to his father's house. At first he sat like a guilty man — his mouth hidden within his beard and his hands held tightly together as if they were tied. The noise from the train wheels seemed to say, *"Tch tch tch.* Terrible, terrible, terrible. Oy, oy, such a worry, it digs in my heart." He leaves a wife and a child. He's not satisfied. Why does God give him troubles? A big problem he could understand, he could fight. A fire maybe. He could run inside and save everybody. Or a pogrom. He could hide, he could go with Tzeepeh and the child to the fields and protect them. All right, with the first wife it didn't matter. She was quiet, peaceful. She didn't ask anything, she left him alone. If she was healthy, he could have been happy with her. How could he know Tzeepeh was becoming mean and driving him crazy? She wasn't the same. How could he help that?

The train arrived at his town in the early morning. It was a cold spring day, and he couldn't stop shivering. He got out of the train and saw people were leaving. No one was coming but him. Somebody tapped him. "Dauvidel Dauvidel! What is it?" He saw it was Heimie. "Why are you here?"

"How are you?" David asked. "Why here?"

"Where else? I'm living here," Heimie said.

"Here?"

"I married by you a cousin. Who knows? Fourth, fifth, tenth? A relation. So now I'm in the family. But you —"

"You're going on the train?" David asked.

"To Warsaw, for business."

"Glass, maybe."

"Aha!" He looked at David like a doctor would. "It doesn't go so good in the glass? You're not starving?"

"I have enough to eat."

"They'll be surprised you're here. I haven't heard anything. You're all alone? Where is your wife?"

"I'm by myself."

"Troubles?" Heimie closed one eye and stuck his head out to David like a rooster. "Dauvidel. Dauvidel," he stuck a finger in his chest like a knife. "Both, hah? Both you and me, study and study and learn and we are here — nowhere. For what? Are we better off, all the time in the yeshiva? Questions, questions — what good is it? Give me a for instance."

"What are you asking me?"

"I'm asking, for what are we asking? They take us, young boys with nothing in

67

our heads but a good taste for life, and they're stuffing us with questions — If a man's ox gores another ox, who's to blame? What does it mean that Rabbi Akiba gives straw to a stranger? If God loves the poor, why does he not support them? 'Because,' says the Rabbi, 'God wants to give the rich a chance to be good.' Is this an answer? Are these questions? Hah? Listen,'' he grabbed David's lapel, ''when a Jew can't ask, is he a Jew? Listen, listen.'' With two hands now he pulled David. ''I can't ask. It's all gone, the questions.'' Tears in his eyes. ''What do I ask? I ask, what good does it do me? I'm afraid the ineffable one is going to punish me. My heart pounds. God listens. He waits until I think it's all right, I'm satisfied — then he'll put his finger on me. What can I do? I'm scared and I'm busy. I pray and I buy goods for the shop. Cloth. We're not rich, but we're not poor. It's a business. Dauvidel, tell me'' — his big eyes were popping out of his head — ''in my place, what would you do? More questions? More swaying in the synagogue three, four times a day?

Already" — whispering now — "already I don't talk every minute on the train. Do I sit and read from the commentaries? I look out the window. 'Look, look,' I say to myself. 'The sun is shining such a beautiful shine! It's a pleasure! Am I wrong? If I am wrong, why doesn't God throw a stone at me? Is He waiting for a better day when I don't expect?"

The train was blowing like a nose and smoke was coming out of it. David pushed Heimie and said, "Go in good health!"

"May God hear you." Heimie stuck his head out the window. "Will you be here when I come back?"

"I don't know!" David yelled, and the train made a cry and such a smoke as it was leaving.

The same thing happened when he walked into his parents' home. In those days things didn't change like today. Three years he was away. He was twenty now.

He walked into the house like always. "Ma?" he called. Oy, she saw him and turned white like a sheet and gave a clap on her heart so hard he had to hold her up. She almost fainted. A loud wet kiss she gave him. "My son, my son!" and she cried like her heart was breaking, she was so glad. Finally, she said, "Look, look, so skinny like a finger! Oy, it kills me. Come, my son, I'll give you what to eat. Fresh, what I made this morning — sponge cake, your favorite, and you'll have with buttermilk and cheese a piece. You have to *eat*. Nothing but skin and bones. Oh, my God. Does she give you to eat, your wife?"

"Yes, Ma."

"She makes good meals?"

"Yes, Ma."

"How can it be good if you don't eat? But I won't say anything. I'm leaving my children alone — let them live their own lives. What do they want from me, the mother-in-law? Tell me, how is she, the baby, the blessed one, the beautiful darling? Oh, it hurts me, I can't see her. She wouldn't come with you, your wife? Why couldn't you bring them, too — your wife and my grandchild?" She stuck her head into the living room. "Gershon! Gershon! Come look who's here!"

The father came into the kitchen. "David! My God, I thought I was dreaming of your voice!" He gave his son a hug and a kiss on the cheek, smack. "What? You're home? Look, Leah, a father! A grown man already! How long is it? God knows. More than three years? In three years the young change to old and the old to beauty. Nu? How is it by you? Where is your wife? Where is my grandchild?"

"They're home, Pa."

"Home? And you, where are you?"

"I'm home, Pa. I'm here."

"Don't bother his head with questions," Leah said. "Let him eat something."

"I'm not hungry, Ma."

"Hungry, smungry, you have to eat. Never mind, sit, I'll give you."

So they talked and she put some food in front by him. Then he ate his mother's cooking. Delicious. Now he knew Tzeepeh didn't put enough salt, or too much salt, forgot a piece garlic, was stingy with eggs, baked maybe too long, too short — you get used to something in your mouth and sometimes forget what is good.

"Let him rest," the mother said. "Poor

boy, look how tired he is. It hurts me. Go lay down. No arguments. Sleep a little!" So he lay down in his own bed, and it felt like heaven.

When he got up, after a good rest, he asked his father about the business. "Not so good. When you left me, I took in your brother, Louis. Nu, he's a good boy and he works as well as he can, but his mind is — who knows? Maybe he'll be the scholar in the family. How can you tell?"

"Pa —" David looked at the floor. "Pa, do you know, I would like very much to be back with you and travel again to Kiev."

"By you the glass isn't so good either?"

"It's all right. It's a living. But it pulls me, the big city."

"To live in the big city? You don't miss your family, your relations, your own town? I didn't understand when you wrote how you were moving far away by yourself to a strange place. Did it bring you something? A man has got to be with his own." David was quiet. He looked at the floor.

Grandmother Leah watched him, and it

gave her a pound in the heart. And she said to herself, "Oy, something isn't right. My son is hiding something from us."

"I'd live here again," David said.

His father shook his head. "In my house you are welcome — it's your house, too. But where? Your room is like a closet, and your wife, she's used to her own. With a baby you got to have a place."

"Never mind," Leah said, "a baby makes room." But in her heart she knew something. She sat next to him and held him by the hand. "What happened?"

Then he started to say that he's not happy with his wife. She drives him crazy. He can no longer be with her. She nags, she tells him this, she tells him that, she can't be satisfied. What can he do? The parents felt bad to hear their son couldn't find happiness again. The mother was crying because her oldest son couldn't find a good wife. She knew that time that the girl was not for him. But she couldn't say so.

The zaydeh and the bubbeh didn't know what to say. Finally, the zaydeh said,

"Maybe she'll change."

"No, Pa," David said. "It's no life with her. I told her she can have the business and be alone. She's not for me."

"What will you do?" his father said.

"I'll give her a divorce."

The bubbeh caught her heart in her throat. "You left her, then? For good? She stays with the baby alone? My God, she'll take care of the baby? She's so mean she'll harm the baby."

"No, no, Ma. Don't say such things. Maybe it's my fault."

"How is it your fault? Don't you give her the best of everything? A good house, plenty on the table, everything a person can ask for? When I saw her, I knew in my heart she is common, prosteh. I couldn't tell you. God forgive me, I should have said something."

"Still," the zaydeh said, "when a person sees he's going to lose a life, he changes. Give her a chance, she'll change back."

"Change back?" said the bubbeh. "She is what she is, and that's all there is to it. The marriage was not made in heaven."

"It's not right." The zaydeh was shaking his head. "He should be with his wife and his child."

"Don't give him headaches already!" She started to cry again in her handkerchief. "Such heartaches he has from this life, don't ask."

"Pa," David said, "can you use me?"

"Use!" His father blew a puff from his cheeks. "You have to ask? Don't insult me."

So David again traveled with his father on business to Kiev, Warsaw, and Odessa. Finally, he started going by himself — business only, no monkey business. He threw himself into his work with all his strength, and he came home very seldom. He didn't think about his wife and daughter. Like a horse he worked and worked, and ate and slept. When he could go to shul, he went and prayed. It didn't bother him — the prayers, the men in the synagogue. Oh, they talked, they asked questions about the Talmud and about business, too, but they left him alone. Heimie tried to ask questions, but David wouldn't answer. He was friendly, but he wouldn't talk. So after a few weeks Heimie didn't ask. What's the use of talking to a stone wall?

Finally, coming home on the train, he saw a mother with her little girl. He saw how the mother held the girl, but the child turned herself and climbed on the seat. She couldn't sit still. Then she came to David on the next seat and wanted to climb on his lap. "No, no, Faygeleh!" the mother cried, but David said it was all right to let her climb. It was the red hair and the red beard that the little girl thought was so wonderful, like fire. She pulled the beard. It was his heart.

Once he was home, David told his parents he was going to see his child. "You'll go back?" his mother asked. "You'll stay again?"

"I'll go to the rabbi there," David said. "I'll get a divorce."

"You'll see, you'll see," his father said. "You shouldn't jump out from the blood vessel. When you get there, you'll see. Maybe things will be different."

"A cow changes to a horse? Different — like a dog with a bone she'll be different. A person like her doesn't change. It's her nature." To David, the mother said, "Only she shouldn't talk you into something else. You have to do it, do it. Don't let her tell you otherwise."

When he left he looked beautiful, like the sun — shining skin, white teeth like stars, his hair like red clouds in the evening. But he sat on the train like an old man and couldn't sit straight. He looked at a book, stories by Tolstoy, but he spent an hour on one page, he couldn't see. All the way he couldn't sleep. He was like a ghost. Again it was springtime and green things flashed by. The muzhiks — peasants — working in the fields, a man behind a horse, with the reins wrapping his neck, and they waved. They liked the train and were afraid of it as if it were a god. Everything was coming back to life again like a child after the bath. Rosy cheeks, laughing, it's a good feeling. But David — for him the sky was empty, blue, an eye behind a teardrop, and the earth was turning over like a grave they are digging fresh.

Finally they came to the Leeteh. It was

as if everybody was expecting him, with the hellos, how are you, where were you for so long? It seemed that he knew each person in the depot. They recognized him and had to say something. It was embarrassing. To this one, to that one, he shook a hand, he made a smile, go with God, God be with you, how's by you? Finally, in a hurry, he ran away from them and walked to the old street — nu, a dirt road that makes dust on the curtains — and soon he came to his house.

It was warm, the front door was open, he heard somebody talking, laughing, a woman, but then a man, too, and Tzeepeh laughed high in the air, like singing from high to low. David's heart was pounding in his ears. He could hardly go to the door, but he went.

It was the neighbor, the fat one; it was Tzeepeh, plump also now, but not so fat like before. On her lap was a little girl with the red hair — Hanneleh. His child. On the other side of the table sat — who? A middle-aged man with a beard already gray and dirty-looking, and on his head was a hat with grease on the brim, and he also wore glasses to show a reader, a scholar, a wise man maybe. All looked at David like he was Elijah.

"Oy," said Tzeepeh. "It's him."

The man got up from the table and bent his head. "How do you do? Shalom." He smiled but didn't look into David's eye. The woman, the neighbor he recognized, sat with her mouth like a cup and didn't move.

"You're home?" Tzeepeh asked.

"Excuse me," the man said. "We were talking, your wife was saying so much about you. This is my sister-in-law, my brother's wife. We came on a visit, my sister-in-law and me, having a nice chat. Nu, we shouldn't stay a minute — Natalie, let the man have a minute's peace with his wife, he's been away so long." Natalie lifted herself up, a balloon, a bowl Jell-O she was. Then she looked at Tzeepeh, at the man, at David, back and forth, back and forth. She couldn't stop, and the man was bending to David and to Tzeepeh, and he grabbed the woman's arm and took her out of the house.

"He comes to visit with his sister-in-law," Tzeepeh said. "He's all by himself, so he has a cup tea."

Hanneleh put a thumb in her little mouth. David saw she was pretty, with red curly hair and blue eyes like his. He held out his arms and was going toward her to lift her up for a kiss, but she pushed him away from her. She made a lip like she was going to cry and put her face on Tzeepeh's shoulder.

"It's already two years," Tzeepeh said. "You're a stranger to her. What can you expect? My poor baby." She held the child to her closely. "Sit," she said to him. "I'll fix you something to eat."

He shook his head.

"Such a long way you come and you're not hungry? Did you eat something before?"

"I came to see Hanneleh. I came to make it final with us."

"Final? What's with a final? All right, you're home, we'll talk later. You're tired, you're hungry — eat first, then we'll talk."

"There's nothing to say."

"Two years and there's nothing to say?

I'm alone two years in the business and the house with a baby after you go away and leave me, and there's nothing to say? Then why do you come back?'' She stood up with Hanneleh and yelled, "What do you want from me?"

"I came — first, to see my daughter. Second, to give you the divorce.''

Tzeepeh let the child hang on to her by herself. Hanneleh couldn't hold on, and she slid down from her mother onto the floor. Tzeepeh closed her eyes. "God gives me punishment. Why do I deserve this? I should die, it should all be over with me, I shouldn't suffer anymore. Why do you bring me such trouble on my heart? Do I deserve such a life?'' She shook her head back like she was looking at the ceiling, and she cried so hard that it hurt her.

Finally, David said to Tzeepeh, "Listen, there's nothing to do. We don't get along, we can't live together in peace. It's done. What else can we do?"

She sat. "You don't love me?"

"And you love me?"

"My parents were right. They told me it's common, it's not good to marry for love. They told me I shouldn't play at love like a common girl. Romance! I should marry a good man who will be with me, it doesn't matter — a good Jew with a head on his shoulders."

"You'll find somebody."

"Oy, I'm so mixed up, I don't know what. I begged God, I hoped and prayed, please send my husband back. Then, you didn't come and you didn't come, so I didn't beg, I didn't pray. I had to live. I had to keep up the business — you wouldn't know it now. I'm making pretty good, I'm even saving money, God help me — you'll see. It's a business!" She stood by him, tears on her chubby cheeks. They gave a little shake.

"We'll go now to the rabbi's house," he told her. "He'll give us the divorce, I'll say good-bye, and you'll be free from me."

She shook her head and cried, all over she shook, sitting down again, and pretty Hanneleh was crying, too — the two together, hugging each other. "I'll go to the rabbi," David said. He looked at her and at his daughter. What could he do? It was the best thing for all of them. They had to do it. "I'll wait by the rabbi's house for you," he said, and he went out.

David came finally to the rabbi's house and knocked on the door. The rabbi's wife was surprised to see him. He went inside and had a cup tea, and the rabbi came, a big old man with a chest like a barrel, with a long beard and a hat always, and the tassels under his vest. "Shalom, shalom," they said, and they talked of his travels, and he told the rabbi why he was there. The wife, she knew what to do. She left them alone.

The rabbi, so big it was hard for him to breathe, laid a hand on the beard he should look wise, and he spoke. "A Jew doesn't divorce his wife. So, she's hard to get along with, God makes it for a reason. Take it from me, with a woman is better than without. The Talmud tells us woman is sinful. Why? Because she's a woman, she can't help it. When the angel told Abraham what is, who listened? The wife, Sarah. Who made trouble for Moses? Miriam. Who was jealous of her sister Leah? Rachel. Who is eating the forbidden fruit? Eve, who else? God bless them, we have to live with them. For the children. A man, he's the father, the provider. But the mother, she's the blood. We are Jews because we have Jewish mothers."

"I'm here for the divorce," David said. "That's all."

"Whose fault is it?"

"Maybe it's me, maybe it's her — so it's both."

"You got another woman?"

David made a noise, a spit, three times with his mouth. "I would kill myself first."

"Your wife, what can she do? She's got to live."

"I don't ask what for myself. I give her the business, the house, everything. I go away with empty hands."

"And the child? A child without a father?"

"Better at peace without than a tumult with. Don't worry, she'll have a father soon enough. My wife won't be without."

A knock on the door — Tzeepeh. She came after all. The rabbi's wife brought her in and they all looked at each other. Finally, the rabbi said to David, "I'm sorry, you shouldn't have it. I know you. I know Tzeepeh. Both are good. You can't divorce. Go and live in good health with God's blessing."

David stood up, red in the face. "Rabbi, I came to you for a divorce. If you won't give it to me, I'll go to another rabbi."

What could he do? Tzeepeh crying, David standing up like a prince, a general, a somebody, like a king. The rabbi's wife was crying, too, she couldn't help it, she wiped her eyes on her apron. The rabbi wrote it out, the "get" you call it, the divorce.

On the second day of the week, the fifth day of the month of Nisan in the year 5640 of the creation of the world, according to the number we reckon here, I, David Eisenberg, son of Gershon Eisenberg, who stands this day in Leeteh, the city situated on the river and containing wells of water, do hereby consent, with my own will, without force, free and unrestrained, to grant a bill of divorce to you, my wife,

Tzeepeh, daughter of Moishe Shimin, who has been my wife from time past, and with this I free, release, and divorce you that you may have control and power over yourself from now and hereafter to be married to any man whom you may choose, and no man shall hinder you from this day forevermore, and thus you are free for every man. And this shall be unto you from me a bill of divorce, a letter of freedom, and a document of dismissal, according to the laws of Moses and Israel.

Everybody put his name on the paper. The rabbi shook his head and gave the paper to Tzeepeh. "Now," he told her, "you are no longer married." She held the paper and cried, she couldn't help it. The rabbi's wife put her arm around her on the couch.

Quickly, David went out of the rabbi's house and walked right to the depot to go home. Then he worked for his father and traveled with the barge. He went to Minsk, Warsaw, and Odessa.

3

My mother's father was named Hyam and her mother Bernice (last name Lutz). They had ten children, six sons and four daughters. Each one went to cheder, Hebrew school, to learn. The sons learned Gemara, where in the Talmud it is saying what it means, and the girls learned to daven, pray. And that's all the girls learned. The four girls were young, but the oldest was sixteen. Her name was Razzeleh (Rachel), and she helped her mother with everything, even carrying two big buckets of water from the well very far from their house, and she poured it into a big barrel for water, and she used to take a big pack of laundry and go for a mile to the lake to wash and lay it out on the grass so it should dry. She would take bread and dry fish with her and eat by the lake. It was so nice to watch the birds, the way they look down at the water, scooping up, like a hand, a fish here, a fish there.

When no one was looking, she would undress and go into the water. In the old country they bathed naked. They didn't know what a bathing suit is.

This time more Jewish girls were sitting on top the grass, waiting for the clothes to dry. You know girls, they laugh, who's this boy, who's that one. We think times are different? What's then is now, what's now is then.

Razzeleh was quiet, it was her nature, and she smiled. Little Naomi was skinny but such a head she had, a scholar's daughter — today she would be a teacher. "Razzeleh," she said, "do you hear them? Nothing but boys — life is a boy, a body, a man. Give them a man, they're living."

"Let them talk," Razzeleh said. "Wait till their parents pick out a man for them to marry. Then they won't talk."

"Then what?" Naomi said. "Then they'll cry?"

"You'll cry," one girl said to her. "Such a man you'll get."

"No, I won't cry," Naomi said. "When the time comes, I'll be ready for him. I don't expect, so I don't dream foolish things. The way I think, I will get the worst — so, when the time comes, I'll be surprised because it'll be better than what I expect. I can't get worse. I have to get better." The girls were laughing. "You'll see, you'll see. You think a man will love you? How much dowry your fathers have for you? Hah? You think a prince from Moscow is coming for you? A poor Jew is coming for you with the smell of fish on his hands. That's who's coming."

"I would run away," one girl said.

"Where will you run?" asked Naomi.

"To the city."

"You know who runs to the city? Prostitutes."

"What if you don't love the man?" the girl asked. "Isn't it like a prostitute, Razzeleh?" She called on Razzeleh because she was older than the others, sixteen.

"Where do you get such ideas?" Razzeleh asked. "Love comes after, with the babies and the home, and everything is good. Do you know better than your parents what a good man is? You are talking like goyim. Ah! I got to clean myself!'' Quickly she threw off her clothes, piled them up neatly, and jumped into the water. It was not so warm, and she had to rub herself hard.

"Look, look!" a girl screamed, and she pointed her finger. From far off three or four boys were coming, Russian boys running toward them, making noise, barking like dogs, jumping together. The girls quickly grabbed the clothes and ran away screaming.

"Razzeleh!" yelled Naomi. "Quick, quick!" But there was no time now. "Give them some kupkes, pay them they shouldn't bother you!" She tried to hold herself by Razzeleh, but Naomi was scared and ran away, too. Razzeleh saw the boys notice her. What to do? Farther away in the water some Russian girls played — naked like her. Most were little girls, eight, nine, ten years old, maybe six altogether. So Razzeleh pushed as fast she could to get there — in those days they didn't swim like now. Maybe with the hands in front to make little paddles. But Razzeleh could swim very well; she was very strong.

The boys came like wolves and they yelled, they threw their bodies around, and they jumped on the clothes Razzeleh had brought and threw them into the water. Then they picked up stones to throw at her — they wouldn't go into the water. One of the stones hit one of the Russian girls.

"Ay!" the girl yelled. She started to holler, my God, like they were killing her. "Mamusha! Mamusha!" she yelled for her mother, and she got scared. All the girls got scared, and the girl went under the water. She couldn't swim well, she forgot. Who knows? She was drowning. Razzeleh saw her and swam so fast, so hard, that the water was making foam, and she grabbed the girl by the hair. In the meantime, when the mother, who was laying clothes on the grass, heard her daughter screaming, she ran to the lake, grabbed stones, and threw them at the boys, who ran away. Razzeleh pulled the girl from the lake and quickly picked up a bed sheet on the ground and wrapped the little girl in it, and her mother was crying and screaming, "Bozheh, Bozheh." That means God.

"She's all right," Razzeleh said. "It's all right." The little girl was crying and shaking like a leaf.

The mother grabbed Razzeleh's hand and kissed it. "Bless! You are an angel! God's blessing on you! May Jesus save you! You saved my Ninichka from those dirty boys!" Then she gave the child a slap. "Did I tell you to go into the water?" The girl was crying, the mother was yelling at her, but they each put a pile of laundry on their backs and went away all bent over.

Razzeleh stood naked and shaking like a fish in water. Her clothes were not there — the boys took them. Maybe the laundry, some pieces — but the laundry swam away. Now the sun was diving into the lake, the night was coming quickly, so fast she could see how the dark ate up the sky. She was alone, afraid — what should she do? It was getting cold. Her mother knew when she was supposed to be home, but maybe her mind was busy with something, maybe she had to go to a neighbor's house, maybe somebody came to visit so she had to stay for tea.

So she bent herself on the ground, she curled like a baby inside herself, she pulled her knees to her chin, and she shook from the cold. She started to cry. She put her hands over the mouth, she shouldn't make crying sounds because maybe the boys would hear her. The wind blew from the water like over a cake ice. She bit on her hand so she shouldn't make a noise. A dog was barking, maybe a wolf. Would it smell her? Still, it was far. A caw-caw and cheep-cheep, the birds. She listened hard — somebody crying, a baby, no, a cat, or a bird, all kinds noises. Like an old man who burps — a frog, she knew, but maybe an old man, and then like somebody in pain, oy, oy — who could it be? An animal in the night?

Now it was dark — no lights, no moon, nothing — so a little bit she sat up, and then a little more. Like she was blind. Oh, how cold! She couldn't help it, she cried, oy, Mama, Mama, would she freeze to death here, would she die and nobody find her — would the boys find her and take her body?

Somebody. A crack, the grass was swishing. She started to crawl on the ground. Something underneath her hand like a snake, she pulled away fast, but it was hard. She poked a finger — a root from a tree. Quickly she touched it, her fingers crawled on it, and she followed. Bigger and bigger it got on the ground, like an arm, a leg, even a body. Finally, it grew to a tree and she brought her body close to it so no one should see, or tell she was not the tree, too.

Somebody was coming, pounding a stick on the ground. Pound, pound, the stick, the grass, her heart, coming closer. "Ho!" A noise, a voice like a deep horn blowing. She gave a bite on her finger. "Ho!" The voice was like a knife to her, and from her mouth came a scream. A black body like a cloud came toward her, and she screamed with all her strength, screamed with her hands over her own ears.

It was quiet. Somebody was putting a spoon hot chicken soup on her lips. A little bit she could swallow. It felt soft beneath her and warm, so good. On top, a feather quilt like a cloud — the cloud was white and soft, warm. "Razzeleh? Razzeleh, darling?" It was Mama. Oy, Mama looked so beautiful, an angel, a light shining around the head, a cloud, gold. "Razzeleh?" She took another spoon soup. Tears came behind her eyes. Oh, God, it's a dream? Let me wake up, God, but I'm too scared. Maybe she was dead.

"Mama?" and she looked.

"Yes, darling. I'm here. It's all right, darling. You're home, you're in your own bed. It's all right now."

From behind, her father said, "Tell me, my child, don't be afraid. What did the murderers do to you? Tell us everything, my child. No one will know. We will be quiet. My poor child."

So good in the bed, so warm. She would go to sleep.

"Razzeleh," her mother said. "We sent the children to sleep. We are alone with you. Tell us, my darling. We want to know from everything."

Her whole body was tired and her eyes closed, but they wouldn't stop bothering her.

"Your brother Isaac found you. He put on his coat and took a big stick for the dogs from the Gentile homes. He came to the lake, it was so dark he couldn't see. But he heard how you were crying in the quiet. Do you know, he put his coat on you and brought you home on his big shoulders. My God, my poor child! What did they do to you?"

She didn't know they thought their beautiful daughter was no longer the same and that the Russian boys might have done the worst thing to her. To her parents, she was lost, her whole life. Now she would never be able to marry.

Razzeleh was falling asleep so hard that her parents also started to yawn. So they went to bed with a little oil lamp that burns all night.

Morning came, the roosters were singing. Everybody had chickens and roosters in the house where there was a big oven for baking bread and challeh for Shabbos. Under the oven was a big place for the chickens. At four in the morning the roosters started to yell. Then Razzeleh's mother jumped up and woke her husband, and they started again to bother Razzeleh. They went to her bed and talked to her. "Razzeleh, are you sleeping, my child? Get up and have something to eat." Her mother brought kava (that's chicory, you know) mixed with boiled milk. The skin from the milk was like butter, wonderful. They held it up to her mouth. "Take, my child. It will make you feel good." From her mother's eyes the tears dropped out. How come her Razzeleh, the pretty one, so good, who worked for the whole family. Vey's mir. Who will look at her pretty face with the long braids, and such big black eyes? She cried more.

Razzeleh's father, Hyam, was standing up to pray with tears in his eyes. "God, why do you let the Gentiles do harm to my holy child, my clean spirit? They make her body dirty. Who is going to take her? She will go out like a candle fading on Friday night. Vey, vey, what should we do, God? Give an answer." He took his fist and beat his chest and talked to God. "Take me, God. I am ashamed for you, my God." He was very orthodox. That's the way he stood and prayed and beat his chest, and tears he had plenty.

Again, her mother talked to herself: "God, maybe I sinned against you. Razzeleh is paying for me." She stayed near the bed with the glass kava, her hands shaking, the tears running.

Razzeleh saw her parents and heard how they talked. But she was so tired and broken that she didn't have the strength to speak.

"Daughter, take a little in your mouth," her mother said. "Look how dry her lips, so pale, her cheeks like snow. Razzeleh, take, take."

Her bones were like nails, her ribs felt like fingers stiff inside her. "Mama," she says, "I want to sleep so bad. I don't want to drink. Later, Mama, I'll get up and eat, and I'll clean up the house. Mama, the clothes — the boys threw the clothes in the river and they floated away."

"Don't worry from clothes. We have

more clothes." And again her mother started to cry.

"Mama, why do you have to cry? I'm not sick. I'm only tired, I was so scared."

Then her father said to his wife, "Bossel, come eat breakfast."

But she cried. "All you have in your mind is to eat when our child is lost to those boys, what they did to her." Razzeleh didn't understand her mother, and she wanted to get up to show she was all right, but her head fell back on the pillow. Her mother saw and gave a scream, "Oy, vey! What the murderers did to my child they did to me!"

Hyam couldn't stand it. He went to the kitchen for a piece bread with kava. He stood up to eat. He was afraid if he sat down his heart would stop. Maybe Razzeleh was saying something now, so he ran back to the bedroom with a mouth full of bread, but he couldn't say a word.

"You should go for the doctor," Bossel said to him. "I want you should bring the doctor right away." A doctor, a felsher, a soldier in the Tsar's army. He knew from a sickness like I know how to be a doctor.

In those days he was like a doctor, but he wasn't a doctor. They used to call him Ponee Doctor, means with respect.

Right away Hyam ran into the street, quickly he walked, his eyes on the ground he shouldn't see somebody who would stop to talk. He heard his name. "Hyam! Who chases you? Hyam! Have you found gold?" and he raised a hand, shalom, but he wouldn't stop. Finally, he came to the doctor's house, a little brown house with hay on top of the roof like the other houses. "Ponee Doctor!" he yelled, and slapped his hand on the door.

The doctor's wife opened the door, one hand on her hip. She held a wooden spoon and saw it was a Jew. She leaned a hand on the door to show how he was bothering her from the kitchen. "I have to see Ponee Doctor," he said.

"You're sick?" she asked.

"No, no, not me. I have a child, very sick — please, I have to see him."

"He can't go for nothing," she said.

"Do I look a beggar? A child is dying, and you're talking money? Let him take everything, so long he comes. Where is he, the doctor? Ponee Doctor!'' he yelled past her.

"You don't yell in my house!" she said, and she closed the door in his face. He pounded with his fist and yelled again, so mad it dripped from his mouth. Finally, the door opened, and his fist was high in the air in front of the doctor.

"What is it?" the doctor asked. A middle-aged man, blond, a tiny mustache, and glasses, the way they wore them in those times, no rims.

Hyam's heart was aching, he could hardly talk. "My daughter is sick. Come to see her. You're a doctor, you have to come."

"There's no question," the doctor said. He brought the little bag of medicines and went with Hyam to see Razzeleh. At the house the whole family took him in like he was higher than the Tsar. In those days they used to show very much respect.

Bernice sent the rest of the children to cheder, the Hebrew school. She didn't want they should find out what the Gentile boys did to their sister. Nobody said anything about what happened to Razzeleh because in this town everybody knew what was going on in the other person's cooking pots.

Razzeleh was worse, with fever. The doctor looked at her closely, in the eyes, the mouth, the ears. He put his ear on her chest, he should listen by her heart. A long time he stayed listening. Finally, he held her wrist and looked at the watch in his vest pocket. Meanwhile, she lay very quietly, her eyes closed a little bit, and she said nothing, only she looked at him with very great respect.

"You will put cold compresses on her forehead," he told the parents.

"Yes, yes," said Bernice. "A nice clean dish towel, ironed, it's all right?"

"And she should drink as much hot tea with lemon as she can."

"The best thing," Bernice said. "You're right." And she ran to the closet for the towels and put fresh water in the samovar.

"She'll be all right?" Hyam asked.

"How did it happen?" the doctor asked. "Was she sneezing?"

"No, no," Hyam said.

"What was she eating?"

"The same as us. Good food, clean, kosher. You know what it means, kosher?"

"Of course."

Hyam was smiling. "Of course. You are a civilized man, I can tell. Some people — who knows what they think? They think kosher is with blood, like we Jews are eating each other. Superstitious! That's what brings all the trouble. By us, kosher means 'blessed' and making sure everything is clean. The rabbi looks carefully on the meat, it should be pure and good."

"I know."

"He knows." Hyam was happy. "An educated man! You see?" he said to Razzeleh. "On him you can depend."

The doctor bent over Razzeleh. Softly he asked her, "When did you get sick?"

Still she was tired, but smiling. The long black hair, not in braids now, was wrapped around her head like she was a painting on the white pillow, now with a face like she was blushing, lips like fire, and she looked at him. Brown eyes she had, but dark like rich earth, and she looked at him standing over her.

And he smiled back. He had to, he couldn't help it. "It came on you, a mystery?"

"She got cold in the night," Hyam said quickly. "She works too hard, she's tired, the cold wind was blowing on her, so you see how she is. How does she look to you, Ponee Doctor?"

The doctor smiled at Razzeleh. "She looks fine."

"Oy, thank God, thank God, blessed be He." He held the doctor by the arm and pulled him toward the kitchen. All the time the doctor was looking back at Razzeleh. In the kitchen Hyam came up to the doctor, grabbed a button on his coat, and said, "Tell me, is she all right? She'll be okay?"

"It's too early yet. We'll see if the fever can go down."

"Sit," Bernice told him. "I poured for you already a nice cup tea. I'll take a cup to Razzeleh and you'll sit a minute, it won't hurt you, a cup tea with kuchen I baked for Shabbos. It will melt in your mouth."

So the doctor and Hyam sat at the table and drank tea with kuchen. "Delicious," the doctor said.

"By my wife's hand everything comes out good," Hyam said.

"You are lucky."

"Thanks be to God," and he knocked on the wooden table. "With the heartaches they give us, we are lucky to stay alive. As long as they leave us alone, we are lucky. What do they want from us, the soldiers, the army, the officers? We are poor Jews. What can we do? I want only my children should be healthy and happy. Is that bad? So I make a living with the hides — I buy the hides of cows, horses, any kind the muzhiks sell me. I clean them up, I hang them to dry, and I sell. Sometimes it doesn't pay, but I have to keep up to feed my children. God put us on earth so we can live by His name, blessed be He. And people are saying it's bad to be a Jew. All right, it's bad, it's a hard life, they punish us because we are Jews. What can we do? Blame it on God, please. Don't blame everything on us."

The doctor took a sip tea. He

was finishing.

"The ignorant only," Hyam said quickly. "You got to understand — not everybody. A man like you, educated, intelligent, you're all right. We have to think on the good side, no? Some people are bad, but some are good, too. Right?"

"I suppose so." The doctor was getting up from the table. "Thank you for the tea and cake. Thank your wife for me, too."

"A pleasure, Ponee Doctor, my pleasure. Listen, you'll tell me if I have to give more. It's all I have now." And he placed in the doctor's hand fifty kupkes (by us, fifty cents). The doctor didn't look at it; he put the money in his pocket and then put on his hat.

"You're going, Ponee Doctor?" Bossel was coming from the bedroom. "Wait. Let me give you a fresh challeh you'll enjoy." She put a whole challeh in his bag, fluffy, gold outside, white inside. A bread? By us now it would be a cake.

"Thank you."

"Take it in good health. My daughter is sleeping, may God bless her. Can you say anything? She looks all right to you?"

The doctor went to the bedroom door and saw Razzeleh sleeping like an angel. He looked a long time. Finally, he gave such a sigh it scared Bossel, and her heart pounded. But he said, "She'll be all right. I'll come to see her again tomorrow."

"Bless you, bless you," both said to him, and he went out.

"Did you ask him?" Bernice said to Hyam.

"What, ask? How can I ask? Is my daughter whole? Can he tell from looking at her eyes?"

"You should tell him what's happening."

"And if I tell him and he tells his wife? Run out in the streets and tell the world my daughter was raped by good-for-nothing Russian boys?"

"Hush! God forbid."

"We'll keep quiet, that's all, and we'll hope for the best. God deliver us from such troubles."

In the meantime, the doctor went home and sat down. "Did they cheat you again, the Jews?" his wife asked. He laid the money on the table and took from his bag the beautiful challeh. She broke a piece and tasted, delicious. "Nikolai," she said, "what's the matter with the Jew?" Zhydovka, she said, like a dirty word, Jew.

"She has fever. She's not well. I don't know what's wrong."

"So it will be one Jew less."

Next day he came again to see Razzeleh. Now she looked better. The color of her cheeks was softer than before, and her dark eyes looked like stars in the sky at night. Her black hair tossed across her white neck. He sat and looked at her. How's she feeling? Better now? Don't talk, you should rest. When he left he wouldn't take the fifty kupkes. "I didn't do anything," he said. "When I can make her better, then you'll pay me."

"At least take a challeh," Bossel said.

"You need it for your own family," the doctor replied. "When I can sit at the table with your daughter and eat it, then I'll have some."

When he returned to his house his wife asked, "Where are the fifty kupkes?"

"They're very worried about

their daughter.''

''I told you they wouldn't pay you. Worried! With them money comes first.''

''They'll pay me when I go to see her again.''

''Where is the white bread?''

''We forgot about it.''

''Yes, they know how to forget when it comes to giving something.'' She grabbed a shawl. ''I'll make them remember.''

He caught her by the hand. ''No.''

''Never mind, no. Where would we be if I didn't go after your money? Your heart is like an old woman. You've got four mouths to feed, a family. Always you act like you're still a bachelor.'' She pulled away from him. ''I'll give it to them, they don't pay us, not even a piece white bread.'' But he grabbed her and wouldn't let her go. ''What kind of a man are you?'' she yelled at him. ''A good-for-nothing loafer! Fifty years old and a child, a baby! He can't even provide for his family. His wife has to collect the bills!'' Their children, two boys and a girl, ran out of the house; their mother screamed before, too.

"Why don't you be quiet?" he asked, softly but to her face.

"Damn you," she said. "Curse you. Son of a bitch!" Yes, she said that to him. "Why did I ever marry you? A doctor! A high man in the world! A Jew lover!"

Ah! he slapped her across the face, the first time. She fell to the floor, so surprised, and lay on her elbows, looking at him. Oy, then she screamed and cried. Finally she got up. "You were afraid I'd make trouble before? Now I'll make trouble! Now I'll make the dirty Jews a lot of trouble they'll remember for the rest of their lives!" But she didn't leave the house.

He came again to see Razzeleh. She was already sitting in bed. He went inside and bowed to her and kissed her hand as if she was high society. "I don't have to ask how you are today," he said. "You are beautiful like always, but today even more. All girls should be sick like you if it makes such beauty. Tell me, how can I treat you if you make me so mixed up when you look like an angel?" She laughed and was blushing.

In the kitchen Bossel had rolled up her sleeves to knead the white dough. She baked very good kuchen with a challeh and put them in a basket covered with a white towel. So, when the doctor came in the morning, she got ready the basket with the baked goods. She brought it into the bedroom, where he was sitting with Razzeleh. She was blossoming like a rose. "Child," Bernice asked, "how do you feel?"

"I don't understand why you keep me in bed," Razzeleh said. "I'm feeling fine."

"You have to stay a little longer," the doctor said.

Bossel kept an eye on Razzeleh's stomach. She gave him the basket. "No no's," she said. "Take it in good health." And she forced on him, too, fifty kupkes. "You're a doctor. It's your business. You have to eat, too, you and your family. Three nice children he's got," she said to Razzeleh. The doctor smiled a little bit, as if he was embarrassed.

When he went home, he laid the money

on the table and gave the basket to his wife. "You see," he said, "the dirty Jew, she sent it to you."

"You think it's a present?" she said. "You made the girl well, didn't you? There's nothing to say thanks for."

Finally, Razzeleh couldn't stay in bed anymore. She got up and began to help her mother, and one day she went to the well. She took two buckets, but when she carried them they made her bend over. At that moment the doctor drove by in his droshky, his carriage, with two black horses, and he saw Razzeleh carrying the water. Quickly he stopped in the middle of the street and grabbed the buckets from her and carried them to her house. In front of their houses the Jewish women sat on benches — a board on the ground with dirt on top of it, and with another board on top of that. They sat with their babies, nursing, and looked at the world and conversed with each other. So they saw the doctor and how he carried the water for Razzeleh, and they talked: Razzeleh, Bossel's daughter, the pretty one, she's not acting nice. It's not nice for

112

the doctor to carry water for her. It came to Bossel's ears that her Razzeleh was going out with the doctor.

"Razzeleh," her mother asked, "it's not true? How can you take a ride with the doctor in his droshky? People are talking to me and I don't believe anything."

"It's not true," Razzeleh said. "The doctor was driving by and he saw how I was carrying the water. He jumped from the droshky and grabbed the buckets from me. I told him I could carry them myself, but he said I wasn't strong yet. Who was telling you all these things?" The neighbors, naturally. They talk about all kinds nasty things. "Let them talk," Razzeleh said.

Her mother felt ashamed for listening to them, and she ran to the neighbors. "It's not nice," she yelled at them, "you should talk about my child. From all her sisters, she's the best and the smartest and a good berrieh — wonderful housekeeper. Everything she does with a *taste*." The neighbors raised a shoulder: Who knows? Did their eyes tell them different?

In the meantime, the doctor always

stopped Razzeleh when he saw her outside. He went by her house morning and night. He made excuses — he had to see this sick one, that one; he had to buy drugs, medicine, and he went in his droshky and saw Razzeleh. He stopped. "How are you feeling? You shouldn't work so hard. It'll be bad for you." She smiled, warm in the face. Fine, she felt fine, she liked to work, to help her mother, and she ran inside quickly so the neighbors wouldn't talk. Bossel kept looking at her daughter's stomach, but in those days the dresses were full, so who could tell? She counted seven months, eight months, nine months. Nothing, no baby. So, thank God, at least she was not pregnant!

"It's time to talk," she said to Hyam. "What future can she have if someone finds out what happened?" She said to Razzeleh, "We want to talk to you about something." So the parents and the daughter sat down, and Bernice talked about the time Razzeleh went to wash the clothes and how Isaac, her brother, had found her and brought her home, and how sick she was. "Now, my child,"

Bernice said, "we have to talk about what to do. You'll get married, your husband will find out what happened, it won't be right."

"If he doesn't know how to understand such a thing," Razzeleh said, "I don't want to be married."

"How can you blame him?" Hyam asked. "A wife has to be pure. Will we lie to him first?"

"Lie?" she asked. "Why should we lie? I was swimming, some boys came and threw my clothes in the water, and I couldn't go home till Isaac carried me. Is that the end of the world? Nu, so I was scared to death and I got sick. I couldn't help it."

"The boys," her mother said quickly, "they didn't hurt you?"

"They threw stones at me in the water."

"But they didn't harm you?"

"They couldn't hit me. One girl they hit, a Russian girl. I told you how I —"

"My God," cried her father, "they didn't knock you on the ground? They didn't — it's hard for me. Do you understand?"

"What?"

"We thought they raped you," Bossel said.

Razzeleh couldn't help laughing, but she saw her mother was crying already and how her father's mouth turned down, so she held their hands. "Why didn't you ask right away? I would have told you. I didn't know. How could I know? Such a mix-up it didn't have to be. How could the boys touch me? I stayed in the water. When I came out with the little Russian girl, the boys had gone away."

"God bless, God bless!" her father yelled. "Oy, you don't know how we were going crazy! You're all right? They didn't do anything? Thanks be to God! God is good to us." And he cried. That's the way they were in those days. So happy they were.

Now Razzeleh turned seventeen and became beautiful like the sun. The doctor couldn't eat, couldn't sleep; it was a pain for him to look at his wife — she didn't keep herself up. She couldn't say a good word for anyone, an unhappy woman, that's all. He tried to keep busy day and night. Everywhere he thought he saw Razzeleh, and his heart was in his mouth when he saw a shape that looked like her. When he saw it wasn't her, his eyes became hollow like the dead.

Finally came a day when Razzeleh went to the market for vegetables. He saw her buying and pushed toward her as if he was blind. "Rachel!" he cried. "Rachel! I have to talk to you!" She looked at him in the middle of all the people, everybody looking, and she tried to turn away from him but he wouldn't let her go. "I have to tell you something," he whispered, but everybody could hear. He looked around like he was stealing something. He couldn't hold her, he couldn't drag her away, he couldn't talk to her quietly. So he laughed and picked up a bunch beets from a stall. "Take to your mother," he said, loud, and paid for the beets he gave her. But while he was giving them, he whispered softly to her, "Let me talk with you please. Tonight, outside your house when it's dark. No one will see us. It'll be all right. Say yes." He looked at her so hard she got scared and turned away.

After supper that evening, after the dishes were washed, the table was scrubbed, and the floor was swept, Razzeleh said "excuse me" and took the oil lamp with her, like she was going to the bathroom — only, then, the bathroom was the tiny house outside, in back, so no one asked anything. She came outside, among the crickets and the frogs, it scared her, ever since the darkness by the lake. The wind was blowing the light, she was afraid it would go out. Where was he? A shadow by the wall, a shape like she saw at the lake that night, and she put a hand over her mouth so she wouldn't scream.

"Rachel!" the doctor said softly. This time a half moon was shining, so he put out the light with his fingers and held her hand, looking at her in the moonlight. She was so delicate. She couldn't see his eyes, black holes. He kissed her hand, held it to his cheek. She tried to pull it away but he wouldn't let her. She let him hold it. "I've been waiting for so long," he said. "I was scared you wouldn't come outside. We'll walk a little bit."

"No, no." She wouldn't do it.

"All right. Here is better than nothing."
He took both her hands and held them to
his lips, to his heart. "Rachel — Razzeleh
— yes, that's better — Razzeleh, it's you.
Can you hear how my heart is pounding?
If I had a weakness in my heart, I would
die now from you. I wish I could die now
from you — I mean it. Would it be better
if I should die?"

"No. Oh, no," she whispered.

"I can't stand it anymore," he said. "I
have to tell you. I have to hope for
something, or I have to know absolutely.
Razzeleh, Razzeleh, my darling, I love you
more than anyone in the world.
Everything comes to me now like dust —
only you are real. Love me, Razzeleh, my
darling, my little darling — let me live,
too. I know," he said. He wouldn't let her
talk. "I'm crazy, my head is in darkness,
too. I can see how I'm walking and
talking like a madman in the street. I
don't sleep all night; I walk and I walk,
and she says to me, 'What are you doing
in the middle of the night? What's wrong
with you?' like she doesn't know. She
won't say, but she knows. All right, let

119

her know, let her understand she's dust in my eyes — I wash them out with my tears for you. Shall I kill myself? Will that be better? I get down on my knees in the middle of the night and I pray — to what do I pray? I don't know. I don't believe in anything but you now. I pray to you. Love me. Love me and save me, Razzeleh." He held her in his arms, so tight she felt her ribs would break.

"Ponee Doctor," she said. He let her go. He breathed like a broken animal. She looked at him.

"Say it," he told her. "I have to hear you. Wake me up with a cold pail of water in my face." He started to sob. "But even if you say you don't love me, I won't believe it. It isn't possible. You must love me." He fell on his knees. She couldn't help it. She came close to him and touched his head. He put his arms around her legs, his head against her, and she stroked his hair, and he cried.

"My doctor," she said. "I am a Jewish child. I am seventeen years old, the same age as your son."

He looked up at her. Now she could see

his eyes, how they were shining with tears in the moonlight. "I'll give you everything. I'll leave my family. I don't care. Anything you say, I will do it. Even if you won't marry me, I'll give you everything I have. I'll go anywhere you want."

"Your wife will make a pogrom on all the Jews."

"I'll kill her! Is that what you want? I'll do it."

She pulled him up. She was making him stand up, and he held her close to him and kissed her hair, her eyes, but she wouldn't let him anymore. She pushed him to the end of her arms. "You are an educated man. You are an intelligent man. You are a good doctor. And you have three children." She smiled at him. "God should bless you for your goodness. To everybody, yes, and to the Jews in our little town. I thank you with all my heart for what you did for me. My doctor, I respect you with every bone in my body. But I will marry who my father and mother say. I will marry a Jewish boy. Love? Love comes after, with the babies and the home. It's up to God. Maybe your wife is not loving to you because you don't show love to her. Show her love, she'll love you back.''

He looked at her a long time. The wind blew like somebody saying oy, oy, and the cries came no more, no crickets, no frogs. Only the wind blowing their hair, and he looked, holes in his eyes again — she couldn't see them. Finally, he put her hands to his lips. He let go and walked away quickly. Just at that moment a cloud was coming over the moon; it was dark. Everything was turning to shadows.

But a light came, yellow and skinny, from the door. It was her mother. ''Razzeleh? Is that you? Why are you standing in the dark? Come inside quick, you'll catch cold.''

''Yes, Ma.'' He must have walked. No horses, no droshky. He was gone.

Next day she found out he went away with his family. No one ever knew where.

4

Two years passed while David was in Kiev. He stayed there to put all the things he bought for his father in the barge. His father would come to Kiev and take the barge back by himself. David stayed in the city alone. He lived with an old couple in the Jewish section. What could he say to them? He worked hard, he kept to himself, he got lonesome. So, in the end, he came home again and his mother, Leah, didn't know what to do, she was so happy to see him. Now he was dressing like a prince. All the girls in the town were running to the windows to see David. Their parents were yelling at them they shouldn't look. The fanatics, so close they lived by the Laws, they used to say bad things about David. "There goes the Kiever bum," they said, because he shaved his face. He had very nice mustaches and he was wearing a short coat with patent leather boots and no hat. With a beautiful cane he walked. You see? they said. A good-for-nothing! A goy he is, not a Jew, they said.

In those days a small boat used to take the business people down the Dnieper River. They went from one town to another, and then they took a large boat, or maybe the train, and went back to their own towns. So, on Shabbos all the girls and boys went for a walk to see the small boat. They went over an old wooden bridge, and when they walked on it, it shook like an old man, but they laughed and held on to the railing. This day, this Shabbos, Razzeleh went with Naomi to look at the boat. A nice, warm spring day, just right. And David was walking, too, alone. Nobody was friendly to him, not even Heimie. Heimie liked David, but he couldn't afford to walk in the street with him. It was bad for business with the religious fanatics. Sometimes at night Heimie went to David's house; he liked to talk.

So David was standing alone on the bridge with a cigarette. He saw a pretty girl with another one who was not pretty. He looked at Razzeleh and couldn't take his eyes off her. She was also looking at him.

"What are you looking at?" Naomi asked in a whisper.

"I'm looking," Razzeleh said.

"You're looking. He's a shaygets, not a Jew."

"So a Jew is somebody with a beard and a hat?"

"My father told me not to look at his face because it is the face of a goy."

David smiled at her and Razzeleh couldn't help smiling back. Then the boat came and everybody hurried to look. The bridge was shaking like it would fall on top of the boat. David looked and looked at Razzeleh, too, how she held the rail like it would collapse and she was scared, but laughing, and her eyes bright and her long neck, the way she was leaning to see the boat go underneath. All at once gives a crack! The bridge. Like sheep and goats everybody was jumping to get out from the bridge. And such screaming! The boys ran, a leap, a climb, and they're gone. But the girls in their long skirts couldn't go so fast. Naomi fell and screamed, so Razzeleh had to pick her up. But Naomi was so scared she grabbed Razzeleh's dress, and they couldn't move. The bridge was like a sick person in the stomach. David looked back and saw Razzeleh and Naomi in the middle, on the boards from the bridge, with Razzeleh trying to lift Naomi. So he ran and took Naomi in his arms, while she was yelling and screaming and kicking her legs, and finally he brought her with Razzeleh to the side of the bridge.

David, looking on the bridge, was still holding Naomi. She bit him on his hand, nu, and he dropped her like a stone.

"Naomi!" Razzeleh yelled. "What's the matter with you? He saved maybe your life and you are biting him!"

"He didn't have to hold me," she said, crying on the ground.

"How else could he carry you off the bridge?" Razzeleh asked. "Without holding you?" To David she said, "Don't mind her. She's scared, so she bites you."

"I was carrying the wrong one," David

said, and he smiled at her.

"If I was so scared, maybe I would bite, too," Razzeleh said. "You can't blame her."

"Your bite on my hand I would enjoy."

Her face got red like fire and she didn't know where to look. She gave Naomi a hand and picked her up, and they started to walk home. David took his cane and walked by Razzeleh's side. She held Naomi's hand.

"Nobody can trust the bridge now," he said. "That's the way it is. They wait till it's too late, then they'll fix it. First, somebody has to get killed."

"You think the bridge will fall down first?"

"Maybe."

"Somebody should tell the mayor, the constable."

"That's the way it is. Somebody should tell them, but who is somebody? Each person says somebody should tell them and nobody tells them."

"I'll tell my father, he'll go to them."

"And your father is somebody? They'll listen to him?"

She looked at the ground and kicked a tiny stone.

"I mean," David said, "who listens to us Jews?"

She let go Naomi's hand so she could fix her braids. One was loose. While she was fixing, she looked at him, her arms raised, her head bending. It gave her such a shape he could hardly breathe. "You shouldn't be so sad," she said. "Some people listen to us."

"Who? The Tsar maybe? The Cossacks? The Gentiles all over the world, they're not persecuting the Jews?"

"Here nobody is persecuting. Thank God, here we are happy."

He looked at her like he was going to cry, but at the same time he smiled. "I hope you will never wake up."

Naomi said to him, quick, "You should be in shul." But he wouldn't talk back to her. He looked at the ground and Razzeleh looked at the ground. Only Naomi was watching everything. David walked, his hands behind his back, like he was studying the earth. Razzeleh, too, was reading something there. "Are you walking with me?'' Naomi asked her. "This way," and she gave Razzeleh's arm a jerk to go in a different direction. David stopped. To go with them in such a direction would be to crawl after them like a puppy. Razzeleh looked past her shoulder at him. Naomi pulled her. All around the boys were yelling and running, the girls were laughing, skipping and it was a fine day. Only David stood still and watched Razzeleh. When she was gone, he walked again, slowly, with his cane now tapping, and he rolled another cigarette and smoked.

Next day David and his father went on business, shop to shop, house to house, taking orders. And so they came to Hyam's house, where he was busy in the yard with the hides hanging out to dry. Shalom, shalom to each one, and they talked business. You need maybe yeast? Flour? New brushes? Whatever you need. Razzeleh came out to hang the clothes — not near the smelly hides. But David could see her in back of the house. So he took a little stroll.

"So you are here," he said.

"Yes."

"It's nice."

"Yes." Then she put a white tablecloth in her mouth to fold. The wind blew, a good wind. She could hardly hold the tablecloth in her mouth. All of a sudden, she gave to David a corner of the cloth. "Hold it," she said, as she gave a tiny laugh. Before he knew what's happening, he was holding one end of the tablecloth for her. "Hold hard!" and she gave a yank so the tablecloth would be smooth. Then she folded it in two and gave him to hold again. "Hold it!" she said, and gave such a pull it fell out of his hands. She laughed. "What's the matter, you're not strong enough?" She put the tablecloth in the basket for ironing. From where she was bending, she looked up at him. "Thank you." She threw him a smile so warm, so good, like he could taste it, like something came to his head, he didn't know what. All of a sudden she was the world and he couldn't find anything wrong with her. Not like before, with Tzeepeh. How good it was to be in love. Now he was afraid and he was fighting

— no, he didn't want any more heartaches. But she was beautiful when she bent down, when she rose like a flower, a cat stretching, a leaf in the wind, her face pure, her red lips, her nice round shoulders, and where she tied a belt at her waist, it was no waist, he could put his hands around her. God forbid, it was a woman he had to have, it was so long, he needed to hold love in his arms again? He knew it was bad, a sin, to look at her and to think how he wanted to touch her — to touch maybe anybody, any woman? But he saw her younger sisters come in and out of the house, each one was working. They could be women, but they didn't appeal to him. He looked at Razzeleh and his heart was getting soft. It was Razzeleh he had to have. To have? God help me, he thought. Will she have me? He couldn't force himself. But maybe she liked him; maybe when she would know him better she would love him. Maybe after they were married. Oy, such a dream he was having!

She went into the house. She stopped at the door with the basket on her hip, and she smiled at him before going inside.

All week he could think of nothing else. Every chance he had, he walked by her house, but he never saw her. She was busy inside, or she was not inside, or he didn't know from what. The women sitting on the benches watched him, so he couldn't wait; he couldn't even look a long time. Sometimes he went at nighttime and stood outside her house. All of a sudden his head was no good but for her.

Comes Shabbos, at the table David said to his father, "Pa, I want to ask you something."

"So ask."

"I want to ask tonight. After the blessing."

His father made the blessing and ate the Shabbos challeh. Later, when everybody had left the room, David's mother and father stayed with him.

"Nu?" his father asked.

"There is a girl," David said. "The daughter of the hide seller."

"Which daughter?" his mother asked. "They have more than one."

"Her name is Razzeleh — Rachel."

"I know her," his mother said.

"I would like to meet her."

"They buy yeast and flour from us," his father said. "We know them. You were there with me last week."

"We know they have a beautiful girl," his mother said. "People talk about her not very nice, Dauvidel."

"What do they talk?"

"That she's meeting sometimes with the Gentile doctor who used to be here."

"He was an old man already," David said.

"The old men are the best," his father said, and he laughed.

"So, people talk. Who knows what's true?" his mother said. She didn't laugh.

"Ma, they talk about me, too."

"The good-for-nothings, they talk. They like to make trouble from nothing. Why do they have to talk about you? There's nothing to talk."

"Pa," David said, "can I see her? Will you help me?"

"All right," his father said, "if you want it. I'll talk to her father, Hyam, in the morning, when I go to daven."

"Maybe she'll like me, maybe she won't. I don't want to force her."

"So we won't talk weddings yet."

"Give her a chance. I don't want a wife who hates me." They were quiet. This time they wouldn't argue.

In the morning Gershon went early to shul to daven. It was cold there, they could see their breath inside; plain windows it had, plain walls, nothing fancy, but in front of the altar with the gold cloths with the lions embroidered on, the Torah behind the velvet curtains, and when they carried the Torah, on their shoulders, the scroll, in the velvet case with the bronze chains and tassels, everything was beautiful. It's not like American synagogues, everyone quiet, listening; in shul everybody talked at the same time. They sing, they daven, they sway with the prayers in their bones. In between they talk business. So, Gershon stood next to Hyam, they davened, they talked a little business. Finally, Gershon said, "All of a sudden I hear you have a beautiful daughter."

"All of a sudden?" said Hyam. "It's

not a surprise to me. I have beautiful daughters, as many as you like — four, can you imagine? God bless them, they are healthy and good. Six sons, four daughters, that's a mouth to feed? Let me tell you, they all work hard. Alone, I couldn't do it. My sons, may God give them long life, they are my right hand. Isaac the geeber, like a fighter, he's the strongest. He's afraid of nothing. And Louis? Listen, Louis —"

"Thanks be to God you've got His blessings. Talk to me about your daughter."

"Which daughter?"

"Rachel."

"My Razzeleh? An angel. She's the oldest. She's — let me see. Last year, this year. Maybe she's sixteen, seventeen, no more."

"You promised her to somebody?"

"Razzeleh? Nu, it's time she has a husband. She should've been married two, three years already. What can I do? She doesn't want it yet. A hundred are asking for her, she doesn't want. So far I don't force her. But the time is coming, she should have a husband, a family."

"My son is interested."

"Which son?"

"My oldest also. David."

"Oho. The gentleman. I haven't seen him in shul since a long time now."

"He comes, he won't make a big show of himself. The troubles he's had, he likes it quiet and peaceful now. But your daughter, Rachel, she appeals to him."

"My Rachel? My Razzeleh?"

"Didn't I say before?"

"So, maybe I didn't hear you." Hyam pulled his prayer shawl around his head.

"Why are you scared? My son is a good looking boy, handsome, and also good in business. He went to the yeshiva, he knows from the Gemara and the Talmud, a regular scholar. A learned man. He knows besides Hebrew also Russian and Polish. What more can you want?"

"So," Hyam said, "maybe he is a Rabbi Hillel, but it's my understanding he also had two wives and a child. It's not true? A man married two times already and a child on his hands —"

"It wasn't his fault. It's my fault

altogether. I mixed his head with a sick girl. Her father wanted her to have a husband before she died, so he came to me, and I, like a fool, all right, then it sounded good, so I went ahead. David knew from nothing. A thirteen-year-old child. Nu, he is a Bar Mitzvah, and the next thing he is a husband. What does he know? To him, it came like death, like a bolt out of the sky. God knows, I should be punished, not my son. I swear to you, he didn't touch her. What did he know? A child in the bedroom with a child.

"Then, later, he meets a good-for-nothing, she catches him, and this time I want to keep out altogether. So, what do I say? Nothing. When I should say nothing, I say, and he's punished for it. When I should say something, I don't say, and he's punished for that. Oy, my fault he married the girl. Who knows what she is? All right, she comes from a good family, but herself, she's no good. She makes him miserable and he does everything for her. You don't have to worry, she's not here, not close. And he got a divorce by the rabbi. The child, God bless her, stays with the mother and it's like she's dead. We don't know from her. So, my son is alone and he's clean. A kosher boy, I tell you. We are the proudest in the world from him. If you're asking anybody who does business with him, they'll speak only the highest about him. Yourself, you see how he helps me. He makes very good and your daughter, Rachel, would live good by him." Time for more davening, so they davened, the cantor sang, and they sang. "Listen," Gershon said, "you don't have to give any dowry with food."

"Dowry, smowry," Hyam said. "I want my Razzeleh to have the best."

"I'm not asking your daughter to run like the blind beggar to marry. Let her see. Let her say hello to my son and he'll say to her, and they'll see. They'll talk themselves and we'll see what happens. If she says no, all right, it's no. We can't help it."

"And if she says yes?"

"Then we'll talk, you and me."

Hyam gave a sigh like he was worn out. "What will be, will be."

So, Hyam came home and everything

was ready on the table. He washed his hands, made a moetze over the bread, and sat down to eat with the whole family. "Razzeleh," he said, "now you're sixteen years old?"

"Foolish!" Bossel said. "Don't you remember anything? She is seventeen."

"Ah. So old already? And we are not grandparents yet?"

"We have plenty of time," Bossel said. "Who knows? If God is willing."

Then the whole family, Razzeleh's brothers and sisters, started to tease her, how old she is, how maybe the old rabbi himself will ask for her, or maybe the shoemaker with the wart on his nose. She smiled.

After, when the children were gone from the room, Hyam called Bossel from the kitchen. Razzeleh washed the dishes with her sisters, but she knew what they would talk about. She prayed to God in her heart, please don't make me get married to someone I can't stand. What would she do? She thought about David. Why did she have to see him in the first place? Now, her heart would ache with someone else.

In the living room Hyam said to his wife, "We got to talk over a marriage for Razzeleh."

"So, we'll talk. You'll bring a matchmaker?"

"What? A matchmaker? Is she so ugly and we so poor we have trouble finding her a husband? Somebody is asking already."

"Who?"

"Eisenberg."

"Who Eisenberg?"

"Gershon Eisenberg, with the wife Leah."

"So the boy is their son, the oldest, the know-it-all, with no beard, with no payess, with no hat — a goy already? He is for Razzeleh?"

"We'll talk."

"The one who had two wives already and somewhere a child, who knows what, who knows where? So maybe he needs more so he can leave them, too?"

"He's a learned man, not only Hebrew, the Gemara, the Talmud he studied in the yeshiva, but also he speaks Russian,

Polish, Latin, English, I don't know —"

"How old is he? With two wives already? And he stays in the house with his father? He can't make a living by himself?"

"He's with his father in the business."

"I won't let her be with such a goy. A beautiful girl and a dowry you'll give her. We should throw her away to a good-for-nothing who can't keep a wife? Is Razzeleh a dirty rag, a piece furniture?"

"Eisenberg is by me an honest Jew, and he's got plenty of money, you don't have to ask. And the son, David, he works hard, he's running the business in Kiev, in Minsk, in Odessa a long time, and, on top, he's a scholar. He reads, he studies, he can talk with the best —"

"No more!" yelled Bossel.

"We'll talk!" yelled Hyam. He gave a pound on the table and he walked back and forth across the room. Finally he looked at his wife. "All right, it doesn't thirst in my mouth I got to have the boy for a son-in-law. Enough is enough."

"Listen," Bossel said, "I didn't tell you. I'm talking last week by the rabbi from the yeshiva. A genius he's got, a young boy from the country, he studies the Gemara in the yeshiva. Such a head! A scholar, somebody to be proud of. He's so religious he can die for it. By him, a girl can bring honor to her family — and no worry from the dowry. She can marry him, someday a great rabbi."

"Who?"

"His name Mottel. I don't know, Feinberg, Weinberg, something. For Razzeleh, it would be the best thing. She'll have all the honors. Nu? What do you think?"

"Let me see the boy first. Why do you want to hurry?"

"And why you?"

"We'll see, we'll see."

Bossel ran to the kitchen. "Can you imagine?" she asked Razzeleh. "Somebody put in his head for you to marry the goy." Razzeleh looked, what goy? "The Eisenberg boy, the loafer from the big city. Leah's oldest."

Razzeleh tightly held a dish, her heart like the wind. "David Eisenberg?"

"David — he's a curse to such a name.

Don't worry, it won't happen to you."

"Ma . . . I wouldn't mind if —"

But Bossel didn't know what was in her daughter's heart. "I would die first," she said. "If your father made you, I would kill myself. Oy, my poor girl, such troubles and he wants more for you." She held Razzeleh like a little girl, even if she was taller by four inches. "You'll have the best. Don't worry, a match you'll make, it'll be made in heaven. I got myself for you a good young man, a fine scholar, everything a person can ask. Did you see by the yeshiva a boy, Mottel?"

"Ma," Razzeleh was still holding the dish, "if David Eisenberg is asking —"

"No more his name in this house! God forbid it!" and she spit three times to keep out the evil spirit.

David waited at home for a word from his father. "No news," Gershon told him. "Each time Hyam says to me, 'My wife is against.' 'And you?' I'm asking. 'Me, I'm not against, I'm not for. I don't want to give you an insult, but it's better not. Your son is a fine catch, all right, you have nothing to worry about. He'll marry

143

who he wants, but it's better not Razzeleh.' "

So, David walked by himself in the nighttime. He went by Razzeleh's house and watched in the dark. It was not safe because if some Russian boys saw him, they could break his bones, and if a family saw him there they would make trouble. But it was very dark, no lights except the lights from the houses, lamps and candles, and he walked. He was only afraid the dogs would bark. One barked and then another and then another, until finally a man came out of his house. David stood behind a tree. The dog barked but the man yelled, "Sharrop!" and the dog was quiet. After a while they all were quiet. David stayed by the tree. There's her house, he thought. She's inside, maybe her bedroom is there, maybe she's in bed already. What does she think? Now she must know he wants her for a wife. Does she refuse? So her mother is against, but Razzeleh? Is she against, too? Foolishness, foolishness. Why does he pick out someone he can't have? Let him pick out a nobody, then everybody will be satisfied. What's he done with his life? Every time he's bad luck. Was it Tzeepeh's fault after all? What did he want from her? Love? Where does he get such ideas? He's not a good Jew, he feels. Maybe he should never have been born.

Nighttime, bedtime, David saw the family go outside one at a time, in back of the house, to go to the bathroom. My God, it's a sin to watch, but he couldn't help it. He walked quietly around the house so the dog wouldn't bark, and he could see where they go to the bathroom, one at a time with the lamp. Finally, he saw her, the last of the children. She went inside the little house in back. Oy, it was so bad to watch, but what could he do? So he waited.

The little door opened and she came out. "Razzeleh!" he whispered.

"Oy!" She gave a little jump, bit her lip, and looked hard into the dark. She would scream in a second.

"It's David Eisenberg!" he said.

She stood like a statue.

"Gershon Eisenberg's son. Do you remember me?" He came closer by till the little light from the lamp, dancing in the night wind, showed on him. "Can I talk?" he asked.

"You scared me," she said.

"God forgive me. I had to see you. In the daytime, I couldn't. It would make trouble for you. Where else can I find you? You see how crazy I am in the head? It's a terrible thing to stop you here. Will you talk with me?"

"My parents will come out to see why I'm so long."

"Can you go with me where people won't look at us so we can talk?" He was close to her now, and she held the lamp by her eyes so she could see him, the two close together with the dark all around. The wind was whispering in the trees.

"My parents wouldn't let me," she said.

"You can tell them you are going to your girl friend for Shabbos evening. You can fix it up with her — the one with you on the bridge. Won't she help you?"

"How can I tell my parents a lie?"

The back door opened. "Razzeleh?" her mother said.

Razzeleh quickly put the lamp down by her side. "I'm coming, Ma."

"Why do you stay outside?"

"I'm looking at the stars, Ma."

"Stars? How can you see stars? I don't see any." She stepped from the door.

"You have the door open, that's why. Too much light. I'm coming in now."

But her mother closed the door behind her and came out. She looked up to see. David quickly bent over and went quietly away like a cat.

"I don't see," her mother said. "What can you see?"

"Maybe some clouds are coming," Razzeleh said.

"I don't like it — your standing alone in the dark. Come to bed."

"I haven't — I'm not through yet," Razzeleh said.

"You didn't go to the toilet yet?"

Razzeleh could hardly talk. "No." So quiet her mother had to ask. So she said again, "No."

"We're waiting. Such a foolish girl. Go. We have to go, too. We can't wait all night."

Razzeleh walked slowly toward the bathroom, the little house in back. When her mother went inside, opening the door and letting out the light, David bent like a stump, and the door finally closed. Then Razzeleh stopped and covered her mouth with her hand. She was laughing. "Now," she said, "you know everything."

"Well," David said, "by me it's no secret. At least I know you are a human angel." And together, close by her light, they laughed quietly.

"I must go inside quick," she said.

"You'll meet me?"

"I'll go to my friend Naomi on Shabbos."

"We can meet," David said, looking, thinking, and he pointed, "there, in the woods a little way inside."

"I will go to Naomi's."

"Only a few minutes we'll meet, to talk. I have to explain to you."

"All right." Quickly she ran to the house.

"When?" David called softly to her.

"When I come from Naomi's home."

"It will be dark. I'll smoke a cigarette,

you'll see it. By the woods there.''

She ran inside. Did she say yes? Maybe she talked to get rid of him. No, no, she wouldn't do that. She was too polite, too good. David looked up to see the stars. On Shabbos a moon would be starting.

On Shabbos David looked for Razzeleh in shul, where the women sit upstairs in back. But he couldn't find her among all the babushkas that were there. Each time he thought he saw her, it was someone else. Besides, he couldn't turn around all morning in the shul. So he davened, but he thought about Razzeleh. Instead of each word in the prayer he said, ''Razzeleh.'' Later in the afternoon he wouldn't go back to shul like his father. Instead he went walking. He had to walk to push the sun, it should go down faster. He walked around the whole town, field after field, this road, that road, till at the end he was covered with dust, and still it wasn't suppertime yet. He went home and took a bath. Inside a big metal tub he stood and washed himself. Then he put on clean clothes, nice patent leather boots, a short coat, not a long one to the shoe tops like the religious fanatics.

At supper he couldn't talk. He pushed the food into his mouth so the others wouldn't talk to him. He heard like they were in a different room. "Sonny," his mother said, "you don't feel well?"

"I'm fine, Ma," he said.

"Then what's the matter?" she asked.

"Just thinking."

"Thinking? Always he's thinking."

"So don't bother him," his father said. "Let him think, God be praised."

Supper finished, his father said, "I'll go to shul a little bit. David, you're coming?"

"No, thanks, Pa. I'll take a little walk."

"He thinks and he walks," his mother said. "It's not good all the time."

"It costs money?" his father asked. "Let him think, let him walk. When I was young, I was the same."

"From what were you thinking?" she asked. "For where were you walking?"

"When you're young, it's no problem, thinking, walking. I know what it is. Don't bother his head with questions."

David came to the woods behind Razzeleh's house too early. It wasn't dark yet, just a little gloomy. A path went through the woods where people walked, a little path still green on the bottom. David sat on an old dead tree, lying down, and he made a cigarette but did not yet smoke. He wouldn't use up all the tobacco and paper; he wanted to be sure to smoke so she would see where he sat. A little squirrel looked at him; then it ran up a tree like David would chase it.

A sliver of the moon finally came out; soon they wouldn't be able to see. Soon she would be too scared to come, it would be too late and her parents would worry, and he wouldn't get to talk to her. If she came too late she would have to leave right away, and he would be like a child reaching for the stars.

Now he had to light the cigarette, or, if she was coming, she might not see. He wouldn't puff, it should burn slowly. He was there, behind her house. Her brothers and sisters went in and out, and he was afraid maybe a little one might run to play in the woods. But it was too late, he knew, she didn't care, a foolish shlemiel he was, and the dark was coming faster, he could hardly see, and he felt maybe he would stay here all night. What did he care? He would sleep on the ground, so miserable, and the cigarette, he had to put it out.

"Oy! Mama!"

He jumped when the voice came. Someone out in the open, near the beginning of the trees. He ran quickly. My God, someone lying on the ground. "Razzeleh?" he whispered.

"It's me. Oy, I'm a fool," she said.

He went and put his arms around her and held her tight. "What happened?"

"When I saw the cigarette," she said, "I started running, and something, a bush, caught me like a hand and pulled me. Oy, I hope I didn't tear my clothes." Maybe she didn't see he was holding her. She felt all over her dress and down by the ankle. "It scratched me."

"By your foot?" David asked.

"My ankle. It's wet. Oy, I think it's bleeding."

"My God." He took his handkerchief

152

from his pocket, white like snow, and gave a shake. "Let me."

"I'll do it," Razzeleh said. She took the handkerchief and pulled her dress up a little bit so she could wrap it around her leg. He was so close to her now. With his left hand he gently held her left shoulder, her back on his chest. And he bent his head so he could put his face in her hair. "Ah," she said, and she sat against him harder, her cheek all of a sudden by his lips, and he kissed her. She pulled away.

"Forgive me. I couldn't help it," he said. They sat quietly a minute. He wanted to tear out his heart. "It's all right, your foot, now?"

"Yes," she said. "Later I'll wash your handkerchief and give it to you."

"I won't take it from you. My gift to you — a handkerchief? I want to give you the biggest, the richest cloth in the world." She was quiet, so he said, "I was afraid you wouldn't come."

"Naomi, she wouldn't let me go. She wanted to talk. She was crying she'll never get married, her father can't find a husband. She's a year younger than me, and she's crying she's an old maid."

"And you?" he asked. She wouldn't answer, so he sat by her and for a minute both were quiet. "Here it's dark everywhere," he said. "You don't see, you don't hear, no one knows what's going on. In the big cities they are more civilized, they go to the big theaters, and life there is very different. Here they don't know what's going on in the world. All they know is on Shabbos they go for a walk on the broken bridge to see the small boat." She let him take her hand. "Six months more I'll be here," he said. "After, I'll go again to Odessa."

All the time, you see, Razzeleh swallowed up every word from him. She felt so warm in her heart, oy, it was good to sit by him, hand in hand, but she was living a lie because she was supposed to be still at Naomi's. What if Naomi came to her house for some reason? It was not so far. If they should say, "Razzeleh, you lied to us," what could she do? She would die. Still, to pull away her hand, to get up and run to the house — she felt like she drank too much Pesach wine, she didn't know what she was doing, like she didn't care anymore. Then, down there, at the house, she saw the back door open up, and her mother looked outside a minute. Razzeleh grabbed David's hand. Finally, her mother went in. Razzeleh stood up quick. "Did you see?" she asked.

"I want you to go with me," David said quick. She looked at him, scared, and she started to run away. He caught her. "Don't you know? I want to have you for my wife." She couldn't help it, she started to cry. For what? Happiness? She was too scared? She felt all mixed up. "I'm so terrible to you?" he asked.

"How can I go against my parents?" she asked him. "I must do what they say."

"And if they say it's all right, then what do you say?"

They stood close now. She looked at him, in his eyes. Like a breath she said yes. He held both her hands to his heart and bent over to kiss her, but she was frightened. She didn't know why, and she pulled away from him and started to run home.

He yelled to her, "Again, Shabbos?"

"Shah!" she said, her finger to her lips, and she looked to see if anyone could hear.

He ran to her. "Again, Shabbos? We have to talk yet."

She smiled at him and nodded and ran quickly to the house. From the door she saw only the dark behind her, but she gave a wave anyhow.

Her parents didn't ask. They knew she was with Naomi. In her room her twelve-year-old sister was sleeping, so Razzeleh could go to bed quietly. Finally she lay down and looked far away with beautiful thoughts, but it bothered her he was going away in six months and she wouldn't see him again — unless she could go with him. What if her parents said no, it was so quick, they didn't like it, he looked bad in their eyes. It made her afraid and she wrapped herself up in the quilt, and that was how she fell asleep.

Next morning she woke up very happy and started to clean the house. On Shabbos they couldn't wash the dishes or do work because it's the holy day, the blessed day, so everything was saved for

Sunday. Razzeleh washed the dishes and sang to them like a bird in the spring. In the hide room separate from the house, where they hung the hides so they wouldn't smell up the house, Bossel was helping Hyam. She heard how Razzeleh sang Russian songs, strong and happy. "You hear?" she asked Hyam. "You hear how Razzeleh sings?"

"What's to hear? A girl sings, let her sing."

"She's happy."

"Thanks be to God."

Then Razzeleh, since she was the oldest, made a meal for everybody. The other children went to cheder, and Isaac went to learn how to make furniture. He had a good head. Hyam wanted him to be a rabbi, but Isaac didn't want to be a rabbi with long curls and a long coat. When you have children, you got to expect.

Came the Shabbos again, in the evening, and Razzeleh said she would go to Naomi's. Nu, let her go, it won't hurt, her parents said. This time she told Naomi she could stay only a little. Last time was too late for her parents. Already she told another lie and she felt sinful, deeper and deeper she went. Again she ran to the woods in back of the house. She saw how the cigarette burned like a star. This time she was careful not to fall, and she walked toward David. He was standing, waiting. It was not black, the moon was big, and they could see. Again he held her hand, he gave a kiss on her fingers, and he put them on his cheek.

"Now I'm not good for my father," David said. "I don't know what I'm doing day from night. I look on the numbers, the figures from the business, and I see 'Razzeleh, Razzeleh.' And when I should say, 'We have all kinds rope, twine, string we can buy for you,' I hear myself saying, 'We have beautiful braids like silk, dark like night with flashes fire,' and the customer shakes his head. 'Meshuggener, crazier I haven't seen in all my life.' 'What's the matter you're talking crazy?' my father says, and I laugh like I'm playing a joke. Do you see? 'You're bad for business,' my father says. 'Maybe I would be better off without you. You'll ruin me.'" He watched her closely.

Razzeleh couldn't speak. She looked up at him like he was the only person alive. And he couldn't stop, his face on hers, his lips on her cheek and on her lips. She didn't know this was how it is, so warm but shivering, too, how weak she was, and she held on like she would fall. She pulled him, she wanted him closer, even to hurt her ribs, she couldn't be close enough. "It was never like this before," he said, finally, quiet, his lips by her ear, and he held her tight. "So now it's love, what all the books say, how you don't know what happens, it comes. No one else, no one else," and he looked in her eyes. "And by you?" he asked. "Who am I for you? What do you feel for me?"

The moon was behind him. She couldn't see, a shadow, the shape of a man, and she heard him talking quietly so his voice didn't sound the same as he whispered. Was she dreaming maybe? What could she say to him? She was a little bit scared of the way she felt — maybe this was how babies come? She knew but she didn't know. The stories people told, the ways girls talked — they think they know, but they know from nothing.

"Razzeleh, my Razzeleh," he was saying as he held her. And then some leaves were brushing, some twigs were snapping, and somebody was walking.

In Russian someone yelled, "Look what we caught!" A young Russian man in a shiny shirt, and then another one. "Lovers in the woods, by Christ!" they were yelling, each with a bottle in the hand, high up like lanterns, and they bumped each other as they came near David and Razzeleh. One leaned toward her. "Do I know you?" he asked in Russian, and then he looked at David. "Sir, your Honor, you shouldn't take our girls from us. It's bad for you. You have to leave something for us, sir. Forgive me, your Excellency. Would you have a drink with us?" He held out the bottle to David, who quietly held Razzeleh. "It's nice," the other one said, and he reached out to touch her braids. She put her face on David's shoulder, so scared she was, and she could feel the man holding her braids. "You take from us only the best," he said, and he fell backwards holding her braids, and it pulled back her head, all of a sudden out of David's arms before he knew it.

"Take your dirty hands away from her!" David yelled in Russian, and he gave the man such a kick in the stomach that he dropped the bottle and fell on his back. The other Russian, a young one, was laughing, he thought it was funny, and he grabbed David's arms from behind.

"Your Highness," he said, "forgive us, but it's not right." Then the other one held Razzeleh's ankle, and she screamed with all her heart and tried to pull away, but he pulled back and she fell next to him, crying out while David was kicking. What should he do? The man on the ground with Razzeleh was putting his wine-soaked face on hers, and she gave him such a hit on the nose it made a noise like the twigs underneath, and he let go of her.

"Run!" David yelled. She couldn't leave him like a prisoner, but he yelled, "Run! You'll help me if you'll run!" The Russian holding him was laughing, so he didn't hear it was Yiddish David spoke. As he saw Razzeleh start to run away, the Russian let go of David to catch her, but David threw himself on him.

How did they fight? Not like here, what you see in the moving pictures. There they gave kicks with the boots, they bumped their heads on their stomachs like goats, and with a thumb they pushed into the eyes, the nose. With the fists, they hit like they pound a table. The two young Russians were tearing up David's clothes, but he wouldn't give up, and he hit with his hands and his feet and his head. One gave him such a knock with an elbow that he fell down on a piece wood, a branch. "Where is she?" one of them asked, as he went like a blind man with his arms out to find Razzeleh. The other was bending down to grab David's coat and give him another knock. But David took the branch, a big one, and hit the Gentile so hard on the head he fell down.

Now David stood up; by the mouth he was bleeding, his face looked like a rag, and his legs were shaking and folding up underneath, he was so tired. But he was wild like an animal, and he called out, "Razzeleh? Are you here? Razzeleh!" He couldn't see the other Russian but he heard something, the voice and some laughing. Oh, my God, he was going crazy. Did the Russian have Razzeleh, he wondered. He ran that way, this way, looking where the voice came from, and he carried the big piece wood. There, he saw, the other one was bending over — my God, with Razzeleh? With her underneath? And David ran with such a yell, like a lion, and he hit the Russian on the head with the piece wood, such a hit, the goy fell like somebody was cutting off his legs, and he lay like a log. David looked and looked. Nothing, thank God, nothing. Razzeleh was not there. "Razzeleh?" he called softly. "Razzeleh, it's me, David. It's all right now. Are you here someplace?" Nothing. It was quiet, not even crickets or birds, not even a dog. All right, thank God she went home. He prayed she went home, please, God, let her be safely at her house.

He looked at the Russian. Maybe he was dead. He went to the other one.

Maybe he was dead, too. So torn and bloody was David, like soup was spilling from his mouth, he could hardly walk. Like a wounded animal he went home, into the back of his house, where no one was watching, everyone was sleeping now. He took a pitcher of water and poured into a big bowl and washed himself around. Then he took his clothes — the fine shirt like a rag now, the short coat from the city that looked like a mop now — and he put it all in a cloth bag that he hid, so no one should find it, in the pit outside by the garbage. But his forehead, his neck, and his cheeks were torn.

When they found the two Russians, maybe they would be dead. All right, the people would think they beat each other up. But if the two Russians got up and went to the police, they would start a pogrom on all the Jews. Oy, he was so tired, how could he think? What did he make of his life? Why did God pick him out?

In the morning, when his mother saw him, she was scared. ''What happened with your face?''

''I cut myself with the knife when I shaved,'' he said. ''I didn't know something happened to my razor. When I go to Kiev I'll buy a new one.''

She listened to him and said, ''Go, my child. Wash your hands for breakfast.''

But David couldn't eat. How was Razzeleh? How did she feel? How could he find out? His mother was busy with the nine children; his father went by himself to the stores to take the orders and he went himself to Kiev now, so they didn't tell him.

In the meantime, Razzeleh woke up with swollen eyes. What happened to David? They were two and David was one. Maybe they killed him, God forbid. No, it wasn't possible. He couldn't be dead. So all night she was thinking, she couldn't sleep, and she cried. How could she find out? She ran out of her room to find someone, maybe Naomi could ask for her, maybe they would be talking already about what happened. Her mother said, ''Oy! Razzeleh, what is it?'' She felt her glands under the ears. Nothing. ''Is someone sick? Does Naomi have something, a fever, a swelling, what?'' She ran to the hide room. ''Hyam, come quick! Razzeleh is sick!'' she shouted.

Hyam yelled to his wife, ''What happened?''

''I don't know,'' Bossel said. ''Her eyes, swollen like a disease, she can hardly see.''

''She'll be all right.''

''You got to see!''

''In the middle of work,'' Hyam yelled, ''you bother my head.'' But he came and looked at Razzeleh. ''What's going on?'' he asked. ''Go get the doctor.''

''Ma, Pa, it's nothing,'' Razzeleh said. ''Last night I opened the window in my room. I was hot, I washed my face with cold water, so I caught a little cold.''

''A cold with the eyes closing?'' Bossel said. ''I'll get the doctor.''

''Ma, no!'' Razzeleh said. ''I'll be all right!''

''You're sure?'' Hyam asked. ''Nu, she'll be all right,'' and he went back to his work.

''Doctor or no doctor,'' her mother

said, "today you'll stay in bed."

"I'm all right, Ma."

"She's all right, but you can't see her eyes," Bossel said. "You'll go to bed, we'll find out if you're all right."

Like a prison, she couldn't go out — her own fault, again a lie, and more trouble. Razzeleh sent her younger sister, Sophie. "Find out what's happening."

"What do you mean, what's happening?" Sophie asked.

"If something happened, an accident, something, come tell me quick."

"Why should something happen today? Is it something special?"

"Don't ask," Razzeleh said. "Find out, bring to me what you hear."

"I have to go to cheder," Sophie answered.

"You'll tell me when you get home."

What happened, Razzeleh and David could put together, a word here, a word there, like stitching — Sophie told her, but everyone in town talked about it. In the morning the goyim went to the fields to work. When they walked by the woods, they saw the two boys lying with blood on them. The peasants got scared and ran home, and in one house they were all screaming, everyone together. So someone brought the constable, the policeman, with everyone talking and yelling, but he gave such a yell, with his fist in the air, and he brought it down on the table like a gun, and everyone was quiet. Then a small boy fourteen years old said, "Ponee, we saw two dead boys lying on the ground in the woods."

The constable, named Vasil, tall, with a big stomach and a fat lump on the back of his neck, and with two mean eyes, not a good man, asked, "How do you know? Did you touch them?" "No," the boys said. "You tell lies," the constable said, and he went himself to the woods to look. One of the Russian boys was sitting on the ground scratching his head. The other was still lying down. "What are you doing here?" the constable asked. "Drunkard, like a pig," and he gave him a kick with his boot, and he kicked again till the boy got up.

Now the parents were there. "God, God, someone beat up our children," they said. And they picked them up and put them in the big wagons with the hay to take them home. Now the whole shtetl, the town, was yelling that someone beat up the boys. The goyim raised their fists and there was a big tumult. The Jews were scared. What's going on? David and Razzeleh couldn't go out of the house with their faces.

The parents of the first boy called the doctor. He said the boy was all right, just drunk from vodka. So he lay a little in bed. The other boy, whom David hit harder, couldn't open his eyes. His parents undressed him and found broken pieces glass in his pocket. The mother was fanatically religious and wouldn't call the doctor. She wanted by her the priest. So the priest came, a big white beard, white long hair. He came into the house, one room with a roof of straw. One bed they had, made from boards, the whole family slept together, parents and children. And a big oven in the room. Also in the room, they kept some animals. When they give the pigs to eat, they fill a big wooden bowl with food.

So, the priest came and the whole family, big and small, fell to their knees and crossed themselves three times. The batushka, the priest, covered his nose because of the bad smell, and he talked to the boy: "Andrei, what did you do that you are so sick?"

The boy could hardly speak a word. He crossed himself and kissed the priest's hand. He talked with trembling lips. "Forgive me, holy batushka." He told the priest how he and Vasil went for a walk in the woods, how they had little bottles vodka and started to sing, and the night was very pretty with the moon. "Holy father, the moon was so big in the sky. We saw two people sitting, a girl and a boy. Vasil started to bother the girl. We didn't know who they are. He looked like a Polish prince." The Polish prince used to come and inspect the fields belonging to Kanage Radziwill. "I grabbed the girl, very pretty, with long braids. I never saw one like her. She kicked me and hit me, such a strong one I never saw. I grabbed her braids and I heard Vasil yell, 'Andrei, help me, the prince will kill me!' The girl started to run away, so I wanted to tell her I wouldn't hurt her, but I couldn't find her. And then someone gave me such a big hit, I fell to the ground and was lost." He crossed himself again and was quiet.

The priest started to talk to the parents: "Pray to God the Polish prince will be ashamed, he won't tell his father, the Kanage. If he tells, the Kanage will take away the ground where you plant corn, potatoes, all kinds vegetables." The whole family went through a tremor and started to cry. The priest told them to go to church and pray to God he should forgive them. And they should keep quiet and not talk.

In the shtetl was quiet. Our little town isn't even on the map, but all the Russians got to know what happened by the two boys. The priest said Andrei and Vasil got drunk and fought. When he talked, everyone was quiet, and with every word he said they crossed themselves.

For three weeks already David did not see Razzeleh. Instead, the boy Mottel from the yeshiva went to her house. From

171

all the little villages came many boys to learn the Gemara, and they were very poor sons, so every Jewish family gave each boy one day to eat or two days. So, Mottel came, skinny with two long payess, the hair by the ears. When he came to eat lunch, Razzeleh had to serve him. He ate and looked at her from the corners of his little eyes, with his three hairs on his cheeks. And her mother made sure that Razzeleh would bring something to him every time. He looked at her, such a prize. But day by day she was fading like a light from loneliness.

And David? He talked to himself, a crazy man already. Finally, he said to his father, "I have to talk to you about something. Don't tell Ma or the children."

"All right, good," Gershon said, "we'll go to shul."

It was Friday. David went with his father. The other ones went with their mother. David talked quietly to his father. "I saw the girl, Rachel. I think she'll have me."

"My poor boy," Gershon said, "it's hard. By her father, maybe it's possible.

But the mother, she's like a fire — you can't put her out. If I send a matchmaker, the mother will throw him out. If you go yourself, she won't say a word to you. What the father says goes. That's how we think. What the mother feels, that's how it is.''

''Can you talk with the father?'' David asked. ''You can tell him it's all right by his daughter, she'll marry me. Maybe you can tell him we've talked on the street a little.''

Gershon saw that David was talking wildly, like a man in his sleep having a nightmare. ''We'll see, we'll see,'' he said.

''Talk to him, Pa. Right away.''

''I'll talk. In shul I'll talk.''

''Can you go with him to his house?'' David asked. ''If you see the mother, tell her I'll give my life for her daughter. I'll work my fingers to the bone. I'll stay. I'll go. I'll do anything. Pa?''

''If I can. I won't force myself. Maybe Shabbos after shul. We'll see.''

So, that evening in the shul Gershon again stood by Hyam, and in between the prayers they talked. ''What can I do?''

Gershon asked. "My son is going crazy over your daughter. In Kiev he can get the richest girls with plenty dowry, but he's in love with your daughter. He'll marry her without money. Do you understand?" Hyam played with his beard. "Why so quiet?" Gershon asked. "I have to know. My son is going away pretty soon to Kiev for six months."

"Maybe my daughter doesn't want your son," Hyam said.

"She wants, she wants. Forgive me, but they talked a couple times. In the street, in plain daylight, in front of everybody. Ask her yourself."

"When she hears," Hyam said, "her mother will give a scream. I can't do anything."

"All right," Gershon said, "is your wife so different? She's not a human being? Let me talk to her."

"You?"

"Why not me? I'm the father of my son. A glass tea tomorrow, Shabbos, after shul, she won't refuse me. Let her think I come to see you for business," Gershon said.

So, next day, after shul, he went home with Hyam. They went into the house, clean, with a nice tablecloth, brass candlesticks on the table. It was very nice when Bossel and Razzeleh came in from the kitchen. "A good week to you and to all the children," Gershon said.

"Go make the samovar," Hyam said to Bossel. "We'll drink tea. Razzeleh, bring us to eat."

So, she brought in baked goods and glasses and the samovar while Bossel put the children to sleep. Everything was falling from Razzeleh's hands, she was so nervous. Her father then told her to go out and send in her mother, who came in and sat down by the two men. Razzeleh was hiding behind the door to the kitchen, and she held her breath so they shouldn't hear her.

"Do you know, Bossel," Hyam asked, "why Gershon comes home with me today?"

"How should I know?" she said. "Maybe for business? Otherwise he has nothing to do here."

"She talks like a woman," Hyam

said to Gershon.

Bossel didn't say a word; she just poured the tea.

"A man wants to talk like a human being," Hyam said, "you have to listen."

"I don't have to," Bossel said. To Gershon she said, "What do you want to say?"

Hyam talked. "Do you hold in your heart something bad toward our friend? How long do we know each other? How many years? And all of a sudden he is a piece dust in your eye? For no reason."

Bossel put a sugar cube in her mouth and sipped tea. She looked only at the table; she wouldn't look at the men.

"Listen," Gershon said, "no arguments please. For that I didn't come. In all the years you know me, do I put on you a cloud? Am I a bad name in the shul? I have respect. Ask anyone, am I a stranger? I work hard to raise a good family, all my kids are good. God bless them, I am proud of them. All right, my oldest, David, he doesn't want a beard. On him it itches, so he's more modern. You should see the way Jews go in the cities. No one has a beard on his face. He is highly educated, my David. He knows the Gemara like his hand, and any language you can think of, say it, he can speak. From the books he reads all the great writers. And he knows, he has experience — the world he's traveled." In those days, when somebody went to the big cities, one, two, he was traveling the world already.

"Your son," Bossel said, and she looked at Gershon, "that's your business. I'm not interested."

"He's a fine boy, a good man," Gershon said. Now he was mad. "No one can say bad things about him. Why should he have heartaches? What are you holding against him? You can be the proudest in the world from him, and I don't ask even —"

"What proud?" she asked. "Why should I be proud of him? I have nothing to do with him."

"You have plenty to do," Gershon said. "From the way things look, it's up to you."

"What's up to me?"

"My son, David, wants to take your daughter, Rachel, for a wife."

Bossel gave such a jump the glass fell out of her hand and the tea burned her. She gave a yell, "Vey's mir!" and she started to cry. "It will never be!" she shouted. "A Kiever bum he is! A good-for-nothing with two wives already, and somewhere he hides a child. Who knows, maybe he has more. A goy wants my daughter? First I'll kill myself!"

"Quiet!" Hyam gave a bang on the table, two big candlesticks fell down, Bossel had to grab them quickly, a fire shouldn't start. "I'm not here anymore?" he asked. "It's not my house now?" Bossel was standing with a candle in each hand like a statue. "Put down the candles," he said. She pushed the candles back into the holders. "Sit down." She sat quietly, with tears running down her cheeks. "The boy is a fine boy," Hyam said. "When he married the first one, he was a child. He didn't even know what a wife is. With the second wife, he couldn't live — a wife who mixed in his business, picking and picking. Such a woman you shouldn't be with."

Gershon said, "My son, in Kiev, girls with a lot of money, learned, they want him. And with a business, too. But my son, God bless him, he's fallen in love with your daughter."

"How does he know her?" Bossel asked. "He never saw her."

"She walks on the bridge, so he sees her and finds out she is Hyam's daughter," Gershon said. "He wants her."

"Why talk?" Bossel asked. "Razzeleh knows from nothing that he wants her. Loves! A fine boy who learns in yeshiva loves her. He eats two days in our house."

"Mottel?" Hyam asked. "A stick of wood? Him you want for her? I feel sick to look at him."

"He'll be a big rabbi," Bossel said. "You'll see, and all the Jews by us will respect him, and she will have such a husband, educated, of the highest. What do you want for Razzeleh? The biggest honor, or a man who shleps her, carries her who knows where? He'll divorce her, too, when he gets tired of her."

"I don't want to hear more," Hyam

said. "We'll talk over, we'll see."

"Never mind the dowry," Gershon said. "Never mind giving to eat, a big party, nothing. I'll take care of everything. They'll live by me, or they'll —"

"Oy!" Bossel said, as she ran out of the room. Razzeleh had to run quickly from the kitchen door to her room. "Razzeleh?" her mother called. "I have to tell you something. Do you know the tramp with two wives already, a child also? God knows. Your father wants him for your husband. Can you imagine such a thing? They don't want a dowry even, he's so bad. Don't worry, I'll never let you fall into those hands. A goy he is! What does he know from Jewish? Look at Mottel, how he sits day in, day out, studying the Gemara, his mind on learning, not on bad things. Such a boy, he is worthy of you."

"I don't want Mottel," Razzeleh said.

"He's only nineteen years old. When he is older and you marry him, he'll mind you and he'll be a big rabbi. Everyone will admire you for having such an educated husband. How old are you, seventeen? For a girl it's not good when she's already getting older. The boys don't want her. Me, I was almost fourteen, and I never saw your father till the next day in the morning, and you see how both of us are happy."

"Pa is a handsome man, a mensch, not like Mottel."

"What's the matter with Mottel?" Bossel asked. "You think looks make the world? The great men, all good-lookers? Maimonides, your father says, was an ugly man. Who can tell? When he gets older and has a nice beard and eats better, then you'll see how handsome Mottel will be."

"I don't want to talk," Razzeleh said. "Let me go to bed."

"Razzeleh!" her father called to her. She ran to the dining room but Bossel ran, too. She had to hear what Hyam was saying. Razzeleh was wiping the tears from her dark eyes and her cheeks, and they became even redder. When Gershon looked at her she watched the table.

Gershon was thinking his son knows what he wants.

"Bossel," Hyam said, "take the dishes out." So she had to take the dishes into the kitchen. To Razzeleh, "My child, do you know why Gershon comes here?"

She wouldn't lift up her eyes. "Maybe for business."

"No, my child. He wants you for his son. You don't know him — David, his oldest. We want to put you together, you should meet each other." Her cheeks were like the red from brick when the oven is hot. She started to shake. "You don't have to be scared. Just to see him. When you do, maybe yes, maybe no."

In the kitchen, behind the door, Bossel dropped the glass she was wiping and it broke into little pieces.

Gershon said to Hyam, "You'll see, an engagement will come."

Then Bossel ran inside, her face white, her eyes popping out, her lips shaking. Gershon was scared, and he said to her, "If something breaks, it's a good sign for you."

"Maybe for you," she said, "but not for me, not for my daughter. My God, you want to ruin her whole life!"

"Bossel!" Hyam made a face she couldn't look at. She had to close her eyes. "You won't insult my friend! We have to show respect in our house!" She cried and sat like a stone. "Now, we'll make up something together. David should go out with Razzeleh for a walk. Let them walk and let the two children talk over between them. Then we'll know what is. They'll tell us. Good?"

"Good," Gershon said. "No one is forcing. They'll decide."

"Then it's enough," Hyam said. "Razzeleh, do you understand?" Yes, she nodded and smiled, and she was like a baby with a doll, only so red was her face. Hyam kissed her forehead and she bowed to Gershon and went to her room light like a feather. "And you, Bossel?" Hyam asked. She held her apron over her eyes and ran out of the room. "Never mind," he said. "More she is against, more I am in favor. A home is not good when a woman is a rabbi in it."

All night Bossel was talking in Razzeleh's room, she wouldn't leave her alone, she should not see that goy, David, she should not throw away her life, she should listen to her mother, she knows best how terrible it is to marry a good-for-nothing. He'll take her far away, God knows where, and leave her like he left his second wife — if a second, so there will be a third. And who knows what happened to his first, a young girl like Razzeleh? Her father will be mad, but better he should be mad. She will be happy. Nu, she'll get used to Mottel. If not Mottel, all right, someone like him, a good boy, religious. Respect he'll have from everybody.

She talked, talked, and talked till finally the daylight came into the room and the roosters crowed and everybody got up. But Razzeleh was so happy she kept quiet and didn't feel like she hadn't slept. Her mother was very white.

Comes Shabbos and Hyam and Bossel went to shul, and Razzeleh put on her Shabbos dress and combed her braids, long down the back, and she washed her face and dressed the little children. On the table she put a nice tablecloth and then the dishes and the spoons. Then two big challehs with a bottle wine and a silver cup to make Kiddush. Everything was

Shabbosdich. When her parents came home, the whole family sat down around the table. The father and mother went in the kitchen to wash their hands, and Mottel came in with his long coat, and with the payess, the hair by the ears. Razzeleh could hardly say "Good Shabbos" to him. Together all the children said, "Good year, Mottel."

The parents came from the kitchen and Bernice said, "Mottel, go wash your hands." He went out and he came back and sat not far from Razzeleh. The father made the prayers, everybody said "Omayn," amen, and he gave everybody a big piece challeh for a moetze. Then Razzeleh went with her mother to the kitchen and they opened up the big oven covered with rags.

They took out the food — potatoes, meat, beans, and onions — and gave everybody separate, and Razzeleh served first to her father. Then Mottel and the mother and finally the children. Afterwards they had a big kugel for dessert.

When they were finished they all sang

Shmirez. Then Hyam went to take a nap and Mottel davened with tefillin. Razzeleh cleaned off the table. Finally, she went by the door. Her mother saw.

"Why do you leave Mottel?" Bossel asked. "Listen, you'll be old and homely, and you'll be sorry you lost such a wonderful boy who didn't talk loud and who learned so good the Gemara!"

"I have to go," Razzeleh said.

"So you're going?"

"Pa wants me."

"What does he want? A goyisher son-in-law?" Bossel asked. "You'll stay home and I'll tell him. Let him hit me, whatever he wants, you don't have to go outside on the street with such a beggar."

"Please, Ma," Razzeleh said. "I'll be all right. You can't hurt Pa that way."

"Hurt Pa?" Bossel stood like Razzeleh was throwing water on her face. Then Razzeleh gave her a kiss, quick, and ran outside. It was too late to stop her.

She went to the bridge by herself, turning this way, that way, all the time with a fear in her heart that they would see her, friends, relatives. By the bridge

she was looking for David. She couldn't
see. All the sky by the ground was like
somebody cuts it, a wound, and black
clouds on top, they were curling around
the blue parts like big mouths — the day
was going, still warm, but she began to
shiver. Where was he? Maybe it was a
mistake? How did she know him, a man
from the world with two wives already?

A grab on her elbow like someone hit
her whole body. She jumped. It was
David. He breathed fast and looked
around, his eyes wide, like maybe he was
scared or mixed up. He looked different,
thin, like the Jewish boys with the caps
and the long black coats. "You're here,"
he said, and he grabbed her arm too hard,
it hurt. "I have a good place." He pulled
her along the street, and she had to walk
fast, the way he went. By us stood a big
church on the hill. Shabbos, at night, no
one goes to it. So David took Razzeleh
way up high, where they were alone by the
church, gray, and the windows were
purple, and the top was like lots of little
bald heads, and the wind made noise like
an old man in pain. David pulled her

down on the grass and looked at her.

"I went crazy when I couldn't find you," he said, "and if I killed the two muzhiks I didn't care. I thought they harmed you. I could kill everyone in the world for you. They thought I was the prince, did you hear? And you a beautiful peasant girl or maybe a princess, and it could have been a whole mishmash with a pogrom, but, God be praised, everything is all right, except I didn't see you for so long. I can't eat, I can't sleep, like I'm dying. Razzeleh, Razzeleh," and he held her shoulders like a vise till tears almost came to her. "Would you like to live in Kiev or Ekaterinoslav or Odessa?" David asked her. "Where? Wherever you want, away from here, such misery. There, in the city, everybody goes on Shabbos to the theater and they go to the Tsar's garden, and the most beautiful music plays. In Odessa they bathe in the Black Sea. What is here? It's dark and there's no light or nice music. No one here to have a conversation, like a graveyard, everybody sitting dead or running like animals, only money they want, like dogs running after rabbits — no, no, like pigs for roots. They have to do it, they don't enjoy. Razzeleh, Razzeleh, you'll go with me the whole world around! I know what life means. I know it very well." So excited he gave her a shake, but she couldn't talk. Slowly she pushed away his hands. He swallowed and took a big breath. "Do you love me?" he asked. It gave her such a scare, he felt it. "Tell me what you feel. Don't worry. I won't go and cry like my father is yelling at me."

What could she say? She looked at him and then at the ground. How could she leave the town where she was born, and her parents, brothers, sisters, everything?

Softly he said to her, "I want you should be my wife. Before, I thought — something is different? You have someone else?"

"Oy." She looked into his eyes. "My mother, my family —" and she put her head into her hands, looked below, at the lights coming from the houses, the little smokes from the chimneys.

"It never came to me you weren't sure," David said. Now he was quiet.

Razzeleh couldn't stand it. She put her hand on top his head and tried to talk, but she couldn't. She looked at him. Slowly he leaned toward her, carefully, and on her open lips he put his own. Her heart didn't let her hear anything, only itself. "My wife," David said. "You will be my wife. Tell me. You want to be?"

"Yes," she said, a breath, a sob. She stood quick and he, too.

"Then what is it?" David asked. "We say yes, our fathers say yes."

"I'm afraid of my mother," Razzeleh said.

"Who counts in your family more — your mother?"

"No."

"Then why are you afraid?"

"She talks in my head."

"What? I'm a loafer, a goy, no good for you?" David asked. He let go of her. "Maybe she's right." Razzeleh tried to see him better, she was so mixed up. "If you don't believe me, if you think maybe she is right, then maybe she is. How do I know from you? Maybe you are no good for me. But I love you — that's all.

Who's right, who's wrong? I don't know.
Only I love you, maybe it will kill me, all
right. But I don't have any questions." He
took one step away from her and she
threw herself on him, her arms around his
neck.

"I love you!" Razzeleh cried. "It tears
my heart, but that's how I am — my
family, my town. I'm afraid. Was I ever
away from my home? When I go out I get
scared. Will you take me to the city? How
will I be there, a little town girl, I don't
know the city. You hear how I can't talk.
What do I know from conversation? All
my life I know only to work in the house,
getting ready for Shabbos and the meals,
the cooking, the cleaning — that's my life.
If I come to the city, I'll be lost. Will you
stay with me, a country girl? You'll be
ashamed."

"May God strike me dead first," David
said. "Ashamed? Of my Razzeleh? How
can you say such a thing?" He held her,
softly now.

What's wrong with me? she was
thinking. I love him, I want to be by him
forever, but I'm scared. Why should I be

scared? "I'm scared," she said.

"Before a flea should harm you, I would die."

She smiled at him. "How many times can you die?" She grabbed him hard. "I don't want you should die. Don't say, it's bad luck."

"Then you have to marry me. Without you I can't live. You will. You will. Nu?"

My God, she wanted, she should say yes, but in her ear were her mother's words, and she was afraid he would take her to the city like a storm at night. She was scared, like the night at the lake with the Russian boys, and every time with David was like God looking down, making a punishment, but she couldn't help it. She loved him, all right she would suffer, she had to speak —

"Who is there?" a deep voice shouted in Russian. "What do you want?" A giant floating, black flies with wings shaking, flap, flap, in front like a big knife, a butcher blade where a face should be, a hole opened. "What are you doing?" the voice shouted, and Razzeleh screamed. She wanted to run but David held her, and she pushed but he held on like he was bringing her for sacrifice, and here was the Angel of Death, who wanted her.

"Razzeleh! Razzeleh!" David said. And in Russian he said, "Your Excellency, we were sitting and talking."

"Who are you?" A voice like a drum.

"We are Jewish," David said. "We had to talk alone, so we came here."

"Talk, hah? There are two of you? From up there it looks like one person, so close you talk."

Razzeleh moved her face away from David's coat and saw the priest, his robes and silver beard shining.

"You could be in trouble on church property," he said. "Somebody catch you, it would be bad for you." Like Moses he looked. "You think you are the only ones who come here? A regular lovers' hill it is. You," he asked David, "you're married?"

"No, your Honor."

"And she?"

"We are going to get married if she'll have me," David said.

"What's the matter, can't you wait?" the priest asked. Then he looked at

Razzeleh. "You'll have him?" She couldn't talk, so scared. "Don't let him ruin you here on the hill. Plenty girls are ruined here. A holy place, they think that makes it all right. Still a sin, you understand? He'll have you and then he'll leave you. Marriage first, then he can't hurt you." The priest put his finger, long like a wooden spoon, under her chin. Then he raised it to look at her face, wet from tears, her eyes like wells with stars in them. "Your mother knows you're here?" he asked. "Listen, be a good girl, go home, let him come with his parents like a gentleman. If you have to meet secretly, something is wrong." He stood straight, the church was behind; like the church he stood over them, higher on the hill. He shook his head no, sadly, "Go with God's blessing on you," he said. "It's dark. You should be home now. Shalom."

"Shalom," David said, and he smiled. The priest went flying with his robes back to the church, standing like a castle. He looked like he floated in the air. "Shalom," David said. "I wonder he knows Yiddish, too." And he laughed.

"The batushka, the lord priest." He took Razzeleh and they walked down the hill. She was wiping away her tears. So, she was scared, it was all over, but she couldn't stop crying.

So David let her cry, but he kept one arm around her. When they came to her house, she saw her mother standing in the door. Quick, Razzeleh pulled David's arm away from her, but her mother saw and ran out, shouting, "Where were you so long? Don't you know it's late? It's dark already. I'm dying from worry and you come like it's nothing." She threw knives at David with her eyes and she looked at Razzeleh's wet face. "Oy! What is he doing to you? Proster!" she yelled at David. "Common! If you harm a single hair on her head, I'll kill you!"

"Ma," Razzeleh said. "Stop it."

"Stop it? So my daughter now talks back to her mother?"

"She's perfectly all right," David said.

"From you, now, you have to talk?"

"It's no use arguing," he said. "Razzeleh will marry me."

"Over my dead body she'll marry you,"

Bossel yelled. "A goy she should marry? You — you should grow like an onion, with the head in the ground. Trash!"

"Ma!" Razzeleh shouted. "I won't hear it!"

"Get in the house! Go!" and she gave Razzeleh a slap on the cheek, hard, and David made a step toward her like he'd hit her, but Razzeleh looked at him, please, no, and he put down his hand. "You see?" Bossel said to her. "You see what he'll do? He'll do it to me, he'll do it to you, worse. Get out!" she yelled at him. "Get out of my house! Leave her alone!" And she pushed Razzeleh into the house and bang! She slammed the door. David stood like someone was shooting him, like he was dying already.

Soon he came home. Only his mother waited. The children were in bed; his father stayed yet in shul. "Nu?" his mother said. He shook his head no, he couldn't talk. "She won't say?"

"It's the mother," David said. "She's the trouble."

Leah gave a deep sigh. "It will be all right. You'll see. Go, my son, go to sleep.

You look tired." So he went to his room and lay down and thought of Razzeleh. He couldn't rest, so much he loved her. How he wanted to have her by him and to fly high to the skies and to hold her close to his heart and to yell out, "She's mine, she's mine forever!"

With Razzeleh it was a different story. By her, too, the children were sleeping and the father was in shul, but inside Naomi was waiting. She was here to spend the night — such a time, Razzeleh didn't want Naomi now. "Go to bed," her mother said. "Wait till your father comes, what I'll have to tell him. Go. You should be ashamed, so late. Where were you?" She looked closely at Razzeleh, all over, her dress, too, front and back. "A good boy would not keep you so late alone," Bossel said. "How can I hold up my head in front of people? You think he cares what people say about you? Just for himself he cares. Nu, go to bed. Naomi, talk to her. To me she won't listen. Go, go."

The bed was filled with hay inside the white cover; the whole room smelled of fresh hay, which was put in daily. On top

197

was a white bedsheet made from heavy linen.

Razzeleh and Naomi sat on the bed.

"Did he do something to you?" Naomi asked, her eyes like pieces money.

"So beautiful he is," Razzeleh said, and she cried. "I don't know what's the matter with me. Am I a broken dog, I have to do only what the master says? A sheep. By myself, I'm lost."

"One thing I could tell you," Naomi said. "How could you go out with such a goy who already had two wives?"

"You would refuse him? You think Mottel is better?" Razzeleh asked.

"Mottel is educated and he's quiet, and your mother wants him for you."

"You would like him for a bridegroom, Mottel?"

"Me? If my mother would want, maybe I would marry with him," Naomi said. "He eats by you twice a week. You know him better than I."

"So bring him to eat by you," Razzeleh said. "I don't want him. I can't stand to look at him."

"You think everybody has to look like

David Eisenberg?" Razzeleh wouldn't answer. "He's still like a goy and no one wants him. You better not go with him because no one will come to your wedding. They'll talk very badly about you."

"Oy, vey, my head turns and I'll fall down and faint," Razzeleh said. "Maybe it will be better for me I should die before I have to go with Mottel to the chuppa to marry."

"Why worry?" Naomi asked. "Love, it comes when you have kids, your husband sits regularly by the table, in the shul. Years from now, you won't remember what happened tonight." Razzeleh's own words she threw back at her.

Razzeleh couldn't go to sleep. She lay on her bed and looked far away and thought about what she could do. Finally, open her broken heart to her mother and tell her, "I want David. If I can't have him, I don't want to live. I don't care what you want." She should say that? That's how she was that night, talking to herself in the dark, with Naomi kicking her side and pulling on the cover. Razzeleh's head was turning and tears were running down her pillow. Her heart was pounding so hard she was scared it would jump out and she would fall asleep forever. When the roosters started to crow the whole family woke up, but Razzeleh didn't even hear Naomi getting out of bed. Then Bossel came into the room and shook her. "Get up, it's late," she said. Razzeleh sat up with such a headache, her eyes closed, her red cheeks so pale, that her mother was scared. "What's the matter?" Bossel asked. In those days a sickness could take a child and you couldn't do a thing.

Razzeleh couldn't talk, and she started to cry.

"Today comes Mottel. You have to give him his meal," her mother said.

Razzeleh tried to hold back the tears. All right, she would give him the meal.

"You couldn't sleep? Something hurts you in the stomach? I'll give you a spoon oil." And Bossel ran to the kitchen, and in a dish she poured a half glass sour pickle juice and a half glass castor oil. She mixed it up and took it to Razzeleh. "Drink it up, you'll be like a new Razzeleh."

Razzeleh looked at it and felt sick. "Ma, it doesn't hurt now. I feel all right. Now I feel good."

"You have to drink it. Drink, I tell you," she yelled and forced her to drink. "Now, hurry up, it's late. You'll make for Mottel a good soup with chicken." And Bossel had to go out to the barn to milk the cow. Razzeleh got dressed, went to kitchen, and started the soup, her tears falling into the pot. Soon came her father; he wanted a cup tea.

"Razzeleh? How goes by you and the Eisenberg boy?" her father asked. "When I came home from shul last night, you were already in bed. What do you think, he appeals to you?" He saw her eyes full of tears, how they were running down her cheeks, so what could he know? "You don't have to cry, my child. If you don't want him, it's not necessary you should cry. You don't have to marry him."

"Oh, Pa, I want to but I'm scared," Razzeleh said. "Ma hates him and she wants me to marry Mottel. She says I have to."

"Hah?" Hyam jumped like someone would bite him. "Where is she? Where is she?" One of the children, Bessie, said she's milking the cow, so he ran out to the barn and gave such a thunder the pail fell out from between her knees and the milk spilled out. Bossel sat like in cold water on the hay. "I'll chase him out of the house!"

"Who?" she said finally.

"Who? You know who! It's enough I give him to eat twice a week!" Hyam yelled. "I don't want you should mention his name! You want to take such a beautiful good child and marry her off to such a stupid boy? You are to blame for Razzeleh's sickness! He doesn't even know the Gemara well! What do you know is going on in the world? Him, a husband for Razzeleh? We would have to give him to eat all his life!"

"So, better she should marry a goy?" Bossel asked. "He'll bring his child to us, we'll have to raise her, too?"

"One thing I want from you," Hyam said. "Don't talk to me no more calling him a goy. It's a shame for me to hear such stupid words. You talk like a gossip who has no brains. So better be quiet. It'll be good for us all."

Razzeleh came out of the house and stood by the door. Her father left the barn. "I'll talk to Gershon," he said. "We'll talk." She threw herself on him and kissed him. At the same time, like her stomach was turning, she was scared of her mother. Hyam went inside the house and Bossel came out of the barn. She looked at her daughter.

"Razzeleh," she said. "I want to have happiness from you. You are my oldest daughter."

"I want you should be proud of me," Razzeleh said. "I don't want you should be ashamed."

"So what are we arguing, you and me, your father and me? We want the best for you. I'll tell you the truth. I'm scared of David Eisenberg. His kind I know. Fast he marries, fast he is divorced. How long do you know him? All right, he's more modern — that's good, modern? Who is a Jew anymore when he looks like a goy, acts like a goy, and lives like a goy? The best way to get rid of the Jews, let them act like they're not Jews. You'll be happy in a house trayf?" Again Razzeleh cried and ran into the house.

In the middle of the week, one day, Hyam said, "Bossel, I'm going to see Gershon about business. Maybe I'll be home late."

"Why should you go by him?" she asked. "Better let him come to us and talk business."

"And you should chase him out of the house?" Hyam asked. "I don't want to be ashamed."

"I won't say one word."

"Never mind. I'll go to him."

Bossel's face was white. She knew why he was going. So he dressed very Shabbosdich, combed out his black beard, and went to see Gershon. When he came in, Gershon and Leah gave him a very nice welcome. Leah called David and they all sat by the table and drank tea. A little conversation — how's business, what's a Jew to try in this world — and then Hyam started to talk: "I come to talk over with your son. I want to know what you were talking about with my daughter, Razzeleh.''

"She won't give me an answer," David said. "I know she loves me but she's afraid of her mother."

"Her mother, God bless her, has her heart set on the yeshiva boy, Mottel. He's so religious he could die for it. And he doesn't have himself what to eat. My foolish wife wants him because he can read the Gemara."

"My son can do just as good with Gemara as Mottel," Leah said. "If you want to hear from my son in Gemara you can."

"I know already," Hyam said. "What happened before, with the wives, the child, who knows, what's past is past. So long he'll be good to my daughter. That's what I want. Better to talk about shiddach. When we make the engagement, then we'll talk over the date for the wedding."

Leah said, "Your wife knows you are here to talk about the shiddach?"

"My wife will do what I say," Hyam said. "And I see what is good for my daughter."

David said, "We are in love very much. We don't have to wait too long to get used to one another. You don't have to give me a dowry and I don't want you should give me to eat. To tell the truth, I don't want I should sit and eat and learn the Gemara — the Gemara I learned already. I can make a good living, my wife won't work to support us, and she can even go with me to Kiev to live there."

"No, that I don't want," Hyam said. "By us she's the oldest and we want she should live here in our town. In our house she can live till you start something here for yourself. Then we'll see that you have your own house."

"There's nothing to say," Gershon said. "He has to be with me in the business."

"You have more sons," Hyam said. "They're growing older. You should take the other sons and teach them the work." Gershon raised a shoulder. Why not? All right, he won't argue.

So they talked and they made up between them that in one week they should make the engagement. Then the two fathers drank wine. L'chayim, long life, and Leah and David were both so happy, oy, what their son was through so much in his life. They all four were drinking wine; then Hyam went away very pleased.

Razzeleh was standing by the window, watching her father come in. A chill went through her whole body. Hyam saw her and said, "Call in your mother. I have to talk to her." So she went to the kitchen to call her mother, her legs shaking. They came back to the living room together. "Well," he said, "you could give me mazel tov." Bossel got black in front her eyes; she could hardly sit down, her face so white, and her lips started to shake. "Why are you so scared?" he asked. "You should be very happy our daughter falls into such a beautiful family. And the boy, David, how does he read the Gemara? Like an angel. Better than a rabbi. You'll hear how nice he can daven. What do you want from him? You got to be happy we don't have to give him a dowry and two years to eat." Bossel looked at him and her tears fell on her dress. She couldn't speak.

Razzeleh felt like she was under water and she couldn't hear well, everything looked like it was slow and waving. Maybe, she thought, maybe she should go out and leave them alone, but her father said, "Don't go, my child. I want you should hear, in a week we'll make the engagement with Gershon's son, David. I want to know if you are satisfied with him." So excited, she looked at him and at her mother, who was still crying. "You have to say," her father told her.

"Ma," Razzeleh said, "can't I have your blessing?" Her mother cried. "If I can't have David, then I'll never get married. For nobody." Still her mother cried. "Maybe that's the best thing."

"You should sacrifice yourself for a mother's tears?" Hyam asked. "Bossel!" he yelled at her. "What is with Mottel so much? He's so dear to you?"

"Nu, Mottel," she said, a wave of the hand, and she cried.

"So, if you can't be without Mottel, let him marry Zelda."

"Zelda?" She stopped crying.

"She'll be how old? Sixteen? He'll be good for her," Hyam said.

"What are you saying, sixteen? Fourteen."

"And how old were you when I married you? She's a good girl, Zelda, never complains. So, she's not strong, but she is quiet. Finally, you'll marry a daughter to the scholar, we won't argue anymore."

"How can Zelda —" she started to say.

"Zelda or no one," Hyam said. "Now you'll make preparations."

So, when Shabbos came, Leah baked mandel bread and Gershon had wine from Kiev. Bossel wanted the engagement by her house because Razzeleh was the oldest, so, all right, Hyam said in their house. Razzeleh couldn't keep busy enough all day Friday before the Shabbos; she did her work with such an appetite. What she usually did in one day, she now did in two hours, and no one could understand where she got the strength. Like a fire she was, so fast, everything singing in her heart.

Shabbos evening everybody came from shul to Hyam, all the friends and relatives, and David with his parents and brothers and sister. When Leah saw Razzeleh, she took her by the hand in the kitchen. "Where is the salt and pepper?" Razzeleh didn't understand but she gave the salt and pepper to Leah. "Give me a handkerchief," Leah said, and she put the salt and pepper into it and tied it up and told Razzeleh to put it in her bosom. "Now," Leah said, "if someone gives you a kayn aynhoreh, you are safe." By us kayn aynhoreh means the evil eye. People used to come to her and she would say a prayer and the person felt better. Even goyim used to come, and she never took pay. She did it for a mitzva, a good deed, it should help her with God. "Now you can go in," Leah said. "And no one who looks at you can make you ill."

And they went in. Everything was on the table, made from boards and wooden horses and wooden benches. When Razzeleh came in with Leah, who wore a beautiful sheitel, a wig, and gave a look at David, her whole face was blushing. Her heart was dancing. Everybody was looking at both of them, and they put them at the head of the table, and by the sides were the parents and at the ends were the guests and the children, the shochet, the special rabbi who kills animals for food, and the rabbi and the cantors, too. Then they poured wine. Razzeleh held an end of a handkerchief and David held the other, and the rabbi said a prayer, and the shochet, too. The cantor was singing, holding the wine, because it was Shabbos night, Havdala, the end of the Shabbos, and the week begins. Then Gershon gave the plate to David and he threw it on the floor. When the plate was broken, all in one voice yelled "Mazel tov!" "It should be with mazel," the rabbi said, "and they should live out the years till one hundred and twenty." Then they started to eat herring, good mandel bread that Leah baked, and they were eating and drinking and singing Chasidic songs, and the men started to dance. Hup! Hup! Clapping the hands, making circles, fast, fast!

Razzeleh sat in a tumult from happiness, making with her feet a little dance no one should see under the table, and David found her hand and squeezed it, also under the table so no one should see. Mottel sat, too, with half-opened eyes like he couldn't stay up, only sometimes they opened to grab a look at Razzeleh. He held a piece bread like someone would take it away from him. Bossel made her daughter Zelda sit near him.

"Nu," Leah said to Bossel, "a beautiful couple."

"God be willing," Bossel said.

"Why not? They are good children. My David, what he could be, whatever he wants — so intelligent, don't ask. From all the languages, he knows perfect. Oy, you have to hear how he sings Gemara — a cantor! So, he likes the business with his father. He likes to travel the world. Whichever place he goes, everybody recognizes him. A mensch! Such a beautiful Jew, like a diamond."

"Like also a diamond, Razzeleh," Bossel said. "An angel. You'll taste how she cooks, better than me — a touch, she has! And she works, like a hundred she works, cleans the house top to bottom. I don't have to say twice to her. She does it by herself. The best — what can't she do?

And all the time smiling, singing like a bird. Wait, you'll see how she dances, the feet so fast you can't see, like a drum. All the men are crawling on her feet, so beautiful she is. Who can't she have?''

''My David, he pushes away the rich girls in the city, they all want to marry him,'' Leah said.

''Razzeleh, already ten times they want to marry her,'' Bossel said. ''But she says no. So, now a man with two wives —''

''His first, a girl older than him, and we didn't know she was sick, dying. They fooled us — oy, such aggravation, my poor David, you don't know what he went through. Thirteen years old, a child yet, he knew from nothing. And the second —''

''What is with the child?'' Bossel asked.

''The little girl is with her mother,'' Leah said.

''When they are married, maybe David will take her by him?''

''Who knows? First let them be married.''

When it was very late, everyone went

away, a little bit drunk but very happy, and Razzeleh and David were so happy they couldn't talk. The wedding would be in several months. First, David had to go with his father to Minsk, and they had to stop in Kiev.

Now they could see each other and not hide. David came every night to Razzeleh but they couldn't be alone. Her mother sat, all the children looked. So they had to sit in the house, and they couldn't say love words. Finally, came the day David had to leave. It was hard for him, and Razzeleh was getting a sore throat, so much she won't let herself cry. She wouldn't see him for two months, but what could they do? He gave her his mother's watch, with a chain to pin on a dress.

On Shabbos Razzeleh put on a nice dress and the watch and she went for a walk with Naomi. Sometimes she went to Leah, who told Razzeleh what David liked, what he didn't like, and that sometimes she'd have to help him out with the business. Razzeleh listened closely. But where would they live? She was too scared to ask.

Passed two months, David with his father came back from Kiev. He brought very beautiful things for Razzeleh, don't ask, and they started to make the wedding. David brought silk from Kiev and they gave it to a dressmaker. Leah took in two women to bake the cakes. The day came for the wedding. Razzeleh was fasting. When they dressed her and put her on the chair, no one could take their eyes off her. She was blossoming like a rose.

Everybody ready by the shul; again David went first to the chuppa, the canopy. His four brothers held the sticks of the canopy and the music played. Everybody in the town was running to see, and they talked, the old women, how Razzeleh fell in with such a man, already two wives he had and a child, and how it was a pity on Razzeleh, so beautiful and herself a child — a big tumult they made. So? They got married anyway, with the singing, and David looked at Razzeleh. Her face was covered with a silk scarf tied in the back. The rabbi said be happy, they drank wine from the glass, David and Razzeleh, and he put it under David's foot, and then he broke it. Mazel tov!

Then they ran home, everybody, and Zelda, Razzeleh's sister, put out a tray wine with a big challeh, and she stood at the door and held high the tray, and when the bride and groom came, they took the wine and the challeh into the house and everybody sat down to eat. The rabbi with the bride made a moetze. Then Bossel took off Razzeleh's scarf and cried. At the table she put Zelda near Mottel, who was sitting like a statue. When they made the prayer he rocked, and when they finished eating and started to pray, with all his voice he prayed, with closed eyes. Bossel looked at him, her hands folded on her stomach. Ah! So nice, she thought. David looked at him and said to Razzeleh, "Why is he shaking himself, the big horse?"

"Never mind," Razzeleh said, and she looked at David like his face was the heaven, the stars. "Now we are married."

5

David went to Kiev for long periods of time; Razzeleh was home like before. Was that marriage? She didn't want he should go away and come home twice a year. To go with him to Kiev now was too expensive — and she was scared. In a small town the wife has to stay by her parents. Hyam saw how she was wilting, dried out — tea wouldn't help, and she couldn't sing. She could hardly do work in the house. Like a guest she was. So Hyam convinced Gershon they should build a little house, one big room, across from Razzeleh's parents. Hyam and Gershon bought the lot and they built a house and put David and Razzeleh there. One room with a big oven, the floor dirt. Then David bought a big lake. In those days it didn't cost so much, and he started to raise fish there and Razzeleh raised geese. That's the way they made a living.

"How long will it last?" Bossel asked Hyam. "He is in the city, so he'll be satisfied in the fish? No more now the fancy goyisher clothes with the patent leather boots — from fish they'll smell. A nice how-do-you-do, we marry our daughter to a fish peddler. A scholar from fish already."

"When he makes plenty money from the fish, then it'll be perfume to you, the fish," Hyam told her.

It was a little house, but Razzeleh loved it. So clean she kept it. On Friday, when David came from the lake, there was nothing to do. The house was spotless. Shabbos, they had to visit the parents, sometimes by her, sometimes by him, sometimes all together, but at least in the evening they could be alone, and they couldn't get enough of each other. At first, Razzeleh was scared, she knew but she didn't know — what could she imagine? After, she couldn't be close enough, even when he tired her out.

But nine months passed — nothing. A

year, still nothing, no sign. "You see?" Bossel told Razzeleh. "David is not a match for you. It's not made in heaven, the marriage. Didn't I tell you?" Alone, at night, in her little house, Razzeleh cried. She lay with her eyes closed and talked to God: "Why don't you give me a child? Do with me what you want but give me a child. Only bread and water give me, but God give me a child, I should make my parents happy. They love me. I'm the oldest by them. I make them embarrassed." In those days, when a woman is living with a husband ten years and there won't come a child, then you have to divorce. "If you, God," she said, "won't give me a child, I don't want to live. Take me away from the world."

"The trouble is," Bossel said, "God punishes David. Didn't he leave a wife with a child? So he has to suffer."

Leah called Razzeleh by her and made all kinds spices in a little bag. She should wear it and not tell anyone, not even David. She told Razzeleh to go home and that God would help her. Razzeleh kissed Leah on the hand.

That's the way time went by. One year, two years, and Razzeleh still didn't have a child. Leah was scared, and she told David he should bring his little daughter, and maybe God would help him to have babies. "So Razzeleh's got plenty time," he said. "What's to worry? I don't care. Leave her alone already."

"Plenty time?" his mother asked. "She's already nineteen years old. Don't you see how it hurts her, so ashamed she is? People talk, let them talk, but Razzeleh, she loses weight, she can't eat. All day she's cleaning — better a dirty house with children than a clean house without."

Finally, David hired a droshky with a chauffeur, and from his father he got four black horses. Day and night he traveled to Moozer, where Tzeepeh now was. From her family everyone was dead but the bubbeh, the grandmother. Tzeepeh had never married again; she worked in a factory where they made matches, and the bubbeh kept the child.

So late in the evening David and the chauffeur came, a tiny man with a nose like an onion. They stopped by a kretchmer, a place for eating and sleeping, for muzhiks. A big room with long tables and benches, a dirt floor. It wasn't clean.

Next day, in the morning, David went to the bubbeh's house — like his little house but old and falling down, dark. Finally he came to the door. He could hear someone talking, and a chair was moving, and a long time he waited. Tzeepeh's bubbeh, with skin like bark from a tree and warts on her face with hair growing out of them, and she had no teeth. She shook in front of him like she was davening. "Who is it?" she asked.

"It's David Eisenberg. David Eisenberg — Tzeepeh's husband, used to be. David, from years before!"

"Who knows?" she said. "Who knows? You should have a long life, you'll see what a curse. Oy, close the door, I can't stand the light. I can't see and I can't look at the light. You have to talk loud. What? Sit down, I'll make tea."

"It's not necessary. It's all right!" Anyway she made tea. He was afraid she would burn herself the way she wobbled.

She brought a kettle water and sat like a bundle rags. "Where is Tzeepeh? Tzeepeh! Where is she?" David asked.

"Tzeepeh?" the grandmother said. "Where should she be? She works. Where they make the matches. What do you expect? How else can we eat? We have nothing in the house."

"And Hanneleh? My little girl, Hanneleh!"

"I can't take care of her today. It's no use; I don't have the strength."

"Where is she?"

"Who?"

"Hanneleh. Where is she now?"

"Where else is she? With her mother."

"With Tzeepeh in the factory?"

"Four years old and she's watching how they make matches. So smart! Pretty soon she'll make matches herself. Why not? We have nothing in the house."

"When are they coming home, Tzeepeh and Hanneleh?" David asked.

The old woman looked at him, her eyes like little slivers wood. "What do you want from me?"

"From you, Bubbeh? Nothing."

"Who are you?"

"I'm David. The father of Hanneleh."

She threw her head this way, that way; she looked at the floor; then she looked at him.

All day David walked around Moozer with its wooden houses. Now it was the fall, cold, the muzhiks were wrapping themselves to keep warm. Before they put on their boots, made from hides, they wrapped rags around their feet. David passed the peasant women, too, strong like the men, carrying wood. The women all rolled a piece of rough linen across their foreheads and put a small piece wood in front; then, over everything, they put heavy linen, with two strips hanging down the back — warm like an oven they kept their heads.

Where was the match factory? David asked a young muzhik. Near the church, he said. A factory? By us a house, bigger than most, where they sat at tables making matches. Over there, he pointed, by the church. David went.

A bunch of muzhiks in shiny boots came out from the church. A big man,

223

young, with a black mustache and white teeth, went first, and a young girl followed perfectly in his footsteps. He wore only a red blouse and brown pants, and she a pink blouse and green skirt. They were covered up like nuns. More people from the church started to sing and yell, and a priest stood by the door and waved his hand like a cross. Aha, a wedding. Everybody climbed inside a wagon and they stood together singing; the driver gave a yell and a snap of the whip and the two big farm horses rolled like thunder down the street. They would go to the bride's house and in the back yard they would dance polkas to the music of drums and a violin. The bride would go inside to put a lot of wood in the oven and make a fire and cook something to show. Then she would dance with the groom and they would go into a shack with hay and would be there for two hours while the people outside were eating, drinking, dancing, and singing. Then the couple would come out and the groom would drink and dance a wild dance all alone; the bride would look at the ground and she would blush like a fire and everybody would pat her on the arms and the toches, the bottom. Then the parents would go to the shack to find out if the bride was kosher (still a virgin). They would come out, everybody would kiss the bride and they would jump and laugh, so happy.

David watched. Then it was quiet, the sky was like an old sheet not washed for a long time. Everybody's breath came out like smoke. The bells from the church started to call out and David felt like he was lost for Razzeleh, but as though he were far away, never to go back, like she was only a dream in his head. Now he would see Tzeepeh; he could remember how she looked when he first met her on the train and how they walked by the river. After, the bad times, he remembered, too, but the young face he knew, the white teeth, the first love. Now it was gone and he loved Razzeleh, but how would she be, Tzeepeh? How would she look? How would he feel? His heart was pounding, like knocking on a door.

No question. There it was — the factory. Stinks sulfur, you couldn't stand it. A gray house with two stories and four chimneys. Should he go inside? You never can tell how they will act toward you, the Gentiles. But he was there, so he would go inside. He saw a hall with stairs. On the second floor he saw one big room with women sitting at tables. Far away, at the end of the room, a man stood at a machine. Everyone looked up from their work, quiet all of a sudden, and one got up from the bench — Tzeepeh.

Tzeepeh. Still the same but not the same. He saw now what he had seen on the train: the eyes, the hair red but not so bright like before, and like the young Tzeepeh not so fat, maybe even skinny, but hanging like a goose in the neck. And he saw something on her skin, near the collarbone, on top the bosom, blotched like maybe she was dirty, but he saw it wasn't dirt.

"David," she said. "Oy, David, it's you?" Something had happened to her voice. Before, it was high up, clear like a bell; now it was like she had a cold. Something rattled in her throat, low, rough. "How did you come here?"

"I'm here," he said. "How's by you?"

She wanted to touch him. Her hands were moving like she was picking glue and paste from the fingers. They wouldn't stop. "You know I work here?" Tzeepeh asked.

"Your bubbeh told me you were here."

"We can't talk — the owner will complain." She looked at the man behind. "Maybe I can ask him, he'll let me go early. I'll tell him it's my husband who's come to see me." She put three fingers on his arm. "You look the same as always."

"Where's Hanneleh?" David asked.

"Oh, you have to see her," and she grabbed his arm and pulled him to one side of the room, where there was a box with a quilt in it, and on the quilt a child was sleeping, a little girl with red hair. "Nu?"

"Tzeepeh!" The owner, a fat Jew after all. "You want to work or you don't? It's up to you."

She whispered to David, "He pays by how many matches you make."

She went to talk to the owner; he looked at David, mean, like something hurts in the stomach; a face he had, only black eyebrows, a bush. Now all the women were talking like the steam coming out of the kettle. David looked at his daughter. Two little hands, thin, palms together, underneath her cheek as she slept.

The owner came over like a barrel. He had to twist his whole body with each step. He looked closely at David. "So he's the father. Also the husband?" David shook his head, yes. "You say so, hah? It's your business. By me, as long as she works good, I don't care, I have my own troubles. What's the matter, you can't wait another two hours?" Two fat lips; the top lay on the bottom one, like sausages. "You're so anxious. Why do you run away? All right, it's Friday anyway, then go early."

"A good week to you," David told him.

"Good Shabbos," he said through his nose, and he looked mean.

Tzeepeh put on her coat. David saw Hanneleh was already wearing hers, and he folded the quilt and bent over to pick her up. Quick, like someone dropped her, she pushed her arms straight out, her eyes opened, she gave a jerk, and she looked at David and screamed.

"It's all right, it's all right," Tzeepeh said. "You don't know — it's your papa. You see? Papa." But Hanneleh grabbed Tzeepeh and looked at David like he would harm her, her lips shaking and her voice as if she would yell each time. So Tzeepeh picked her up. Now he could see her better, curly hair, big blue eyes, and skinny, vey's mir, like a finger.

"Hanneleh," he said softly. "Don't be scared. You don't remember Papa? Come to me, my darling." But she wouldn't let him touch her. So Tzeepeh had to carry the child in her hands.

When they came to the house, Tzeepeh was worn out. Inside, the bubbeh was sleeping sitting up. "I let Bubbeh take care of the baby," Tzeepeh said, "but I don't like it. You see how she can't stay awake." Hanneleh ran right to the bubbeh and put her head on her lap. The bubbeh jerked her head; all around she looked but she couldn't see. At last she found

Hanneleh's head, and she put her hand, like a piece twig, on the red hair.

Tzeepeh made tea, all the time smiling, a tiny smile, like she was scared. "So you found out I am in Moozer?"

"People talk, they tell me," David said.

"Me, they don't tell." She put a glass tea in his hand. "You're in business still with your father?"

"No. Now I have a lake. I am in the fish business."

"It's good?"

"A living."

She sat by the table, put a cube sugar between her teeth, and drank. "I couldn't keep up with the glass," she said. "What do I know, glass? You have to cut good all the time, and I didn't care anymore. So I broke more than I sold." She looked at him. "It's a man's work, finally." He was sipping tea, so hot. "I had plenty men who would have me," she said. "Them I wouldn't have. A marriage has to be made in heaven. By me, it's a sin a wife can't love the husband, it's matchmaking with the parents and the couple, they don't know each other till the chuppa." She sipped tea also. "So, how are your mother and father?"

"In good health," David said.

"Thanks to God. You stay all the time by them?"

"I have my own house."

"Ah. It's a nice house?"

"Now it's nice. Later, we'll fix up."

"So you stay by yourself in the house?"

"My wife stays."

Tzeepeh's face was like someone pulled down the cheeks, with red spots on her white skin. Quick, she sipped tea, too much, and she burned her tongue. She looked at David and said, "Maybe you'll have a piece bread with shmaltz?" No, he didn't want. So she gave Hanneleh the bread.

"Nu?" said the bubbeh. "You got company? Challeh we should have, not a piece bread. It's a shame. We have nothing in the house."

"Hanneleh," David said, "come here a little bit." But she stayed by the bubbeh. He took from his pocket two kupkes, pennies, and held them out to her. "Here. For you, Hanneleh. Go ahead, take."

"Go ahead," said Tzeepeh. "Your papa gives it to you." She bent over to grab Hanneleh and push her toward David. But the child didn't want. "Take, take," Tzeepeh said. "It's not nice." She gave a little push. In front of David, Hanneleh stood with a finger in her mouth. Slowly, she took the two kupkes out from his hand; then she ran to Tzeepeh and buried her face in her dress.

"Two years I'm married," David said. "But we don't have a child in the house. My wife stays in the house all day alone. The parents are close, hers, mine, a small town, everybody knows one another. For children it's very good. They are happy there. For Hanneleh would be very good."

Tzeepeh grabbed Hanneleh. "Now I know. A fine business," she yelled. "It's not enough! You have to have everything from me! Get out of the house! I don't want to see you, filthy!" She let her tears fall in Hanneleh's hair.

"My wife, Rachel, she has a good heart," David said. "She can't do enough for me. A perfect housekeeper and a cook, the best. Clean, careful, she knows how to keep a good house, a kosher house, too. Children she loves. It tears her heart out she can't have a child yet. Like the holy book she would take care of it."

"And I don't take care? When you were by me, I didn't clean and cook and scrub and bake and prepare and keep the house nice? A mother, I was no good? She has a man, he provides, it's so hard to keep a good house? I'll have a husband, I'll be perfect, too. Better than her! Go tell her!"

"Who's going to marry you with a child to take in, too?"

"Plenty want me! I can marry tomorrow if I want!" she cried. Now she sat straight like a board, facing him but with her eyes shut, and she cried.

"What will you do when the bubbeh won't be here?" David asked her. "Can you leave her in the house now? Can you take a child to the factory every day? And later, when she's bigger? You want her to work in the factory at six years old?"

Tzeepeh stopped crying. "No one needs you."

"It's better for the child she should be in a normal home. How can you take care of her?" David waited. The kettle was making steam. The bubbeh breathed like she was sleeping, but her eyes were open. Hanneleh played with the two kupkes in her mother's lap. "I want to know," David said. "Tomorrow is Shabbos. I can't travel. After shul I'll come and see how you feel." He stood up. "Sunday morning, early, I'll go back home." No word, so he started to go. By the door he stopped. "Maybe I can bring you something so you'll have a good meal?"

"I don't want anything from you!" Tzeepeh said, like a dog with its teeth showing.

"Bring, bring," the bubbeh told him.

"Maybe I'll have to buy from the goyim."

"God says when you have to eat, it's kosher," the bubbeh said, and she laughed, her gums showing.

So he found by the Gentile stores some black bread, some smoked fish, potatoes, sour cream, a bottle wine, and even a piece halvah. Better he shouldn't eat by Tzeepeh, so he left the food with her and he took eggs he bought to the kretchmer, where he ate. So, he ate, eggs and a little wine. The chauffeur he didn't see. He took care that the horses should eat something and then he went to bed.

Next day the chauffeur was sleeping and David woke him up, he should remember the horses. Then David went to shul, a stranger, so they welcomed him there and he talked business, fish, and how's by you. All day he spent in shul.

In the evening he went again to Tzeepeh. The oven was hot, so the room felt good, and they sat again with tea. Tzeepeh wouldn't say a word. For Hanneleh, David brought sugar candy.

"Nu?" David said at the end.

"Tzeepeh," the bubbeh said. "You have company." In a saucer she poured a little tea so it would be cool, and she sipped from it. To David she said, "She's a young girl yet. Wait, you'll taste from her the challeh she bakes, like honey. A young girl. What does she know from life? For you, she's very good. So, a husband she had — for how long? Two days only. A good-for-nothing, he left her alone, in the air he went. He's dead somewhere. Like a fool he went at night into the city, and the Cossacks, they took everything from him and left him in the street. An innocent girl, how could she know him? You'll be happy —"

"Bubbeh!" Tzeepeh slapped herself on the leg and said to David, "I have to fix myself up. I have to get clothes. I must have to eat and to make the house it should look nice."

"I'll give you what I can," David said.

"You'll give? How do I know you'll give?"

David reached inside his coat and took out his wallet with some money. "I need for myself to travel home. Later, I'll send again."

Tzeepeh counted the money and folded it. "You'll forget."

"I won't forget."

"How can I trust?"

"May God strike me if I forget."

She looked at her hands. "Tomorrow I have to go to work early."

"I'll be here before." David stood up and held out a hand to the little girl. "Hanneleh, you'll let Papa give you a kiss good-night?" But she was hiding by Tzeepeh. "It takes time."

"God help me," Tzeepeh said.

Next morning, even before a rooster could crow, David and the chauffeur came to Tzeepeh's house. David knocked, maybe they weren't up yet. But Tzeepeh opened the door. She and Hanneleh were already dressed.

"Hanneleh," David said, "you're all ready to go? Look, you see how beautiful the droshky with the horses? Four nice horses, how fast they take us!" Hanneleh held onto her mother by the leg.

"Close the door!" yelled the bubbeh. "You think it's summer already? You want to kill me?"

Inside Tzeepeh picked up Hanneleh. "Handlen, it's your papa. You'll go with him, he'll give you candy and he'll take a ride in the droshky with the four horses. You'll be a good girl —" and she started to cry, Tzeepeh.

"Come, my darling," David said, and he took Hanneleh, but she started to cry, too, kicking and pushing him.

"Oy, vey's mir!" Tzeepeh grabbed back

her child and hugged her like she would break her. "She won't go! She won't go by you!"

David lowered his head. What could he do? All right, God wills it. He put his hand on the door so as to leave.

"She'll go!" the bubbeh yelled, and she lifted herself up. "Hanneleh, my little heart," she said to her. "Hanneleh, you'll go to your father." Then she picked Hanneleh up and carried her to David. "Take, take." She looked at him hard. "Before she knows, take her. God be good by her." Hanneleh was crying and kicking again. "She'll forget. Comes a time you'll have to tell her how she left us. She'll forget." Then, lifting a fist like a rock: "If you harm one hair on her head, I'll come, from the grave I'll come and I'll give you! Do you hear? Such a pound in the heart I'll give, God will know!" The bubbeh pushed him on the back and slammed the door behind.

David stood with the child in his arms, and he hugged her, held her, patted her, and he rocked along with her like he was davening. "Hanneleh, Hanneleh, I'm your papa. I love you, my darling. You'll go home with me and you'll have everything in the world. Maybe dolls you want? Such dolls you'll have, with real hair. You'll sleep in your own bed. Maybe a little horse? You'll have a little horse for yourself? See, a little horse, smaller than this, for you alone," and he went close to the horses and put out his hand, and she looked, she stopped crying a little bit to see what was. He patted the horse and took her hand to pat, too, but she was scared, so he didn't force. "You see how the man will drive us? We'll sit in the droshky and we'll go, fast, fast! Look, how nice," and he showed her the blankets in the droshky, the big fur rug to cover their laps and their legs. "We'll be warm like an oven!" He put the blanket and the fur over them and she felt it. She felt the long fur with her fingers. From a bear it was. "All right," David said to the driver, but Tzeepeh came running out of the house with a bundle clothes.

"You don't know," she said, and she gave Hanneleh a wet kiss on the lips, dropped in the bundle, and ran quickly inside the house.

"Go! Go!" yelled David, and the chauffeur gave such a crack with the whip the horses stood on their hind feet, and then they gave such a pull on the droshky, like a snap. Hanneleh was screaming, "Mama! Mama!" and David held her tight, he had to force.

Finally, an hour maybe she was crying, he took out his watch with the chain so she could play with it, and it helped a little bit. Soon the droshky was rocking, it was warm underneath the blankets and the fur and next to David, with his arm around her, and she wasn't crying.

In the meantime, Razzeleh walked the whole night, rubbing her hands, twisting. God, she asked, let her husband and the child come in peace. Finally, the daylight came and she lay down and fell asleep. But the roosters crowed so loud that she soon got up, dressed, and went out to give the chickens and geese to eat. Two hundred geese with how many chickens? And two cows. Where the geese were staying in the barn there was a string fence with a hole with a wooden trough underneath to hold the feed and the water — the hole big enough only for a goose to put his head through. When they finished eating, Razzeleh cleaned it out and put in fresh for the cows. Then she milked them. Next, she sat down to make nets to catch fish.

Time to eat at noon and still no David. Quick, she ran across to her parents' house, full of brothers and sisters, her father in the back with the hides.

"You don't hear from David?" her mother asked.

"I'll go crazy if he doesn't come pretty soon," Razzeleh said. "I'm scared for his life. Maybe some robbers stopped him and he has some rubles and they'll take away the horses — I don't care, as long as they don't harm David." She was sitting and crying, she couldn't stop.

"You think it's close by, Moozer?" her mother said. "It takes a long time to ride with the horses. A droshky he had to hire. In a wagon he would be safer. No, he has to show, they should rob him."

Comes night and still no David. Leah, his mother, was scared, too, and she went to Razzeleh's house. Bossel was by her already, and they sat and waited. Leah spoke so quietly, they didn't understand, but they knew she was praying.

"Vey's mir, what happens to my child?" Bossel said. "All kinds trouble fall on her. Such a man she's got to have. So, maybe God will do what's best."

"Don't say such words!" Razzeleh yelled at her. "I'll go crazy. I'll go drown myself in the lake, you should talk to me like that."

Leah took her around. "Shah, shah, my child. He'll come, don't worry."

"How do you know?" Bossel asked.

"In my heart I know."

"He should never have gone to bring the child," she said.

"And who tells him to?" Leah asked.

Jingle bells, bells from the horses, tiny at first, like a tinkle in water, then louder, and Razzeleh ran out the door and she saw the droshky coming from the hill, and she ran fast. She came to it and saw how David held the child, asleep, wrapped up in a blanket, a quilt. "David! David!" Razzeleh cried so loud he was scared, and he told the driver to stop and take the child. Then David went to grab Razzeleh, and he kissed her on the cheeks, the eyes, and she couldn't come to herself. Then the two mothers came out. Leah he kissed. "You go home now," he said, and he looked at Bossel, too. He knew she was a troublemaker, and she wouldn't move away.

"Ma," Razzeleh said finally, "go home, leave us now. You'll come tomorrow."

"You see?" Bossel said to Leah. "How a child gives to her mother. Be a mother!" and she went to her house like a machine. Leah gave Razzeleh a kiss and went away quietly.

Then Razzeleh saw the goy holding the child. Quietly, carefully, she went up to him and slowly took Hanneleh from his arms. David told the driver to let loose the horses in the barn and he paid him and sent him home. Then they went, David and Razzeleh, into the house, and she put the child on top a feather pareneh, full with fluff, soft.

"So tired," David said, looking at Hanneleh. "The whole day, the whole night we spent."

"You, also," Razzeleh said to him. "I have tea, challeh, cheese — you want I should make you fish? Chicken maybe — I can heat —"

"Stiff like a board I am," he said. "A glass tea with challeh, and we'll go to bed." He held her, a crush. "Now it's all right."

"Your wife, how's by her?" Razzeleh asked.

David laughed. "You are my wife. Tzeepeh — she's old now. I have to send her some money."

"She's not married?"

"No. She'll be, she'll be."

Razzeleh was shaking inside his arms. "God be willing," she said quietly.

When David woke up next morning, Razzeleh was working, pouring the corn for the geese, and she sang softly so Hanneleh would still sleep. He went by the window to hear how beautiful Razzeleh sang, how she stood so proud like a bird, so straight. Then he washed himself and made ready for the new day, but Hanneleh opened her eyes then. "Bubbeh! Bubbeh!"

she called, and she rubbed her eyes. David ran to her and picked her up. Now she was no longer afraid of him. He went outside with her on his arms and into the barn, where Razzeleh was milking the cows. She saw them and jumped up. In the light she could see Hanneleh better.

"She looks like you," she told David, and she held out her arms for Hanneleh, but the child held onto her father so tight with her skinny little hands. She was crying, and it broke Razzeleh's heart. She grabbed a pail of milk and a basket of eggs and said to David, "Come, we have to give the child to eat, and you are hungry, too." They went inside and Razzeleh strained the milk with a white piece of cloth in a pitcher. Then she cooked kasha, cereal from groats, and she wanted to feed Hanneleh. But the child turned her head; she wouldn't eat. So David took the spoon and fed Hanneleh, and then he gave her warm milk to drink. Razzeleh watched. She wanted to cry, but she smiled.

Then David took Hanneleh to see the chickens and the geese. She was scared of all those things because the bubbeh used to sit with her in a dark room. So David stayed with her a long time in the barn. Razzeleh threw corn on the ground and the chickens and the geese came close to eat; Hanneleh held on tight to David's pants.

"It's like you're not here," Razzeleh said, "such a dream. I couldn't sleep. Was it hard for you to take the child?"

"You know," David said, "a child from its mother. But she works and the bubbeh is too old and sick. They could see how it's better for Hanneleh to come by us. A little room in the town, cold, dark — it's not a place for my child."

Razzeleh watched her. "I was scared to death for you," she said to David.

Now the helpers came, ten Russians, to catch fish. Razzeleh gave David bread and onions to eat with some fish, and they went off to the lake. Hanneleh cried and Razzeleh had to hold her, she shouldn't run after David. "Look," she said, "look how the goose is drinking the water," and she laughed so maybe Hanneleh would laugh, too. Then she went to the chickens and showed Hanneleh how eggs are laid and how you have to shoo so you can take them. In the field the horses were eating the cold grass. "Nice horses," Razzeleh said, and she gave them cubes sugar so they should eat from the hand. Hanneleh was scared, but she did not cry now.

Razzeleh had plenty to do, but all the time she kept running to Hanneleh with a piece candy, a piece bread, a glass fresh milk from the cow, cheese maybe, but Hanneleh wouldn't eat. She cried, she stopped, she cried again, all day. In the middle came Razzeleh's mother. "Did you ever see a child like this?" she asked. "Won't eat, won't sleep, crying — who knows what to do?"

"She'll be all right," Razzeleh said.

"How old is she? Four? She goes on the floor still?"

"So she forgets. Maybe because she's so scared. It's a strange place, a strange house, strange people —"

"You have to take care of his child, like a serf," Bossel said. "He can't give you children, right away he gives you one by somebody else, not even your own."

"It's not David's fault!" She was making butter in the tub now with all her strength, like she would punish it.

"So who?"

"It's my fault."

"By Pa I can have ten, and by your David you can have nothing, and it's your fault?" Bossel said.

So hard Razzeleh was pumping, the tub for making butter was jumping up and down, and in a minute it fell over and the milk ran onto the floor, and the dirt soaked up everything. "You see?" she yelled. "You see? You throw so much in my face I can't stand it! Go away, leave me alone!"

Bossel shook her fist at her. "So much happiness I get from my children! You had to have him, and I told you! Look how you live, like a muzhik!" Hanneleh was sitting on the floor crying, with milk on her dress. "You're better off now, now you got a child? Maybe he has more we don't know about."

"Leave me alone!" Razzeleh screamed.

"You bring it on yourself!" Bossel said, and she went out of the house with her arms waving in the air, and she talked and talked to no one: "Didn't I tell you? No, you wouldn't listen, you knew better. All right, now you suffer and who's to blame?" All the way to her house and inside she talked to Hyam, but he wouldn't answer, he was busy with the hides.

Then Leah came. She saw how Bossel ran out of the house, so she waited and then looked at Razzeleh through the door and went inside. Right away she picked Razzeleh up from her knees and made her sit down. Then she picked up Hanneleh, who kicked and yelled, but Leah said, "Don't be afraid, my darling, shah, shah, oy, my little lovely, such a sweetheart." But Hanneleh wouldn't stop, so, finally, Leah had to put her on the floor, where she stood with her fists over her eyes, and she cried and cried.

"What will I do?" Razzeleh asked.

"Don't pay attention. You'll see, she'll get tired, she'll stop," Leah said, and she helped Razzeleh clean up and pick up the churn tub. Razzeleh then made tea with butter, and cheese she made herself on the table. Leah gave her a kiss on her forehead. "You are the best housekeeper," she said. "Dauvidel got the best from everybody." She looked at Hanneleh. "When he was little, that's how he looked. Exactly!" Sitting, she bent toward the child. "Like your father!" she yelled and laughed. "Exactly. Do you know how you look, Hanneleh? Like your father." And she laughed. "Come, darling," Leah said. "Come to your bubbeh. I love you. Don't be afraid." And she pounded on her chest with her fingers. "Bubbeh. It's Bubbeh, darling. Come to your bubbeh and sit on my lap." Hanneleh looked at her with eyes full of tears.

Razzeleh put out her hand. "Go to Bubbeh, Hanneleh. Go to Bubbeh." And she took the little arm and slowly made the child go to Leah. Leah took Hanneleh and held her on her lap. A hug and kisses and "Oy, my darling, I love you. I love you!" A smack, so loud the kiss. "Hanneleh! It makes my teeth hurt, so much I love you." To Razzeleh, she said, "She'll get used to me. I'll take her for Shabbos and you can rest."

Comes Friday morning, David brought a wagon fish to sell at the market for Shabbos. He didn't have then a place to put the fish because he didn't have ice, so he had to carry them right away to sell. All day he stood by the market and he sold, quietly, not singing "Fish! Fish!" like someone else, but he sold at a good price, not too much, a nice profit he made, and people liked, they bought. Fish for Shabbos you have to have. He thought how he would save hard, he wouldn't spend a ruble, and he would make a business so he could travel, maybe live in Kiev finally — maybe Razzeleh would know how to move away from the parents. It will happen, he thought. Tomorrow, the next day, he would find good luck. At least with Razzeleh he couldn't complain. At least he loved her, he had her, he was satisfied. But all day long he had to sell the fish.

The sun was coming down, they all had to hurry in the market. You can't work on Shabbos and the new day starts when the sun goes down. So they sold fast; they didn't argue so much. Finally, David still

251

had a few fish, so he said enough, and he carried them home for the parents and for him and Razzeleh and Hanneleh. Like he was dropping flowers on the table for Razzeleh, he poured out the money. "Count," he told her, but she wouldn't. She was not like the rest, the women counting the money and hiding it in a drawer.

"You should count and hide it," she said to him.

Hanneleh saw the shiny things and she grabbed some from the table and the money fell from her tiny hands onto the floor. David laughed and picked her up in the air, and he squeezed her and gave her a loud kiss. Razzeleh watched and it hurt her, she didn't know why. But she smiled and picked up the money from the floor. Then she cleaned the fish, and David went with Hanneleh into the yard to see the sun set in the branches.

Then David was busy with his father. They were talking about going to Warsaw to buy goods. "You'll go with Aaron," his father told him. "He's a good boy. He won't understand the Russians in the city as well as you, but he will follow what his older brother says. So he'll learn and you can have help from him.''

''I have to be with my Russians at the water,'' David said. ''I owe yet for the lake, I have to pay, and if I don't stay around to watch, they won't work.''

''So you'll hire somebody to watch,'' Gershon said.

''Who can I hire?''

''You'll find somebody.''

''And I can't leave Razzeleh alone in the house.''

''When you go to Warsaw, she can stay by her parents.''

''Such a punishment I won't give her.''

''So she'll stay by us.''

''Where? You don't have enough in the house, you have to have more? You'll add another room in the back?'' David asked.

''Listen, you worry too much. She'll be all right,'' Gershon said.

''I can't leave her alone. I made a promise. She works very hard and she's good.''

Gershon smoothed down his beard. ''My son, let her work. It's the best thing for her. What does she have to do with one child?''

David pounded the table. ''It's not her fault!''

''It's no one's fault, all right, sit, sit,'' Gershon said, and he shook his head. ''What God puts on you, who can understand? It's a shame there haven't been children. Not a son to carry on your name and no one to say Kaddish.''

''How can you hurt her and say she can't have children?'' David asked.

''No one says.''

''No one says.'' David rubbed his hand and looked at it, how red it was. ''I can't go to Warsaw, Pa. I can't leave her so long.''

Gershon shook his head one time, yes. ''Don't worry. God is good. We'll see.''

And David went away with an ache in his heart. When he went into his house, he found Razzeleh with a sweet smile. On the table was a white cloth and fresh challeh and potatoes, kishke, and beans. She made them for Shabbos and baked them in the oven the whole night so they would be ready when they came home from shul.

Hanneleh was standing and holding Razzeleh's dress, afraid she would run away and leave her.

They sat down to eat and David thought maybe she would go with him to Kiev or Warsaw after all, and she wouldn't work so hard and he would show her how nice it was in the city — he could convince her. Now she was not so afraid, she would go with him.

He watched her help Hanneleh eat, but she wouldn't eat herself. He saw all kinds of colors, red, pale, in her face. "Why aren't you eating?" David asked her.

"The child comes first," Razzeleh said.

"Don't you feel good?"

She looked at him, a little smile. "What makes you ask me?"

"You look very white and you don't eat."

"So my stomach is turning."

"You ate something today that didn't agree with you?"

She tried to smile. "Don't talk."

"Sometimes you eat a bad apple, it has a rotten piece inside, you don't know —" David said.

"Oy," and Razzeleh jumped up from the table and ran out to the yard. He heard her vomit, so he put out his hand, Hanneleh shouldn't go out after her. Finally, when she came back inside, he saw how her face was white like a sheet.

"Maybe the food, something?" David looked at the potatoes, kishke, and beans.

"You don't like it?" She looked closely at it. "It tastes bad?"

"Tastes fine. Only, maybe —"

"I fixed special. All day I fixed. Maybe like your mother I can't make —"

"It's good," and he ate a big spoonful.

"Something's missing? Salt? I put in plenty salt. And a little onion — maybe not enough?"

"Perfect." It was dripping from his mouth.

"I can't help it," she said, like she would cry. "I do my best. You'll tell me what's wrong, I'll make it the way you like. I go by your mother — she tells me. A little onion, she says. By her a little is more than by me — I got to put in more."

"No more, no more," David said,

lifting up his hand. "I better see the barn, so cold and with snow, I'll see we have hay by the doors."

"I'll go, I'll go," Razzeleh stood up, but, like the blood falling from her face to her feet, she had to sit down.

"You should be in bed," David said.

"Maybe I'm too much by the oven all day. I'll go outside," Razzeleh said. She got up carefully and put on a shawl, and Hanneleh, too, had to have a shawl, and they went outside to the barn. In those days they used the animal droppings for fertilizer. It makes the potatoes and the beans and all the vegetables rich, more tasty. Today, everything is big and full with nothing — you can't taste. Also, in the barn, they didn't have cement like here, and they didn't clean up. Let the animals step, it made hard the floor. Nu, manure, it smells. So when they went inside the barn, Razzeleh couldn't breathe because of the smell, and she got dizzy and fell on the hay. David grabbed her, carried her into the house, put her on the bed, and brought her tea.

"What's the matter? My God, I'll bring

the felsher (the doctor)," David said. "He'll know what it is."

"No, no, no, I'm all right. I don't want him. Where is Hanneleh? Did you leave her in the barn?"

So David had to run outside. Hanneleh was looking at where the milk came out from the cow. Quick, he carried her inside. To Razzeleh, he said, "I'll get my mother, she'll come. Yours, I don't want." She smiled, all right, and he ran fast to his parents' house and he brought Leah, she should look at Razzeleh. But now Razzeleh was standing, pale, weak, she wouldn't lay down again. Leah brought some castor oil and mixed it with juice from sour pickles and made Razzeleh drink it up, but she had to go outside and vomit, so it didn't help.

Next day she looked fine, rosy, so David didn't worry. Maybe that night he would tell her how they could go to Warsaw and live like civilized people and have good things, clothes, furniture, and servants. But when he came home Razzeleh looked pale and he was scared, so he didn't say anything. All week it was like this. One day she was strong like an ox, the next day like a lamb, so David didn't know what. He tried to bring the felsher, but Razzeleh said she took the castor oil and was fine. Leah came to see. To her, Razzeleh looked thin and white every day.

Friday, David ran home early from the market — so he didn't sell enough fish, they would eat more of it in the house. But Razzeleh looked pink and chubby, like nothing was wrong, and he thought maybe it was all over.

Maybe in bed he would tell her they should move to Warsaw. They were close and they loved like they were newlyweds, so it was three years only, and he put his arms around her and thought what he should say, what she would answer, how he would explain. All of a sudden she shook, like a chill was running through her body.

"What is it? Razzeleh?" She didn't answer, so David said even louder, "Razzeleh! What's the matter? Are you —?"

With shaking hands she covered up his

mouth. "Hush! You'll wake up Hanneleh."

He rubbed her, maybe she was cold. He said quietly, "Why are you shaking? You're feeling sick again?" She made a tiny laugh. "You think it's funny? I worry when you're sick. I don't like —" Again she held her hand on his mouth. He tried to see her, but it was too dark. "Razzeleh," he said.

She put her lips to his ear and whispered, "My husband. My Dauvidel. You'll be a father by me."

Like he couldn't breathe. Finally comes out, "What? A father?"

Her nose was pushing against his ear. "I have a baby in me," Razzeleh said. "Now I can feel it."

"Ha!" David jumped out of bed like he would run outside and yell to the whole world, and Razzeleh fell back, and he looked at her. It was so dark he couldn't see, but he jumped in again and started to hug and kiss her. Then he started to cry like a child, she could hardly make him stay quiet. Finally, he was still; his head was close to hers, on her shoulder.

"How do you know you have a baby in you?" he asked. She wouldn't let him touch her stomach.

"A woman gets signs," Razzeleh said.

"Signs? What signs?"

"What, I couldn't tell you. It's not nice. I feel the baby moves by me."

"You wouldn't tell me before?" David asked.

"I was afraid. It's almost three years already. Now you'll have a Kaddish. Your parents will be happy to have their name live on."

"You have signs it's a boy?"

"God wouldn't wait three years, a girl."

All night they lay in each other's arms till Razzeleh got stiff, she had to turn away, but David couldn't close his eyes. Nu, it was wonderful. God was good to them. Maybe it had to be like this — now he couldn't go to Warsaw. Now she wouldn't leave her parents; a child had to be born in the house by the family. So a little longer with the fish. All right, if a baby comes, it's first. Why else do we live? Maybe after, later, will come the dreams.

Next morning, even before the roosters made noise, David jumped out of bed and put on his clothes and ran, out of breath, to his parents' house. Leah was up already, sitting, making stockings, and when she saw her son, how he ran inside and fell down and couldn't catch hold of his breath, she didn't say a word, and the yarn and the needles fell from her hands, and she ran to him and helped him stand up and made him sit, and then she gave him some vishnik — whiskey from cherries. He raised the glass in the air and said, "L'chayim . . . to life . . . my dear mother! You'll be a bubbeh again." And he drank.

"Oy, oy, oy," she said, her hands on each side of her mouth, and she smiled so much it hurt her. "My son, my child, and we didn't see how she's sick with a baby. Oy, so stupid!" And she laughed and gave him a kiss on the lips, loud. "My child, God helped you with so much happiness. God is good to you. Because Razzeleh is raising your daughter by you, God is good to you." So much happiness, she told David to go home, and she ran to the river because Gershon was there with his son Aaron, waiting for the boat, they had to go away on business. "Mazel tov!" she said, and she told them the good news.

"Thanks to God," Gershon said. "Didn't I tell you you shouldn't worry?"

In the house Razzeleh sang all day. Comes her mother, like always, to see. She was scared when Razzeleh looked bad before. But today her daughter was rosy and singing. "I haven't heard you sing for a long time," Bossel said.

"I am the happiest person in the whole world," Razzeleh said, and she made a little dance and picked up Hanneleh.

"What happened?" her mother asked.

"Ma, sit down. Sit." So Bossel sat and Razzeleh sat with Hanneleh on her lap. Then she put Hanneleh on the floor and took her mother and gave her a kiss. "Ma, you'll be a bubbeh."

So excited, Bossel couldn't say a word, like she was falling from the sky, and she ran right away to tell her husband. But he was cleaning the hides, and she made such a tumult he was scared, and the knife fell out of his hand. Why was his wife so white like snow? She was crying and she could barely speak. "Razzeleh . . . Razzeleh says she'll have a baby!" she said finally.

Hyam laughed from happiness, and he grabbed her and picked her up and danced around with her. "Thank God for such a simcha!" he said. Such happiness. And he ran to see his daughter and took her around and kissed her on the forehead and told her she should not carry the two pails water and not work hard.

Razzeleh then went back to work and sang a Russian song that would make a stone cry, singing in such a sad voice because she was so happy:

Oh, call not to mind dark times
Which we together once with sad
    hearts bore!
Remember not tormenting chimes
Of parting days and grief that
    passed before.

Yet, oh! the joyous moments pure
    and bright!

We knew when hearts were young
  and light.
Are love's first blissful dreams
  so vain?
Oh, cherish them; let them remain!
Cherish them; let them remain.

6

That's the way time passed, and Razzeleh had a daughter. For her parents, a child is a child. A daughter born to a daughter makes no difference. But to David's parents, well, what can you do? They wouldn't put ashes on the head, but they couldn't sing a praise either. All right, comes later a son to keep the name, God willing. And Razzeleh, so happy she had her own child. And that's the way she raised the two girls. When the baby was two years old, Razzeleh was pregnant again, and the second time she also had a girl. Leah and Gershon didn't know where their heads were, lost, they couldn't find the world. "For what?" Leah cried. "Did we do something, God punishes us?"

"There'll be, there'll be," Gershon told her.

"Only girls there'll be. I feel in my heart," she said. "Dauvidel, he's got to suffer. Maybe when I carried him someone gave me a kayn aynhoreh. I remember when I came to see the old woman across from us. She was dying, and she looked at me and I know she gave me the evil eye, and Dauvidel I was carrying."

"Don't be foolish," Gershon said, but he believed it.

Razzeleh cried all the time, why God was mean to her and wouldn't give her a son, only daughters. Her mother told her God wants daughters, too, so let it be girls.

Again Razzeleh was pregnant, and again she had a girl. Leah got so sick from aggravation they had to bring a doctor from Kiev; it took a week till he came on the boat. He said she took too much to herzen and she had to keep the babies off her mind.

That's the way another year went and Razzeleh got pregnant again. But this time it was a son, Abraham. The little town Horeduck was moving on wheels, everybody dancing in the streets. David brought wine and schnapps from Kiev and he invited the whole town, even the goyim. His mother baked, and the whole family and the whole town came to the simcha, such a happy time, to eat and drink and dance. And to the bris, the circumcision, don't ask. It was eight days after the baby was born and everybody came. For the honor of being the godmother, David chose Naomi, Razzeleh's friend. She was married now at last. Do you know to whom? Mottel. David said let her be the godmother, I don't care what she said about me. So Naomi gave the baby to the godfather. David had chosen Heimie, let him have an honor, too. Heimie gave the baby to Isaac, Razzeleh's oldest brother, he should be the sandek, the one who holds the baby for the mohel to make the circumcision. The mohel, an old man, had done it so many times you couldn't count — one, two! So fast you couldn't see, and just right. Then he gave the baby a little cloth dipped in wine so he would suck on it and sleep. And he prayed:

"Our God and God of our fathers,

preserve this child, his father and mother, and let his name be called in Israel Abraham, the son of David Eisenberg. Let the father rejoice in him that came forth from his loins, and the mother be glad with the fruit of her womb." And he prayed more and he said, "And may this child, Abraham, become a great man, and as he has entered into the Covenant, so may he enter into the Torah, the Law, the chuppa for marriage, and into good deeds."

Then he gave the oldest man in the room — how old he was no one knew — the first drop of blood to put on his tongue; then the mohel wrapped clean where the cut was and every day he would make new the bandage. And everybody yelled mazel tov and drank and shouted a toast: "May you have pleasure from your children and your children's children, and in their children," and Leah made a kayn aynhoreh against the evil eye.

Then Razzeleh had another boy, and again a boy, and after that a daughter, and then a boy, and again a girl. Already she had nine children.

In our little town the carpenters didn't have any work. Nu, they had to eat, so what could they do? One night they went out with torches and set fire to the houses with straw roofs. You know how it is, a roof will burn, a wall, a chair, a table, and they will be busy. But the fire started beating and flapping like sheets on the clothesline, and then such a roar, like an animal, or a storm at night and so fast, house to house till the sky was a sun and people were screaming, running, with no place to go because the four corners of the town were shooting flames and cows were burning in the barns and the ducks and geese and chickens made noisy balls of flame. Water in pails didn't help.

Such a tumult. The screaming horses woke David up, and he jumped out of bed to see what's what, and he saw, and thank God at least it was summer, he could pull the children and Razzeleh from the beds, and he ran to the field, where the horses were jumping. Finally, with the children, they pushed the horses into a corner of the fence so they could put on the harness, and they brought them to the wagon and hooked them up. Everybody jumped in, smoke and flames all around, but no one said a word. With all his strength David drove the four horses.

Razzeleh, with the baby in her arms, looked behind her in the wagon — was everybody there? It was bad to count people with the finger because the Angel of Death might find out how many you have and he might try to take away. So she counted the way they did then, "Not-one, not-two, not-three," but it didn't come out right, so again she counted, and she screamed, "It's not all! Who is it? My God, they're not all here!" She pulled on David and grabbed the reins, "Stop! Go back!"

But behind them it was like an oven on the inside, and David was beating the horses wildly, grinding his teeth, and Razzeleh was screaming, fighting him with one hand and crying, "David! David, my God, go back!" and she beat her chest, "Have pity with me, go back!" and she started pulling on her hair, "Oy, oy, God kill me," and she looked behind her like she couldn't believe it, and she counted and counted, but the wagon was bouncing and the smoke was so thick the children started to cry.

Finally, it was dark again all around, and David could stop the wagon. Razzeleh was swaying back and forth, crying. David counted. "Oy, God be praised," he said. "They're here, Razzeleh. All the children are here."

But she cried and she rocked, "Have pity with me, God. Go back. My child is missing."

Again David counted. "Everybody is here. Look, count — no one is missing."

But she cried and she shook her head no, no, oh, God, what are you doing to me, and she wouldn't stop. David held her but it was no use, so he had to drive on, and she cried softer. Maybe she would stop after all.

They came to the village where David bought geese from people he knew, a Polish family. The light was starting another day and David went to their house. Could they let his family rest? Such a question, don't be foolish, and they gave them cheese, bread, and milk because my parents were kosher.

But my mother, Razzeleh, sat and cried, "Oy, oy, my child is missing," and they couldn't stop her. My father told her she shouldn't cry, it's all right, the children came all together, but she didn't see.

The Polish woman counted: "Eight you have. I count, I know — eight."

"They wouldn't come out," my mother said. "He wouldn't go back for one child." She yelled at my father, "You wouldn't go back! Why? One child, he's not worth the world? What kind of father, he can't go back, his own child? Oy, God wants —"

"Nah, nah," the Polish woman said — a babushka she wore, like a wig, all the time. And she took my mother's hand and pulled it toward the children. On top of each one's head she put it: "So it's one. No? One child. Nah." Again she put the hand on the head of one more child: "Two it is. Two children." And on top of each child's head she put my mother's hand, and my mother looked at each one, looked, oy, who was missing? Till they came to six, and she fainted. They put her in bed and she slept the whole day.

Comes night, she woke up and the good Polish woman gave her a glass milk. "How do you feel?" she asked.

"I have to see my children," my mother said. "Where did you put my children? God help me, I can't see my children!"

"Hoo, hoo," the Polish woman said, "sleeping, your children."

"It's nighttime," my father said. "The children are sleeping, quiet and nice. It's all right."

"It's all right. It's all right!" my mother yelled at him, and from her teeth, like a snake, it came: "Suffering, she has to suffer, nobody knows." She looked at the floor, her children sleeping. "My baby," she cried. "You have to take it away from me?" The Polish woman brought her the baby and she grabbed it like from out of a fire, and she started to cry; she shook so hard they were scared she would drop the baby, so my father pulled it away from her and gave it to the Polish woman. What could they do? My mother sat and cried. No one could stop her. Finally, the woman gave her a glass vodka and said,

"Drink up, please. Good for you."

My mother didn't cry anymore. She sat and didn't say a word. Again the woman gave her a glass vodka, and after they put my mother back into bed and covered her, she fell asleep.

Next morning my father woke up and crawled over to look at my mother. She slept with her face to the ceiling, like she didn't move the whole night. My father watched his poor Razzeleh, how beautiful she looked before the light came in, like a painting, pale, he could hardly see. More and more the light began eating up the dark, and he looked. My God! My God! What was it? My father told me years and years and years later, and you say no? It can't be, superstitious, he didn't know, he didn't see? He told me he saw — I shouldn't believe? He was so scared, he started to cry like a puppy, he couldn't hold it in. Razzeleh, her red cheeks pale, her beautiful dark eyes falling in, with circles around them, her beautiful dark hair turned white like snow. Why should he lie, my father? It can't happen? It happens. He yelled so loud the Polish family and all the children came running. What is it? Maybe a fire again? When she saw that my mother's hair was white, the Polish woman crossed herself and screamed, "Bozheh! God! What happened to Rachel?" My father stood like someone hit him on the head.

Two weeks passed. The good Polish woman was like a servant to my mother. She was coming to herself now and she could see how it all was, how her children were there, and how she had lost her beautiful dark hair, how it was white. Nu, she would wear a wig like the religious old women, but my father told her no, he didn't like it. "It looks good on you," he said, "even better." It happens, these things.

The Polish family, they couldn't do enough for them, like angels. Two days after the fire my father went to see what was going on in Horeduck. When he arrived, it was terrible to look at: no more houses, only like lumps black hay and sticks of charcoal, and all over the streets were burnt cows, horses, and pigs already stiff and about to smell. Hungry people.

The muzhiks were bringing them bread.

The carpenters — they were Polish people — felt shame. No pay, no talk, they started to build and everybody helped. My father built a big house in the same place, and when it was ready my mother came back with the children and started to raise geese for the market. Then they dug out a place, deep, like for a freezer, and all around next to the dirt they put in wood, a lining. In the winter they hired muzhiks to cut big chunks ice from the lake, and they put in layers in the hole and pounded the ice and put layers of straw and next ice and next straw until the hole was filled to the ceiling, and then they covered it with hay to the top. They filled wooden barrels with geese shmaltz and covered them up with wooden lids and put them into the deep hole till they were ready to send to Warsaw. They also sent fish in the barrels, and that's how they started to make a living.

And I remember it all — eventually there were fourteen children. Me, I was maybe four years old, five, with two sisters younger than me — Bessie and

Sophie. Everybody had jobs to do, not like today. Already I was making beds, cleaning the table, wiping dust on the windows.

One day the dust on the street was like a cloud with thunder, horses pounding and people yelling and screaming, and I didn't know what. It was Friday and my father was selling fish at the market, so I ran to find Ma. "Ma! Ma!" I shouted. She was by the barn, making the linings for the inside of the hides for coats. How she twirled with a tree branch the thick, foamy glue she made by cooking pigs' knuckles. She looked over my head, in the middle of her work, past to where the horses pounded and the women were screaming. She grabbed up her skirt, with a big apron over it, so she could run fast to the street, and I was running behind her. I fell on her dress when she stood still and I saw the Russian soldiers, the Cossacks, riding their horses round and round, making to dance and kick in the air, and the swords in flashes like the noontime sun blinds you on waving water. Ma started to call names: "Hanneleh!

Natalie! Ida! Abie! Louie! Leo! Faygee! Yasha! Yetta! — into the house." But she got mixed up and looked at one child and called him a different name. It didn't matter, so long as she could push the children inside the house. Then she told the boys, "Run, quick, put the horses in the barn!" And the girls had to go under the beds to hide, and my mother put the baby, Sophie, down by me on the bed. "Don't get out. You're sick, you can't move. Do you hear?" she said. In those days we listened.

Just in time we were under the beds and then comes a pounding on the door like it would break in pieces. It opened, bang, as far as it could go toward the wall. Stood like two bears, with fur hats, fur jackets, red silk shirts, blue silk pants, black boots, long black hair with grease shining, mustaches hanging down to touch the chest, and black eyes, dark skin, bones in the face like they were swollen. "What is it I smell, pork?" A voice like a horn. "A Jew's house. Is it Jewish now, pork?" He looked hard at Ma. "It's a funny one, a freak — see," he says to the other. "She's young or she's old? A girl's face and white hair." The other had little lines for eyes — Mongol he was. "Hey," the first said to Ma, and he grabbed her skirt, my God, where the apron was hanging. "Everything is white?" and he laughed, showing big teeth with space in between. She jumped back but the table was in the way. "What you got to give me?" he roared, and he laughed at her, and he squeezed a hand over her breast. He was pushing her against the corner of the table, sharp, like a knife making a deep hole in her leg.

"Whiskey," she said. "Schnapps."

"Give to him, to Pulo," he said. "First I got to drink you up."

"My children," she said. He pressed more, and he was squeezing and reaching inside and putting his mouth on her face. "They have the scarlet fever," my mother said, pointing to the children. "It comes out on them and maybe me, too." He grabbed her shoulders and shook her in front of him, and he looked at her for spots. "The felsher, the doctor, says everybody keep away from the house," my mother said. "You see how we stay inside. And my babies, you see?" He looked where Sophie lay with me on the bed.

"Pah!" he spit, and gave Ma a push. "It's a lie." In those times scarlet fever was already the grave. On her hands, some white spots showed from the glue, and also on her arms. "Whiskey!" he yelled, and she ran quickly to the kitchen and brought the bottle and she gave it to him. He looked at her like he would spit in her face. "Scarlet fever! It makes white spots, scarlet fever?" he yelled. He drank from the bottle and held to the other, the Mongol, but he shook his head no. "You're afraid it'll give scarlet fever, the bottle?" He looked at it and wiped the opening with his hand. "The hell with it," he said in Russian, and he pulled from his belt his curving sword, and he threw the bottle in the air and made a slash with the sword and broke the whiskey bottle to pieces. He looked at Ma. "I'll make a cure for scarlet fever," he said, and he raised the sword above her and she screamed, oy! God! and he laughed. Came a silver light when he chopped down, and the sword cut a slice from the corner of the table. She screamed and the boys, Abie and Louie, ten years, eight, they ran from the back and threw themselves on the Cossack, they didn't know. But he swept them to the floor like he was pushing crumbs from the table with his arm, and he gave Abie a spank with the sword. Laughing, he raised the blade and started to go out in front.

But Isaac, Ma's brother, the geeber, the fighter, ran in from across the street. He held his fists over his head, and his bottom lip was sticking out, and like two hammers he hit the Cossack on the head. He fell to the floor quickly, a sack of clothes. "Villain!" Isaac yelled at the other. "Get out! You don't belong here!"

The Mongol pulled out his sword so fast it made noise like the wind. Hush! hush! he cut into the air. Isaac grabbed the other Cossack on the floor, like a bag of clothes. He raised him up and threw him on the Mongol. They tumbled in together and Isaac ran to grab both of them, and he shook them and knocked them but all of a sudden he bent over them and stopped like a picture. The Mongol stood up slowly. He put one foot on Isaac's stomach and gave a pull with his sword out from the middle, where it was deep inside. Ma screamed; she ran over and fell on Isaac, lying on the floor with his hands over his stomach, and he closed his eyes and made a noise with his nose. Ma was screaming, and outside people were running, and Bubbeh Bossel came and Zaydeh Hyam and Uncle Aaron, Uncle Joseph, Uncle Velvel, more, and they fell on Uncle Isaac, but the two Cossacks stood up and made signs with their curved swords and everybody went back, but the uncles picked up Isaac.

"Murderers! Murderers!" my father yelled from the doorway. He looked at Uncle Isaac when the others carried him out to their house across the street. Zaydeh said, "Shah! Shah!" to my father, but he went up to the Cossacks anyway. "Murderers!" Then he yelled in Yiddish to Zaydeh, "Run to the constable! Bring him, he should see, with blood on their swords." Zaydeh didn't know what, this way, that way? And my father gave him a push he should go, and he ran out quickly, and my father stood himself with the Cossacks. Ma stayed by us, by the bedroom door.

In Russian, his voice not up, not down, my father said, "Get out of my house."

"David!" Ma whispered. "Come away!"

"Damn fools," one Cossack said. "Now they have trouble. Don't you know better?" he asked my father.

"Get out of my house," my father repeated.

"That bastard, the big ox — what's he, your brother? What do you think, he's going to do what he wants to us? I tell you, he's lucky my friend stuck him like a pig."

"Get out of my house."

The Mongol stood, a statue, his sword pointing down. He looked at Ma. The other one, who was putting himself together, saw Ma and said to my father, "You got the scarlet fever?" My father didn't know what to say. He looked at Ma; he watched the Cossacks. Then one said, "I don't think anybody's got the scarlet fever in this house. Do you? Do you?" He grabbed my father's coat but my father knocked his hand away. "Damn fool Jews. Don't you know better?" He moved, a bear, by the door and he looked around. Was the Mongol coming? But the Mongol looked only at Ma. "Pulo!" yelled the other. Pulo made his mustache twitch; he looked at the sword, the blood already like dark paint, and he looked again at Ma — how she stood by the door to the bedroom, a hand on her chest. "Pulo," said the other Cossack.

Like his stomach was hurting him, Pulo pushed his feet toward Ma, bent his head, and went up to her. My father, in three big steps, came over and reached out, but Pulo, like he could see with his ear, lifted his sword. My father grabbed it and they came together, one on the other. The second Cossack ran over and tried to pull them apart but he couldn't. Pulo held the sword over Pa. My mother screamed and screamed, and the second Cossack ran outside and yelled, "Comrades! Comrades! Give me help!" Then he ran inside to grab Pulo. Like a stone, Pulo stood and tried to push the sword into Pa, but Pa went backwards across the floor. Hooves, horses, yelling and crying, and the leather squealing, and three Cossacks fell into the house and saw Pulo, how he tried to stick Pa, and they laughed like the water rushing over rocks. "Help the bastard!" the other Cossack said. So all put their hands on Pa and they raised him like a doll in their arms.

"Pulo!" one yelled. "He's bothering you?"

"What to do, Pulo?" another one said and laughed.

Pulo grabbed a rope from his belt and threw it on Pa and wound it around his neck. Mama was hitting them, and Pulo, too. The Cossacks laughed and carried Pa outside to the barn with the horses stamping, chickens yelling, and feathers flying. Pulo put the rope around a beam and fastened it to Pa's neck, and they all raised him and let him go. And so he was hanging. He pulled the rope and tried to pull out his neck, but he was hanging and kicking, and they pushed him. So he was swinging on the rope, and they laughed and yelled and Ma pounded on them; she reached for the rope but they held onto her.

"They got whiskey in this house!" one Cossack yelled.

"Ho!" and they pushed each other, who would get inside first to drink, and they ran out of the barn. Except Pulo. He looked at Ma.

"Pulo!" the Cossack said. "They'll drink it up!" But Pulo held Ma when she tried to reach my father. How he kicked and was rolling up his eyes to the roof and pulling the rope; he twisted, he couldn't breathe, and dark blue was his face, purple, and his tongue started to stick out like it was growing in his mouth. "Go inside," the Cossack told her. "Show them whiskey." Like he threw cold water on her face, she looked, and she tried to run but Pulo was holding her. "First whiskey, Pulo!" the Cossack said. "Inside the house is a bedroom with a bed. With a door, Pulo! What do you want with the horses and chickens?" Pulo wouldn't go but he couldn't stay still, and the Cossack pushed them into the house. Oy, such a tumult! Everywhere they were smashing things to find the bottles. "Where?" the Cossack asked Ma. She brought out two bottles schnapps, two bottles wine, high up from the cupboard, and they grabbed and they drank out of the bottles. One took away from the other and they began to laugh, how much they could swallow at one time. Pulo wouldn't drink. He wouldn't take his eyes off Ma.

"Hey!" the Cossack yelled at Abie and Louie, where they stood by the bedroom door. Ma saw and she made with the head so they would go to the barn. They didn't know what. Ma was friends with the soldiers? "Kids!" the Cossack yelled at them. "Get out of my sight!" and he grabbed them by their collars and gave them a kick, they should go outside. Oy, would they see Pa?

The Cossack laughed at Pulo. "I don't see Pulo have a drink! Look how he is, so sad. Is he a man like us? Such an insult, he can't drink with his comrades!" And he grabbed a bottle of schnapps and started to sing:

"Ho! ho! ho! ho!
High the Cossack's heart it's
    bounding
When the battle call he hears!"

And all started to sing:

"Ho! ho! ho! ho!
When the wild hurrah it's sounding
Welcome music to his ears!"

And the Cossack put the bottle to Pulo's mouth. No, no, he shook his head, he wouldn't. And they laughed, grabbing him, he should drink.

"Hurrah! hurrah!
When his horse to fight is leaping
High in the air his sword he's
    swinging,
Thrust and spill
The foe to kill!"

And they poured the schnapps down his throat. He coughed, choked, he couldn't breathe, he got red in the face, blue, purple. He bumped a chair, the table; he knocked the china closet and dishes were breaking.

Ma ran fast to the barn. Abie and Louie were sitting on the ground. Pa lay like he was dead, so white now, his face like chalk and his neck raw, bleeding from the rope. She put her mouth on his and she blew air. She breathed so he would breathe — yes, yes, that's how they did it in those days. And when he opened his eyes he saw it was Razzeleh; it was like a dream, and she held his head in her arms and rocked it like a baby.

So, finally, the Cossacks carried Pulo out of the house and whipped the horses, kicked with their heels, and went away from us. Uncle Isaac was dead. The little town Horeduck cried three days and everyone threw ashes on themselves. To keep his name, lots of baby boys were named after him, Isaac.

7

So, we lived and started to grow up, healthy, white teeth — challeh with plenty eggs in it and the bread you don't squeeze, better than a toothbrush. We all worked hard in the house, everyone helped, but with fourteen children Pa and Ma couldn't keep up.

Came the time when I was eleven, and my Uncle Louis was living in the big city, Kiev. So, big, it was like a small town in America, but in the old country by us it was big. He had a tailor shop — a shop? In his house he made suits and dresses, and he had girls working. Two Singer sewing machines he had. Yes! All over Russia they brought Singer sewing machines, like a miracle, you pushed with the feet to spin. Still, today, I keep my machine and it goes like new. So Uncle

Louis wrote Ma and Pa — why should he hire strangers if he can pay to his own? Send him two nieces, they can live in his house and eat by him, they will be safe, he'll watch, and it'll be good for everybody. We found out he didn't pay so much, but he was never mean to us. Hannah — Hanneleh — was married already to a nice boy from the village, a good wedding they had but they lived in our house till they would have enough. Her husband worked with Pa in the fishing — a good boy, but it was another mouth to feed.

My oldest sister, Rose, sixteen years, was going with a boy, Greesha, who worked in his father's shoe shop. For two years already they were going together — it means he had his eye on her. The parents looked, already they were talking. For Rose, she would marry, it would be all right by her, but when Uncle Louis said to send him two nieces, she said she was excited to go. For eleven years old I was already like a grown person — independent. I could work like a horse and everybody said I was a beauty, with red hair but dark like sable, shiny, with curls, and black eyes. The other children were scared of the big city. Me, I couldn't wait. I had to go, too.

Finally, they said all right, Pa and Ma. They didn't like it, but what could they do? For the holidays, Pesach, Yom Kippur, we would come home on the boat.

We were leaving, like going to the moon, such bundles they made, like in Kiev there was nothing. Everybody crying, hugging, kissing. Ma couldn't stand it — she had to bite her lip. "Go, hurry, he won't wait!" she said, and she pushed us on the boat — two girls by ourselves, my God — and the kids were yelling. Greesha looked like he lost Rose forever, he wouldn't get over it. He was too ashamed to kiss her, but he gave her a handkerchief with embroidery that his mother made. "You shouldn't catch cold," he said. Rose was laughing, so happy. "I won't blow my nose," she said. Tears in his eyes. "Maybe I'll come to Kiev," he yelled when the boat started. They waved to us, handkerchiefs, hats, the hands like butterflies.

On the boat we couldn't sit still, two young girls for the first time out of the little town. We thought the world would be different, like maybe the land would be a different color, blue or red with dots, and the people would walk on their hands maybe, or maybe they would wear silk and big belts like the pictures sometimes on the cans of tea. Like we stood still and the land was going by the boat, we watched. For a long time it looked the same to us, like our town, and we got tired and dizzy, so we lay down on the deck with the suitcases — cardboard — which we used like pillows.

A tumult, the world was falling down on our ears, oy, a thousand cows and bulls in the same throat, pounding like guns, whistles, they could break our bones — Kiev! Already it was getting dark, and the fire poured from the factories with the smoke, the ashes, with the buildings black and blue like bruises. Our hearts were in our mouths, we were holding on to one another like the wind from all the noise would blow us away. We had to laugh at how scared we were, but we were so excited, so happy — it was something new, you see. I'll never forget.

Uncle Louis was waiting for us. We hadn't seen him for a long time, so now we didn't know if it was really him — he got fat. "Rose? Eatkeh?" Like a bear he picked us up. "Ha! Don't you *eat* anything?" He was smiling in our faces and we were smiling back, but he took our breath away from us. Then he grabbed the suitcases in one arm and started to walk, so fast we had to run behind to keep up. The first time in the city we didn't even understand how to walk, so many people, so many shops and buildings, with the pushcarts and the stalls and the dust while it was getting dark — they didn't have what to cover the streets in those days, just the dirt. Finally, when we couldn't keep up, we got scared to death Uncle Louis would lose us, but he went by a door, a house between houses, no yard, nothing, the whole street like one building, all made from wood and without paint. He took us inside, a dark room, the living room and the kitchen together, and another room where the sewing machines were. Aunt Malke welcomed us. She was even more fat than Uncle Louis. "Kinder!" she yelled, with her arms spread open. "Kinder!" And with the hugs she kissed us on our cheeks, smack, loud, so we would know.

So, we settled in, a little room for us, one small bed, and we learned from the Singer sewing machines with another girl, maybe nineteen or twenty she was. She taught us and we worked. Me, I sewed the buttonholes. I go so fast they couldn't keep up, so they let me make pieces on the coats. What did we know? From early in the morning, still in the dark, to late at night, we worked. Aunt Malke and Uncle Louis were never mean, but what could they do? They were poor and we all had to work. We never went hungry, we sent money home, on Shabbos we could rest and go to the synagogue, that's all.

But one Shabbos Uncle invited a student — you know how it is, a student is important, you have to help out. He was tall and good-looking, studying to be a doctor. What could be better? Yasha was his name. He didn't have his parents in Kiev — they lived far away. He was the oldest, so they sent him to the city to study to be a doctor. At the table the first night he couldn't say a word, and Rose laughed with Uncle Louis, how he liked to joke. "So," he said to her, "why don't you put on a few pounds? You're saving me money? You eat good but you don't *show.*" He always liked to tease someone.

Rose covered her mouth with her hand and looked out of her eyes at Yasha and said, *"He* can eat for me," and she clapped again and everybody laughed. Poor Yasha, he didn't know what to do, except smile. But as the days passed, he came to the house earlier and earlier. He sat by the little window in the living room and looked at his books, but he also looked at Rose. He couldn't take his eyes off her. Rose? She had to sew over a piece three times, she made so many mistakes.

Finally, he began talking to her, they drank tea together, and in the evening before bed they went outside to walk a little bit — they couldn't go far from the house. Yasha Segelman — he was very good-looking and educated. Now, at the table, he couldn't take his eyes off Rose, and when he looked at her, like an angel in his face.

One night we were eating special, roast chicken with boobeleh — navy beans you soak in the juice from the chicken, and then you roast — it melts in your mouth, delicious. Then a knock on the door. Uncle Louis got up with his mouth full — who could it be at suppertime? He opened up and somebody asked is Rose Eisenberg here? He came in — Greesha! Oy. Rose dropped her spoon on the floor — bad luck. "What're you doing?" she asked.

"I didn't hear a word from you," he said. "Only from your parents. So —"

"My God," she said, "something happened? Somebody's hurt?"

"No one," he said. "No one, knock on wood," and he knocked on the wall. Then he looked at everybody and made little bows to each one, good evening, good evening, and no one said anything. Who was he? they thought. Especially Yasha.

"All right," Uncle Louis said, "sit. Take a place."

"No, no," Greesha said.

"We got, we got," Uncle Louis said. "When you got beans, beans you got."

So he sat, Greesha. He pushed a chair next to Rose, and once he started to eat, he ate well, hungry. Rose couldn't. She was poking with the spoon, and Yasha was watching and chewing, he couldn't swallow. Everybody else talked, Uncle Louis talked, the usual.

Finally, we were done. We got up to carry away the dishes. I said to Rose, "Why did he come?" She made with her shoulder, how should she know? "Did he come to marry you?" I asked. Why should she start to cry so hard? Then, I was too young. I didn't know from nothing, but I was close to her, like twins — she didn't have to tell me. I could feel. Maybe I didn't understand up from down, but I could feel how something was.

When we came back to the living room, Greesha was talking with Yasha. This and that, who was who. But soon Rose came and Greesha said to Yasha, "Rose is my intended, for two years already."

Yasha turned white like snow. He asked

Rose, "He tells the truth?"

Rose started to cry again. "In our town," she said, "he came to see me like a suitor, yes, for two years." She looked at Greesha. "Greesha, I never told you I was going to marry you."

Greesha got dark in his eyes and he almost fell off the chair. He stood up, he didn't know where to go, he looked at Rose, at Yasha, and then he turned around in a circle, all around, and he opened his mouth, but nothing came out, and he went away, gone, just like that. He didn't say good-bye. He went right to the train and back to our town, Horeduck.

Rose was crying, she couldn't stop. Yasha put his arm around her to comfort her but she wouldn't let him. "Rose," he said.

"Go away!" she cried and she ran to our bedroom.

For a long time he watched to see if maybe she would come out. Finally, Uncle Louis said, "Leave her alone. She's mixed up in the head. You have to give her time." So Yasha went out.

All night I could hear how she cried.

The next day she worked her fingers to the bone. She wouldn't talk, she wouldn't listen. Did she love Greesha so much? She was so ashamed of him? Suppertime, Yasha came like usual, but she wouldn't eat. She stayed in the kitchen. Then he wouldn't eat, and he went out. A whole week passed, he didn't come back. She started to worry, where was he? On Shabbos he came like a guilty man. He couldn't look at her. At the table he sat on one side and she sat on the other, but they didn't look at each other and they didn't talk. Like somebody died.

Next week came a letter from our mother:

Darling daughters,
Everything is going fine but Fanny has to stay in bed, her stomach hurts. Genesha cut her finger, she was bleeding to death. Thank God, bless Him, I wrapped it in spiders' webs and it stopped in time. Pa doesn't complain but his back is killing him, he has to lift the baskets of fish, sometimes the men can't come to

301

help. By me, you know how I keep up. Nothing bothers me, sometimes I can't sleep, Sophie yells, a nightmare, and I have to take her in bed beside me.

I pray God should watch out for you. Such a terrible thing happened, you won't believe. Greesha, he was so interested in you, Rose? Something happened by him, nobody knows, he fell over dead. A young boy, wasn't sick a day before, all of a sudden he's dead. God forbid, who can know? His mother, you should forgive the expression, a witch with poison in her face, she was screaming by me how my daughter kills her son. "Don't you dare!" I yelled at her. "God will punish you for such a thing! They were almost ready to marry, she should kill him? She has a knife that can reach from Kiev to here? What're you talking?" She couldn't control herself. You shouldn't worry, she'll be all right.

Take care, Eatkeh, and take care yourself, Rose. Times are hard but

God will watch us all. Can you come home for Pesach?

I love you both, my daughters.

Ma

At first Rose was almost laughing, she couldn't believe it. She had to give me the letter so I could tell her what it said again. She tried to scream, she put her hands to her head. I had to fight with her so she wouldn't pull out her hair. "Rose! Rose!" I yelled.

"My God!" she was screaming, and she beat herself on her chest with her fists. "God help me! Oh, my God!" Uncle Louis and Tante Malke took her up, and Uncle Louis held her tight so she wouldn't hit her head on the table. Tante dipped cloths in cold water to put on her forehead. Finally, they put her in bed and she cried like a sick baby, softly, all night.

Next morning, like before, she wouldn't eat. This time she couldn't work. She was stabbing herself with the needle, and Uncle Louis was afraid of the scissors, so he told her to rest, to stay in bed, and Tante made chicken soup.

Came Yasha, his face like the earth, so unhappy. "Where's Rose?" he asked. I told him what happened. Sitting down, he twisted his hands, his fingers, and he closed his eyes tight. "I have to see her," he said.

"She's in bed," I told him.

"I don't care. I have to see."

Everybody was cleaning up, getting ready for supper, so, why not? I took him by the hand and went to the bedroom. First I looked inside, Rose should be decent. She was awake in bed. I showed him in and he kept by the door. "Rose?" She wouldn't answer. "I can't help it," he said. "I'm going crazy."

"Oh," she said, and she started to cry. "Oy. Oy. My God," she was crying, water jumping from her eyes.

"Rose, please, I have to —"

"Don't talk to me!"

"Shah. It's all right," Yasha said. "I understand. I want to —"

"I don't want to listen! Oy, God!" Rose shouted.

Yasha made big sighs. "All I can think of is you — day and night. I don't sleep.

304

I can't do my lessons."

She held out her arm. "Go better and learn, and leave me *alone.*"

"You want I should leave?"

"Yes! Go! Get out!"

"You don't care? You loved *him*, not me? You don't care, then I don't care!"

"I can't stand it," she said.

"I don't want to live without you," Yasha said. "Do you understand? I can't live without you!"

"Please!" she yelled. "What're you doing to me?"

"I'll kill myself!" he said. "I'll kill myself!"

She shook her head that he wouldn't, so he ran out of the house.

I said, "Rose. Rose!" But she wouldn't answer, so I ran out, too. Where did he go? It was getting dark. I saw him already far away, he ran so fast. But I could run like the wind, and I was scared, all alone in the city. I watched him, I could see his black yarmulke, the little skullcap, like a ball up and down. Where did he go? My God, straight to the railroad tracks, where the trains were, and he lay down across the tracks. I ran over to him and yelled, "Yasha! Yasha! What're you doing? Get up, Yasha!" But he wouldn't. I tried to pull him away but he was too strong — he lay like stone. Finally, I saw a man, a stranger, a Russian, and I went over to him. By that time, I couldn't speak Russian so good, like later, like I was born with it on my tongue. I was yelling and I pointed to Yasha, but the man laughed. He didn't care, he was drunk anyway.

What to do, what to do, my God? I lifted my hands up to heaven. "Will he die?" I yelled. Came an old man right away, a beard down to his chest, a yarmulke on his head, he was praying and he couldn't look, nothing should bother him, especially a woman. "Help me out," I said to him, and I grabbed his arm. Like a sin, he pulled away and he took a look at me and saw I was only a child, so he could look. What is? Pushing, pulling, I made him go over to Yasha lying like he was dead already on the tracks.

"He's crazy, out of his head?" the old man said.

"He wants to kill himself," I cried.

"A Jewish boy?" The old man was bending over Yasha. "You don't kill yourself, dumbbell. God forbids you should harm yourself. Rabbi Channina said, 'It is better that He should take the soul Who gave it, no one else.' Do you study the Talmud?"

Yasha looked up at the old man. "In Genesis it says, 'And surely your blood will I require.' So, He can have it."

"Ah!" the old man said. He was bending over, lower yet. "The meaning is interpreted where it's harming yourself, it is forbidden."

Yasha raised himself on his elbow to rest. "Interpreted in the book, you see the word 'surely' means how a person strangles himself. So God doesn't care, so long you repent."

"What do you mean, God doesn't care? He cares, he cares. It says when a person is born, all should rejoice. When a person dies, all have to weep."

"Weep?" Yasha said. "In Ecclesiastes you can read it: 'Better is the day of death than the day of a person's birth.' "

"Oy, my God," the old man was hitting himself on the head. "You'll wake up, you'll be in Gehinom." That's how they call the bad place when you die.

"Let it be," Yasha said.

From far away, but already close, the train was yelling it was coming.

The old man was bending down so close, his nose almost touched Yasha's nose. "Didn't God give Moses the Law on Mount Sinai? Didn't Moses give the Law to the people? You are not one of the people? You're not circumcised? You didn't study the Torah? You don't study the Law? The Law is to live with, not to die with. So why do you want to die like a Gentile? Strictly speaking, you have no right — you have to *live*."

Yasha lay down his head again, he wouldn't talk. Like a furnace it came, the train. The tracks were shaking. The old man looked at me. "What is? Why? Why?"

"He loves my sister! He thinks she doesn't love him back!"

"Loves?" The old man stood up and looked this way and that way. "Loves?"

He was bending over Yasha again. "What're you talking about, loves? You want to be married? So, be married. Loves? First you marry, then you love."

Yasha wouldn't look anymore. He lay on the tracks like he was in bed. And the train, it wouldn't stop, started screaming like an animal, a pig maybe, when the muzhik sticks in a knife to kill it. On my knees, I got down close to him and I grabbed his payess, the hair growing down by his ears, and I yelled inside his ear, "She loves you! Rose loves you!"

Oy, not a second — he couldn't believe it, he could, he couldn't. Finally, he did! How close was the train? The wheels made soot on the back of his coat. For me, the steam made a spray on my dress like I was ironing and spritzing from my mouth to make damp. A long time we stood with no air, we had to bend over to catch our breath. The old man was praying, giving thanks to God, and he looked at Yasha to find out who he was, maybe he knew him from the synagogue. "Nu," the old man said, "a stick has two ends. Everybody holds the good and the bad. Oh Lord, our

God, have mercy upon your children."

"Go in peace," Yasha said.

The old man waved his hand by his ear and shook his head yes, no, yes, and he put his beard down over his chest, no one should bother him, he was praying.

So we went back, and I didn't know what would be with Rose. I told Yasha she was upset, that's why she talked bad to him. By the house I said to him, "Wait, let me go inside to prepare with her."

Everything was on the table already, but Uncle and Tante didn't know what to do. Where was Eatkeh? "Oy, my God," Tante said, "where *were* you? My God, you ran out of the house so fast. And Yasha? Where is Yasha now?"

I told them the whole story. "I'll go see Rose," I said, "and I'll tell her Yasha is here to see her."

Uncle Louis made with the shoulder. "See her? Who knows what she wants?"

Her eyes were closed, Rose. Maybe she was sleeping. "Rose?" I said softly. One eye she opened up. I made like I was crying and she sat up quickly.

"What's the matter?" she asked.

"Yasha —" I said.

"What, Yasha?"

I cried more.

She was grabbing and shaking my shoulder so hard, like my teeth would fall out. "What is, Yasha? Where is he? Eatkeh, say something, my God! Where is Yasha?"

"He ran ahead and I could hardly see him, he went so fast. Finally, he went straight to the railroad tracks and lay down —"

She jumped out of the bed like it was boiling water and she screamed, Uncle and Tante came running, and they took her around, but she couldn't stay still. "Where is he, where is he, where?" she cried in my face.

"So he was lying on the tracks and a train was coming — what could I do? I yelled at him, he wouldn't move, no, he wanted to kill himself, so I tried —"

"Oy, oy, God in my heart, my Yasha — what, what?"

"I couldn't, he was too strong. So I asked a man, only he was drunk, he wouldn't do anything. And then I saw an old man with his beard down over his chest praying, but he wouldn't pay attention, he had to pray —"

"Eatkeh! Tell me about Yasha! I can't stand it anymore!" Rose shouted.

"So I grabbed him and I said, 'Help me, help me!" Finally, I pulled him toward Yasha, lying on the tracks, and the old man talked to him but the train was coming, we couldn't move him, and the old man was talking more, how he had to live, Yasha, and the train, my God, like a big mountain with a fire on top — look, how I got all wet from the steam it made on me —"

"Eatkeh!"

"All right! At the end I was yelling in Yasha's ear, 'She loves you! Rose loves you!' *Then* he got up when the train —"

"Where is he?" Rose asked. She looked and looked like maybe he was in the room with us.

"In the street," I said.

In her nightgown yet, barefoot, she ran, she could hardly open up the door, so fast, and when she saw Yasha standing, pale, she threw herself on him, and he nearly fell down on his back. A long time after, finally, Uncle and Tante pushed them inside the house. They couldn't take her away from him. Yasha, at the end, picked her up and carried her to the bed and laid her down nicely. Again she got very sick with a hot fever and sweating and shaking like convulsions. They brought the doctor and he said she was sick from being so scared.

When my sister was beginning to feel good, Yasha made up his mind to get married. Then Rose said to him, "How can we get married, you are still in gymnasium?" That's how they called the university. "And you have so much to learn." His parents, you see, didn't know what their son was doing. They knew only one thing — that he was going to college to study to become a doctor.

For the Christmas holidays all the students went home. Yasha was going on the train — we watched him go, me and Rose. Yasha covered himself and Rose with his big collar. I could see the hot breath from their mouths, and finally one breath they were making. Rose was crying already from loneliness, but when the train went away, and we couldn't see it anymore, she tried to dance home — sometimes a dance, sometimes like she could hardly walk, happy and sad.

Yasha told us later that he came home and said to his parents he met a good-looking girl and he was in love with her and wanted to have her for his wife. Such a tumult! His parents were yelling and screaming, "For a good time we send you to college? That's how you study to be a doctor in college? That's how we work our fingers to the bone so you should look at a girl, a stranger? Who knows what she is, you want to marry her already? No more college, no more the girl!"

He begged them and told them the girl was very pretty and refined. His mother asked where she came from, and Yasha said from Minsker Gubernya, from fine parents. "When you see her, you will love her, too."

Then his mother said, "If such fine parents, they wouldn't send her in the big world alone. Two young girls, they must be shleppers." Shleppers they didn't want their son to marry.

Yasha said, "They come from a small town, everybody knows who they are there. Their parents have fourteen children, so the two sisters went away to work to support themselves."

But they wouldn't listen. Yasha's mother was mean and his father, a nice man, didn't say a word to help him. What could he do? Yasha went away with a broken heart. When he came back to our house in the night, Rose hugged and kissed him, even in front of Uncle and Tante, but Yasha was crying, and he told us what happened with his parents. He said, "What can I do now? I should go to school? How can I go to school, I have no money. And to get married, I don't have a profession."

But Yasha had an uncle, David Schwartz, who lived in Uzefke. He used to make springs for beds. By him worked goyim. He was not rich, but not poor, and he had three children.

"Listen," Uncle Louis said, "why don't you go ask him he should lend you a few rubles to start a business. What can you lose? He'll say no, he'll say yes."

So excited was Rose, and she put Yasha's hand on her cheek. "Oh, Yasha, what do you think? Will you go?"

He smiled at her. "Then you have to go with me."

Her face got red, she didn't know what to say. With a nice breath she said, "You want I should go, I'll go with you. I don't care how anyone talks."

"Why should they talk? A man goes on the train with his wife —"

"Oy!" She clapped her cheeks and she was laughing and crying, and everybody was saying mazel tov, mazel tov, a wedding! But how could they arrange so quickly — it takes time, the day, the rabbi has to know — and Ma and Pa? So much money to come by the boat, can Rose and Yasha and me and the Uncle and Tante, too, go home to our village? How could it be?

"Never mind," Uncle said. "Tomorrow I'll talk to Rabbi Goldfarb. He'll make quick the wedding, a good heart, so long he has no troubles from the families."

"But Ma and Pa will be disappointed, all of a sudden I should be married and they have never seen Yasha, and without their permission," Rose said.

"So, I give the permission," Uncle said. "I'm not your mother's brother? It's the same thing. Don't worry, we'll tell them how he's a scholar and how he'll take care of you. But tell them? After. Then if they complain, it's too late."

You see, Uncle was modern because in the big city the old ideas go away sometimes. People don't care so much. Nu, Tante loaned Rose her wedding dress — too big, we put in tucks. It looked perfect by Rose, like it was special for her. And Sunday morning, in the synagogue, with Uncle and Tante and me and the sewing girl, a few friends of Yasha's, that's all, we made the wedding. Two more couples at the same time, it was all right, everything pretty, flowers on the chuppa, the canopy. The important thing, they were married, happy. My parents, they don't know anything. Later Rose wrote a long letter. She said Yasha was perfect and Uncle Louis made a blessing and stood by her. For the first time Pa wrote the answer. He said, "Ma is crying, but in the end she'll give the blessing, too. She'll remember how it was with us, also, with her mother, may she rest in peace. Go in good health, so long you should be happy and not ashamed to show your face to the world." He was modern, too, you know. Times change. Rose wouldn't cut her hair and put on a wig. She went to the mikva for the dipping, the bath, so she should be pure on the wedding night, a kosher daughter of Israel. But more, no, it didn't matter. So much in love, Yasha and Rose, they looked like angels together.

Then they went on the train, three days later, to see Uncle David. When they both went into his house, he yelled, "Oy, my simcha is so big!" And he hugged Yasha and pounded him on the back. Then he saw Rose, and he couldn't take his eyes off her, and for one minute he stood still, shaking, yes, yes, such a beauty. Then his wife came in and saw Yasha and said, "You're here? The college is on vacation?" But his uncle started to talk, "Who is that pretty young miss?"

So Yasha said Rose was his wife, and he told them how his parents made him get out and not come back, so he didn't know what to do. They sat by the table and ate frischt, like a tea, but Yasha and Rose couldn't eat. Rose already felt like a stranger with her new name, and she looked down at the floor.

Yasha's uncle said to her, "My child, don't be so discouraged. Everything will be all right. Listen, you see how she is, my wife? Before, I was in the army in Warsaw, and when I saw her I fell like a stone from the hand. But her parents, so religious, fanatics, everything had to be a prayer, a no, forbidden, when you cut the nails from the fingers, you have to burn the pieces. Me, so long you should be a good man, you are a good Jew. What did I do? I said to Sarah," and he smiled at her and she shook her head no and smiled, "I said to her, if you love me, come and we'll go to the rabbi and get married and we'll live in another town and I'll find business in the spring. If you want to be with your parents, I'll go away by myself." That's what they did and they went away. "Everything showed for the best," he said, and to Yasha, "That your mother doesn't want you to get married, that's true, you are not even twenty years old and you don't have a profession. That's bad for both of you."

Rose said, "I can work now, by my uncle, to make clothes. And Yasha could do something, too. He is educated."

"You should go to work while he sits in the house all day?" the uncle said. "It isn't right."

"Uncle, what do you think I should do?" Yasha asked.

Said the uncle, "You should open a store for groceries in a little town. Over there, not so far away, is Alchefsk, a nice little town, small, with not very many Jews. They have coal mines where they dig, workers — people have to eat. I'll tell you what — I'll loan you a thousand rubles, Rose will stay in the store and sell the groceries, and you should find work maybe by a bookkeeper, you'll earn money."

Smiling, everybody smiling, Rose clapping her hands and then kissing the uncle on cheek, and Yasha and the uncle hugging. Rose said, "I'll work so hard in the grocery store, we'll pay you back before you know it, and Yasha will find something good —"

"Pay," the uncle said, "it is not necessary to pay so quickly. First you have to settle, and you'll make a home by you, a living. Pay, you'll pay when you get it."

So it was. They came back to Kiev, a suitcase for Yasha, a suitcase for Rose — a wicker, Uncle Louis and Tante gave her. And Rose said she couldn't leave me, will I come, too? Will I come? Don't ask — already I was crying my heart out because I thought I would be alone in the house without her. So happy! The good-byes were like at a wedding, when the bride and groom are going, the crying and the yelling and laughing and kissing, till at the end we were on the train and Kiev was no more.

Twelve years old I was, a girl and woman already. So much I was living through, but enough I didn't know yet. If I knew then what would be — you can't tell from day to day. I was scared of a new place again. That's why I talked so much to Yasha and Rose, I didn't let them say a word sideways. They didn't care, so long as they had each other, holding hands, looking, they couldn't get enough.

Finally, Alchefsk. Oy, a dirty place from the mining, a little town, everything black from soot, and the buildings, the shops, the houses like someone built at night, they couldn't see, a board here, a board there, and no paint, nothing. The train left us on the ground, black dust going to our noses. Which way to go? Rose was scared, too, like someone would steal the suitcase. There were wrinkles on Yasha's face as he was looking this way, that way. "Nu," he said, "it's not so bad." He started to walk and we ran to keep up. Some people on the street — a street? A dirt road full of holes, and some buildings falling down on each side, holding each other up like drunkards together. A shoe shop, a butcher, a barber, a blacksmith, a tavern, a store for cloth, for nails and tools, a saloon — and there was a grocery. Chickens it had hanging and some fish inside a barrel, and inside some shelves, a few things. "We can do better," Yasha said. "You'll see." By the end of the street was an old building, maybe worse than the other buildings, but still an empty building. The window was broken, the door on one hinge only. We went inside — how could it stand up? Dust three or four inches thick, black all over, on the ceiling, in two rooms. "So," Yasha said, "it can't be too expensive. You wait here, I'll find out who owns it and how much."

We sat down on the wicker suitcase to wait. Rose held my hand. I couldn't sit. I got up and walked back and forth in the room, then in the other room. My foot kicked a bump on the floor and I pushed something away with my toe, a big iron ring. Then I saw it was on top of a door. I pulled with all my strength and dust flew up from the door. Bang! It was falling back. Rose ran quickly. "My God! Eatkeh!" she said.

"Look," I pointed. Some stairs went straight down underneath. I started to climb down.

"Eatkeh! You'll get hurt! Who knows

what's down there, maybe full of water, maybe big rats." Rose tried to hold me, but already I stood on the bottom, dirt, and I could see it was a basement. Rose wouldn't come down, she was too scared, it was dark, and she was mad I wanted to see the rest. I saw a big hole, maybe a tunnel where they were digging in the mine. Did it go underneath the ground to another part, maybe another building?

"Eatkeh," Rose yelled. "Come out or I'll write to Ma and Pa you have to go home!"

"It's nice and cool," I said, when I came up, and we closed the door. "We can use it for apples, for preserves, like Pa made the fruit cellar."

"I won't go down there," she said.

"You won't go down, I'll go down. I'm not scared," I told her.

"God knows, maybe we won't need it."

But Yasha came back then, and he said he found the owner and that it was very cheap. So he rented the building, and that night we slept on the floor. Next day Yasha went to see where he could buy groceries, and Rose and I started to clean, to fix up. Two rooms, it wasn't hard after all, and we made spotless, shining, with water from the pump in the street for everybody, a well. We saw only workers with their wives, Russians, and by the saloon a woman with three kids was dumping garbage in the street. One was a girl, maybe thirteen, fourteen. We looked at each other and I smiled — why not? So she smiled and came nearer. "You're living in the old leather store?" she asked in Russian.

"Leather they sold?" I asked. "We'll sell groceries."

"You're Polish?" she replied.

I was not scared. "I'm Jewish."

She was smiling. "That's all right. My name is Katya."

"My name is Edith. Eatkeh they call me. I am pleased to meet you."

"I am pleased to meet you," Katya said.

Very nice, Katya and I finally got to be good friends. She used to like to visit Rose, who would sometimes sew something for her, and we used to eat together. Her mother was very mean, she hated the Jews. Her father was very good, quiet, he kept his troubles to himself.

Yasha found out he had to go to a big wholesale house in Kiev to buy the groceries. But good news he had when he went to the train office for a ticket. He said he was educated and they said maybe he could get a job with the train in Kiev. So he went, and three days he was gone. We fixed up shelves, put nice little crocheted pieces on the edges, and we bought a used bed for Rose and Yasha, a nice little cot for me, a table with chairs, a bureau, pots and pans to cook, dishes, everything. When Yasha came home, he laughed, so happy he was that we fixed up. And happy that he got work in the train office — sixty rubles a month! Only it was bad, he had to stay in Kiev, but he would come home on Shabbos for the weekend. What to do, give up the store in Alchefsk? Already he had paid nine hundred rubles to the wholesale house and he had the groceries in boxes, and they had given him credit for more. We had to stay. "When business gets good," he said, "I can leave the train company and we'll make only by the groceries. You'll see."

So, we were in business. That week Rose and I cleaned and fixed the groceries up nice so people should buy. In the beginning no one came. We lowered the prices, people found out, a woman came, a man, pretty soon it wasn't so bad. It wasn't a living yet, but at least one time, two times a day, a person bought a can plums. All the time we stayed open, day and night. More and more the miners came and bought on credit. Four goyim, big men, covered with coal soot, bought flour, barley, and cans fruit on credit. One night in the dark they came like horses' feet that couldn't find the ground, they had to stomp, and inside the store they yelled they want this, they want that — can we trust? Maybe they'll forget tomorrow when they won't be drunk. But one, with square shoulders like an ox, pulled out some rubles from his pocket, waving them in his hand. "What you got," he yelled. "Give! Everything you got!" They ordered so much, the store was empty, and *cash* they paid. We put everything in bags of cloth, which they carried on their shoulders. "In two weeks," the same one said, "we come, we buy up more!" We didn't know how to explain, but Rose was so happy she took me and kissed me and sang. And when Yasha came home Friday night, Shabbos, with groceries from the warehouse, we told him and he was happy, too. He would bring more next time.

Two weeks passed, again the goyim came, again they bought. The store was empty. The same one, like an ox, said, "They have to pay us yet at the mine. Today, put in the book. In two weeks we come and buy up everything with cash." His name, Gregor Gregorovich. All right, we marked in the book, we added up. Yasha brought more from the warehouse — maybe now he could stop working in the train office, we could be a family.

Two weeks went by. The night they should come — nothing. They didn't show up, the goyim. Maybe they'd come the next day. No one. A few customers, like always, but with the four goyim, nothing. What could be? Yasha said don't worry, sometimes they drink everything up first and have no money. "They'll come, they'll pay," he said. Again two weeks, nothing.

Finally Rose said to me, "We have to find out what's with the goyim. The *money* they owe us, we can't afford it. Go ahead, see if you can find out, so maybe they'll pay." To go to the Russian houses? I was scared. "Ask Katya, you'll go together," Rose said.

So I went by the saloon to look for Katya. Inside, a big room with tables and benches and some chairs. On shelves were bottles of vodka, wine, and kvass, like beer made from barley. On the wall was a hunting rifle. Her father was sitting with a customer, drinking kvass. A nice man he was, so gentle, always smiling. "A pretty girl makes a pretty day," he said to the customer. "Such red hair you see? Dark, like wine. Means she has good blood, a long life." He raised his glass of kvass to me. "A long life you should have, with God's help." The customer raised his glass, too, and they drank up. I didn't see Katya. The father, smiling, yelled out, "Katya! Your friend is here!"

From inside came the mother's voice, like a crow, "Katya! Katya! Pick up the pail of water!"

The father was shaking his head yes, yes, he knows the mother is yelling. But what can he do? "Ah!" he said, "like a serf. Slave driver!" he yelled out. He drank some more and said to the customer, "Katya she likes to beat, and that's how she'll punish me. She knows how it hurts me in my heart for Katya, my favorite. You take my oldest, she don't care, gone from the house like a whore. I tell her, 'You'll make a bad name for me!' She don't care. Her mother drove her. She made a slave out of her, too, so she sells herself. You drive a person like a horse, he'll carry anyone who sits on him." He slammed his mug on the table and the kvass splashed. "No! I won't allow it! Katya! Katya!" He grabbed my arm and pulled me closer. "Take her to your house," he said. "It's better. Hide with her. Don't tell anyone." Then he said to the customer, like it was a secret, "The Jews do better with their children. Do you see a Jewish child crying from work? Do you see a Jewish mother raising a hand on her child?'' To me again he said, ''It's good you are with Katya. She likes better to be by your house than here.''

''Katya!'' Such screaming, but Katya came out of the room and ran to her father, into his arms, like a bundle he held her. Then she smiled, still with tears. So I said, ''Can you come with me a little bit?'' She looked at her father, he gave her a loud kiss on the cheek, and said, ''Go, go, enjoy for change.''

''Katya!'' Like the wind blows open a door. The mother stood holding a wooden spoon and, in her arm like a baby, a wooden bowl for mixing batter. ''I look for water, I don't see. I look for washing clothes, I don't see. I see how you do. You'll teach her like her sister also? Sinner!'' she shouted.

''Look who's talking,'' the father said. ''A sister by the convent? We have the angel in our house?'' He pushed Katya gently. ''Go,'' he said. ''Go with Anuta.'' That was my name in Russian.

''Fine, fine, good!'' the mother yelled. ''Send her out on the street to peddle with

331

a Jew girl yet! Make a Jew whore out of your daughter. Good! I have to take care of everything myself so you can be drunk all the time. Drunkard! What do I kill myself for? Why?'' She looked at the bowl like she would throw it on the floor, and she almost did, and she almost cried, but she didn't. "I can't catch up! He sends out the children. I have to do it all by myself!" She pointed the spoon at me. "Get out! I don't want any Jew girls in my house!"

"Go, before she becomes crazy altogether," the father said to Katya.

"With Jews you let her go? She'll drink blood yet from babies? You want she should be a Christ-killer?" she yelled at him. Her throat was full, she bent her head and stirred fast, fast, hard. I could see a teardrop fall into the batter.

We ran outside and down the street, fast, so we would be far away from the saloon. Katya had to stop and catch her breath, showing her face to the sky, like she had to feel the sun, how warm and good it was. A round Russian face with red cheekbones and blonde hair and pigtails. Finally she said, "Oh, Anuta, what will happen to me? I'm scared I'll be like Sonya, my sister. In bed at night I can't sleep. I think of the men with hair on their lips, how they — they go inside you, Anuta! Holy Mother Mary, why does God make it so? Why does He want to punish me? Sonya, all the time she is hateful, she hates her life so much, how she has to let the men on her like dogs. It must be Mama can't help herself, so mean because she hates." She took my hands and held them close to her chest. "Anuta, why should God hate me so much?" she asked.

What could I say? I didn't know from her God. "Jesus is hating people by you?"

She looked at me a long time, straight into my eyes. Then she looked past me, like to Jesus far away. Softly she said, "Maybe he's mad, so much he had to suffer in his heart, we have to suffer, too? But he never went on a woman. He was pure, good." She looked at me again. "Are you scared that you killed him?"

"I killed him? Katya, I didn't

even know him."

"The Jews killed him."

"They did? How could they? He was a Jew."

Like I threw cold water on her face. She looked, she opened up her mouth, her eyes, she didn't know.

"Katya," I asked, "will you help me? The workers who bought groceries from us — I have to go to their houses, maybe they'll pay something." I showed her how Rose wrote down in the book how much they owed us.

"It's bad where they live," she said.

How could I ask if she didn't want? "I have to."

She took hold of my hand. "We'll go fast."

The miners lived in another part of town, in houses that looked like they were built at night, one this way, one that way, with the chickens and the pigs running inside, outside, and the dogs barking at us, and the Russian boys and girls looking at us, and we were holding hands. Finally we had to ask. At one house I knocked and a man came out. I asked where

Gregor Gregorovich lived. The man said he lived over there, in a certain house. So we went there, not very far, with the Russian boys and girls watching and talking to one another, and I knocked. A man came out whom I had never seen before. I asked him about Gregor Gregorovich. He said he went to the Ukraine and wouldn't come back. Then we went to another house and to another and finally to the last. Like we were carrying honey, the young boys and girls were following us more and more. A young Russian came out of the house. I showed him a name in the book — Peter Stepanovich. The young Russian had no beard, no lines on his face, little eyes like a pig. He was smiling, square little teeth, and he looked at Katya. "Please," I said, "do you know where Peter Stepanovich is?" Now I was terribly worried I would go home without any money, how they cheated us. What would we do?

"Peter Stepanovich," he said, but he spoke to Katya.

I showed him the book. "You see? Here is his name."

He grabbed the book from my hand and let it fall to the ground. Then he stepped on it, under his boot, so I couldn't pick it up. Katya tried to help me get it. He took her two pigtails in his hand and pulled her close to him. "You want Peter Stepanovich, too?" he asked her. Katya pushed him but he wouldn't let go. The more she pushed, the tighter he held her.

"Dog!" she yelled at him — a terrible thing in Russia, to call someone a dog — and she pounded his face with her fists and scratched him. I started to scream, and I pushed and hit him, too, but with his arm he knocked me down. Then, like dogs, they all came, the boys with the shiksehs, the girls, they were running, their mouths open, making growls and snapping sounds with their teeth. They hit with their hands — they didn't know from fists. They poked their thumbs into your face and kicked with their feet and knees. And they tore up the book and yelled, "Hit the Jew girls!" Oy, such a knock on my head, I couldn't feel anything. The world was going around and around. I saw Katya, lying with blood on her mouth, and her blouse was torn. My God, we'll be dead! I thought, and I prayed to God. I told him to help us out! God, don't let it happen. And then came a voice like thunder: "Ho! Enough, what you're doing!"

And they stopped hitting and kicking. Then the voice said, "Speak! Why is this?"

"That one," a boy said. "She started to hit Yoven. Jews!"

"What you say, Jews?" the man asked. He was bending over Katya. A big face he had, with a red beard. "I know her. I go to her papa's saloon to buy beer. What you mean they're Jews. With blonde hair?" He looked at me. He was turning his face — did he know? "This one —" I couldn't move, like I was dead. He raised himself up. "Yoven! Where is Yoven? Bring him out," he said. Then he put his big red handkerchief on Katya's face to wipe away the blood. He would have wiped the blood from me, too, but the boy, Yoven, was coming. I could see him coming out of the house with a towel

337

wrapped around his face where Katya had scratched him. "Speak!" the man said.

"She jumped on me," Yoven said, pointing to Katya.

"She jumped? A child, a baby girl, she jumped. And you, like a ox, she beat you up?" He grabbed the towel from his face so he could use it for Katya. Like a pillow, he raised her in his arm. She was standing to catch her breath, and then she saw the boy. Yoven. She pulled away from the man, went over to Yoven, and hit him so hard in the stomach with her foot that he fell down, and then she spit on him. Then she looked around and saw me lying there with blood on my hands and face. Katya ran over to me and picked up my head and screamed, "Anuta!" So bad was my head, I couldn't hear what she was saying.

"Get out of here!" the man yelled at the boys who were hanging over me. He said to Katya, "I take you home and" — he looked at them standing quietly — "I'll call the policeman." Like he was aiming a gun at them they ran away fast. Then he lifted me and carried me to a wagon with hay in it, and Katya sat beside me to hold my head.

So much shaking in the wagon, like my brain was loose, knocking around inside my head for hours. We would never get home, I thought. But finally Katya was yelling, "Rose Davidina!" We used to call a woman by her father's name. I opened my eyes and saw Rose running after the wagon, crying, "My God! My God! Eatkeh!" When the man stopped the wagon, Katya and Rose helped lift me out of the hay. Everyone ran out of the saloon — the father, customers, and the mother, who was screaming.

"Let me see, let me see!" the father said, and he picked Katya up in his arms and helped her out of the wagon. "You're all right?" he asked, touching her face where there was blood. "How did it happen?" He looked up at the man on the wagon. "It was a bad accident?"

The man shook his head and said, "Some hoodlums, they beat up the girls."

The mother screamed, "They could kill her! Hoodlums! Good-for-nothings! You let them on the streets? And you," she said to Katya, "what were you doing with them?" She screamed at the father, "You see? It's your fault!" Then she screamed at the people, "He sends her out with the Jews! Look at her!"

"Be quiet!" the father said. "Why?" he asked the man. "Why did they do it?"

"The girls tried to collect money," the man said. "I don't know why."

"Aha," the mother screamed. "Money already? Already she's like your daughter, Sonya? You see what you're making her into?"

Rose took me out of the wagon carefully and said, "No. Katya went with my sister to help collect money. They bought groceries and didn't pay."

The mother screamed at her, "You sent her to collect? You dirty Jewess! Why do you think you can do that? I'll teach you, Jewess, with your money!" And she raised her fists in the air and ran toward Rose, who was carrying me, and I was holding onto her so I wouldn't fall. She grabbed my sister by the hand and started to pull her hair. She hit Rose and I fell out of her arms. I couldn't move. Katya pushed away from her father and ran to pull back her mother so she wouldn't kill Rose. She pulled, but her mother was strong, and she gave such a push with her arm, with all her strength, that Katya flew backwards. I didn't hear it happen, but she hit her head on the wagon wheel and fell down.

Oy, God. Her father was on his knees, bending over her. "Oh, God! God, God! She's dead!"

Then Rose picked me up again while everybody was standing around Katya, and she took me into our grocery store and led me to my cot. Outside, the mother was yelling and the people were talking. Finally they went away. "I want to know how Katya is. Find out how Katya is," I said. "What's happened to Katya?" First she wrapped clean strips cloth on my head, and then she went out to see. She was gone a long time. I couldn't wait. So I pushed myself up. My head was like a stone and I was dizzy. I held onto the chair, the table, the wall, and outside I walked near the house, using my hand for support, and I went to the saloon.

Inside, Rose saw me and tried to make me go back, but I wouldn't, so she held me up. She was scared because the people in the room were looking at us like they hated us. They were saying that Katya's father was good to the Jews, and now see what they did to him. I was so weak, but they didn't leave a chair empty for me, so Rose sat with me on the floor.

Finally, a man with glasses on his nose came out — the doctor. Everybody went up close — how's by Katya? He shook his head and said, "In the back she broke her skull. I patched it up as good as I could. If she'll live to tomorrow, then she'll live." From the shelf he took a bottle vodka and went back to the room.

Came a tumult in the room and screaming, and the father jumped out like a bear, like his head was coming apart from his chest, and he looked at us, everyone a stranger, and he looked fast this way, then that way, and on the wall where the rifle was, and behind him was the mother, like she was driving a horse. "Murderer!" she yelled at him. But she saw us on the floor, Rose and me, and she ran over to scream at us, "You killed her! You!" With hands like the claws of a chicken, she would have scratched out our eyes.

But the father's voice was shaking the windows, "Keep back! Away! Witch! You wanted she should be dead!" He held the rifle in his hands. "Hate and spite, that's all!" he yelled.

Came a noise, it raised me to my feet. I didn't know what happened. Only I could see the mother flying backwards like maybe a horse kicked her in the stomach, and she fell next to me with her arm across my chest, and her head banged against the wall.

Then the people in the saloon ran out to the street. They were yelling and screaming, and the doctor came out of the room. The father stood there with the smoking rifle, looking like he didn't know how it got there. They saw the mother lying on me and he ran over to look at her. "What is going on?" he asked.

"Oh," she said. "Oh, my God, he killed me."

"Where?" the doctor asked. "Where

did he kill you?"

She pulled her arm away from me at last and put it on her stomach. "Oh," she was saying, like in her sleep. Her apron was full of little holes, the doctor was ripping it open, and the dress also, and the petticoat underneath, and finally, on the stomach, there was blood. He tore the petticoat in strips and wet them with a bottle alcohol and wrapped them around. She opened her mouth and hissed, and she was screaming "Yi yi yi" while he wrapped.

"Doctor. Doctor, we'll take her to the hospital in Kiev," the father said, holding Katya in his arms. Her head was lying on his shoulder. Her arm hung down stiffly like a piece of wood, like a little branch in the wind.

The doctor got up and looked at the father. "Dmitri Borisovich, she is dead. Don't you see that? She is dead," the doctor said.

"I'll take her to the hospital in Kiev," the father said.

"We'll see, maybe you'll have to take your wife to the hospital." The doctor looked at the wife. "Maybe she'll be all right here, we'll see." He went over to the father and gently picked up Katya in his arms and carried her back into the room.

Then Rose picked me up, but I was able to walk back to our house. I didn't cry until we opened the door, and, like I was holding back the ocean, I started to cry. I couldn't stop. All day, all night, I lay on the bed with Rose, and together we cried.

It was in the middle of the week, so Yasha wasn't home. We had to wait. No one came to buy. Rose didn't even go outside, she was so scared. Next day, when it was getting dark, someone knocked on the door. Finally Rose said, "The grocery isn't open. We're closed up!"

"It's all right," a voice said. "It's Katya's father. I won't hurt you. I want to see how's by Anuta."

Rose opened the door. When he saw me lying like I was dead, he came over quickly to grab my hand and he kissed it. "Poor child," he said quietly. "Poor child. Oh God, oh God, poor child. It breaks my heart. Why? For what?" He sank down on the bench near the table and cried bitterly. Rose had some cherry whiskey that she poured for him, and he looked at it like he was tired, but he drank it up and thanked her. "She went crazy," he said. "She hates Katya. What did she have against my child? Always to the best it has to happen." All of a sudden he stood up, his face on fire, and he yelled, "I'll kill her! She killed my child. I'll knock her head —" and with his fist he was waving. Then, like he saw Katya again with blood on her face, he looked at the wall and dropped the glass of whiskey, his hands shaking. Rose went over to him and took his shoulders, he should sit down. He put his face against her dress and he cried. Oy, did he cry. Finally, like he was swallowing his tears, he looked up at her and said, "Rose Davidina, I beg you, take your clothes and pack up. She's gone away, my wife. She went to her brother in Yelsk, with all the cousins, the relations. She'll tell everything that happened, and from her mouth will come poison. You must run away from here because when she comes back with her relatives, like animals, they'll kill you. Already she told the police how I shot her. They'll be here to put me in prison." He looked wild, and his whole face was wet and his red beard was shining like the rain. "You have to lock up everything, or they'll take." And he ran to close the shutters, slipped the iron bars through iron loops to lock the windows tight and he locked the door in the back and put a chair against the latch and he looked on the front door to see how it should be locked. "They'll come, they'll come," he said. "They hate me anyway, and she hates me, my wife. She hates, they hate, that's all they know. I should kick her out, let her go to them, good! Finished!" He looked at us with sorrow in his eyes. "What happens? When she was a girl, Liza, my wife, like Katya, was small and pretty." And, like he didn't know before, "She laughed! Laughing, happy! That's how she was! I couldn't wait to love her, she couldn't wait — we loved. In the fields we loved! Maybe —" He was holding up a finger to his nose and he smiled. "Before, she was all right. Comes the change of life —'' Then he was remembering, in our house, the little grocery. He could see it and he could see how we watched him. "Pack, pack," he said. "They're coming! They'll break everything apart. They don't care. You have to hurry!" He ran to this side of the room and to that side, like he wanted to pack everything himself, but he couldn't find things.

"How can I take Anuta?" Rose asked. "She's so sick, she's been beaten up. I don't know, can I take her? I don't know where we could *go.*"

"Don't you have relations? Go to them. She can do it." He came over to me and picked up my hand to kiss it. "She'll be all right," he said. "You've got to be all right, little lamb, for Katya." Again he cried like a baby. "You'll go in the night when everyone is sleeping." Like a blind man he went to the front door and opened it. He looked again at the street. "Let them see me," he said. "I don't care." He looked at us. "Lock the door good." Then he waved his hand, like already we were on the train. "Go in health. God will watch." A big choking in his throat, crying. "They'll kill me, too!" He closed the door quickly.

Rose took a piece of paper to explain what happened to Yasha, and she said we would go to Narovlya to get the train for Kharkov. He should meet us in Kharkov, we would wait for him there.

Then she put on as many things as she could wear, one dress on top of another, and on me, too, she put three dresses. She put a little money, whatever she had, into her bosom. I started to get out of bed but I fell back, and she lay down with me in her arms. "Rest," she said. "Rest a little, you'll be stronger." She didn't turn off the lantern, so we still had some light.

Later she woke me up because somebody was scratching the front door. Rose was holding me very tight. Then they went over to the windows. "Can you get up?" Rose asked. I said I would try. I did, but it was like I didn't have legs. Like someone was crumbling paper into a ball, we heard a crackling sound and we smelled smoke. "Oy, God," Rose said. She grabbed a bread, put it in a small basket, and then went over to the door leading to the basement. While she opened that door, I heard the murderers chopping down the front door. More smoke was coming in and I heard the flames start to pop.

Holding the lantern, Rose climbed down into the hole. Then she held up a hand, I should follow her. I almost fell, but I grabbed the ladder and she carried me. Then she closed the door on top of us.

All around the lantern showed the dirt walls, and there was a big hole, like an open mouth, but black inside. On top of our heads we could hear the burning and the chopping. Rose held me up and went into the hole, a tunnel with some wooden beams and boards to hold up the dirt. We went till I felt I couldn't breathe anymore. "How are you feeling?" Rose asked. I started to cry, I couldn't help it, and I fell down. I couldn't go on. But Rose picked me up and told me to climb on her back, no, never mind, I have to do it. She was bending over and waiting, so I held onto her shoulders and put my legs around her. "I beg you to hold on," she said. "It won't take long and we'll be safe.'' Then she started to cry herself, and even though she didn't have any more strength, she kept on walking. Sometimes she stopped to rest and listen. Nothing, no one was coming, thanks be to God. One time a board groaned like a man and we both screamed. All around was dust and dirt, and on the walls were shiny black pieces of coal. I felt dust grinding on my teeth.

Finally some fresh air came. First it felt soft, like someone blowing on us. Then came more, till a wind whistled and it was cool. Pretty soon we could see little lights blinking — the stars. We came out on a hill with bushes and trees. The old mine they gave up a long time before.

Rose put me down on the ground and gave me a piece bread. ''Eat, eat. You have to eat,'' she said. I tried but I started to choke, and then she grabbed me by the shoulders and shook me and yelled, ''Oh, God, let us stay alive! My God, I don't know what to do!'' And she cried like her heart was bleeding. ''Why does it have to happen to me?'' she asked. ''On account of me Greesha died. But it wasn't my

351

fault. I didn't mean he should think I would marry him. God, everyone knows he was not my chosen." We sat and cried, and Rose talked to herself like she was going crazy again. Then came a noise, maybe a stick breaking. Rose jumped like someone stuck a needle into her. She grabbed the bread and picked me up like I was a small child and she ran and ran till she couldn't go on, and then she dropped down to the ground.

We lay there till daylight, like raising the dead, and we saw how everything came alive in the end, and we felt better, but we were still scared. In a little valley there was a stream. Rose brought me some water to drink and to wash — fresh, it returned the blood inside me, and I ate some bread and water.

So, by the sun in the east, we started to walk north toward Narovlya, a little village maybe seven or eight miles away. I felt much better in the head and my legs could move, weakly, but I could take a few steps. Then Rose carried me again, but later I could walk. Finally we came out on the road, empty, thanks be to God, and we could walk better. Springtime, cool, yet so many things we were wearing. It was all right, too warm but not too warm, and everything looked shiny and clean, nice, with the birds singing, happy. Maybe everything would come out okay.

The sun was practically hanging on top of our heads when we got to Narovlya. A few houses were there and a few shops, and a little building that was a depot with a tiny restaurant, four tables, and a samovar. Three or four farmers waiting for the train were drinking tea, and they didn't pay attention to us. Rose bought two glasses tea and she took out the bread and we ate. We sat on a bench, close together, and then we fell asleep.

Rose woke me up soon. "The train is coming," she said. We could hardly pick ourselves up, we were so broken, but when the train stopped, we went in and sat down. I leaned my head on Rose's shoulder, and that's how we rode till we came to Kharkov.

Such a tumult, so many people, like flies. We went inside the station and saw people from all over the world — men, women, children big and small, and so loud we couldn't understand what they were saying. Inside were shops for selling fruit and a grocery, a tailor, a shoemaker, and a baker. Rose took me to sit on a long bench and she said she would go buy something to eat and, maybe, who knows, she'll find Yasha.

I sat not far from a tiny old Russian woman with big wrinkles on her face. She took a little roll from a cloth bag (we didn't have paper then) and began to eat. She looked at me and asked, "Where are you going, little girl?"

I didn't know what to say to her. "My sister is taking me to the doctor," I said.

"So what's wrong?" she asked.

"My feet, they hurt me."

"I see your face is beaten."

"I fell down."

Another little roll she took from the bag, and she gave it to me. "Eat, eat, you'll be stronger."

I took it but my hand was shaking. I was so tired and afraid. Where was Rose? Maybe the bad Russians were running after her, I thought. A chill was coming through my body, my God.

"So where is your sister?" the old woman asked. "What is her name?" Her eyes like little knives coming to my eyes. She grabbed my arm and brought close her face, wrinkled like a worm. "You're a runaway?"

"Who gave you a bun?" someone asked. It was Rose, thanks be to God. She carried two glasses tea. I told her the old woman gave it to me.

The woman didn't know what to say when she saw Rose. Finally, she took another bun from the bag and put it in Rose's hand. So we sat there, eating challeh and drinking tea. Then the woman said to Rose, "You're taking your sister to the doctor?" Rose looked at me. The doctor? "You're not?" the old woman said.

"I am," Rose answered. "I have to take her."

"Doctors," the old woman said. "What do they know? By me, you soak her feet in water so hot that it burns you, and you put in salt, you mix in, with a drop vinegar." She nodded. "She'll be all right," she said, and she smiled with her three teeth, made a little bow, and went away. Like a little chicken she walked, one side to the other.

"I tried to look for Yasha," Rose said. "Maybe he's here, but I couldn't find him. Maybe he didn't get my note. I don't know what to do." She couldn't help it, the tears were coming.

"We should wait here and see," I said. "Maybe he'll come."

What happened? Yasha came home and saw there was no store. Like a fever it went through his whole body. Ashes only, everything burned down. He ran to the saloon but it was closed. Then he asked people on the street what had happened, but they were Russians and they wouldn't say. Finally he came to a house far from our store where two Jewish women lived, and they told him everything. The daughter from the saloon was dead and the mother was in the hospital in Kharkov and the father was in jail, and that's all they knew.

"But my wife, Rose, and little Eatkeh, where are they?" Yasha shouted.

"We don't know," one of the women said. "Everything burned down, such a fire."

"Ah, *God,*" he yelled. "It can't be! Where is my Rose? Rose! Rose!" he cried, and he ran out to the street but he couldn't find anyone who would talk. Even to the police he went, but they shrugged their shoulders.

"Murderers!" he yelled. "You let this happen to my wife, my Rose, my best! Why?"

"Get out of here!" they said, and they threw him out. They didn't care, a Jew.

Finally, he went by train to his uncle, David Schwartz, in Uzefke. Yasha went into the house pale as death. When he came in, his aunt saw him and got scared. "My child, my child," she said. "What happened? I see something bad in your face. Tell me." And she put out her hand to touch his arm.

"Oy, Aunt Sarah, what happened?"

"Yes, yes, all right, you'll tell me later," she said. "Come, you'll eat something and then —"

"Where is the world? Oh, God, it can't

be!" Yasha shouted, looking wild, with his hair wet and his eyes like stones. "Auntie, she's — she's —"

"It's all right, my boy," and she patted him on the arm. "Don't make a worry on yourself. Life is too short."

"Life? Ah, God," and his eyes rolled upward till only the white part could be seen, and then he fell down like a pillowcase full of dirty clothes.

Aunt Sarah screamed and put a wet piece of cloth on his head, but he didn't move, so she ran quickly out of the house to Uncle David, whose little factory was not far. He made springs for beds. When they came back the uncle slapped Yasha's face. Pretty soon he started to breathe, and then he opened his eyes. They made him lie down on the couch and they gave him a little schnapps to drink. When he came to himself, he told them everything.

The uncle had tears in his eyes. "Maybe," he said, "maybe Rose and her sister ran away."

"How?" Yasha asked. "At night they were sleeping, so they burned them."

"Don't talk like that," the uncle said.

"Burned them!" yelled Yasha. "Set the store on fire while they were inside and couldn't get out. My God, the fire, the fire! All around, screaming —"

"Sharrop!" the uncle yelled. "We'll do something. We'll go again to Alchefsk and find out what happened."

"You can't do anything," Yasha said. "They won't talk and I couldn't find out. Nothing!"

"I'll make some soup," the aunt said. "You'll feel better."

But Yasha wouldn't eat and he couldn't sleep. He lay with his eyes closed. The aunt didn't know what to do, so she went around wringing her hands. Finally the uncle said they better bring the doctor. An old man with a few hairs, a beard, what could a doctor know in those days? When he came in, the doctor put his hand on Yasha's head. Then he put his ear on his chest and listened.

"He is very sick from fright," the doctor said. "Give him food even if he won't eat. You have to give him."

And that's the way it was left — that Rose and I were no more.

Now back to us.

We sat all night and a whole day in the station. People came and went. But no Yasha. So tired, we slept on the bench, but then we got scared maybe he would come and not see us and go away again. What to do? I woke up and saw Rose wiping her eyes. We sat and didn't talk to one another. All of a sudden she got up and said, "Eatkeh, take the basket. We'll go to Yasha's uncle."

From Kharkov you can take the train straight to Uzefke, with stops in between. Finally we found the train and Rose bought tickets. Already we felt better. The uncle would take care of us, and we sat like bundles, the way the train was bouncing around. When we came to Uzefke, we didn't care, and so we paid for a carriage with two horses to ride to the uncle's house.

Like beggars we knocked on the door. The aunt opened up, and when she saw us, she fell down and fainted. We didn't know what was happening to her, so both of us started to scream. And the neighbors heard. My God, what can it be, a pogrom? And they ran out of their houses to see what was going on, and they saw the aunt lying on the ground by the door, with Rose on her knees beside her. Finally the aunt opened her eyes, sat up, and looked at us. But again she fainted. When she opened her eyes again, she started yelling, so the neighbors picked her up and took her inside the house to the sofa. "Auntie," Rose said, "don't make a disturbance to yourself. We're all right. Look, it's Rose and Eatkeh."

"My God, my God," the aunt said. "I thought you were no longer in the world. Thanks be to God, it's a miracle. A miracle!" And she started crying and hugging us, and we hugged and kissed her. Finally, the neighbors didn't want to leave, but Rose told them thank you, the aunt had to rest, and like that she pushed them out of the house.

Now, Yasha, we still didn't know about him. From the other room he heard a tumult, but he was weak from not eating and from the medicine. Rose told the aunt what happened to us, and we all cried together. The aunt cried so hard she couldn't talk. She raised her hands to touch us, like she couldn't believe it, and she shook her head yes, yes, even when Rose said, "I don't know what happened to my husband, Yasha. I left a note for him but he didn't come."

Then the tante, the aunt, put an arm around Rose and an arm around me. "Come," she said, and she took us to the bedroom and opened the door. There was Yasha, lying on the bed with his eyes closed and with a white face, like he was dead.

"Yasha!" Rose cried out, and she fell down on him and kissed him, but he didn't wake up. "Don't leave me! Be alive, be alive! My God, oh, my God, if you die, then I will die, too!" It made me feel so cold that I shook. The tante stood, white like chalk, her lips shaking.

Finally, when Rose put her face with Yasha's and made wet his cheek with her tears, he opened his eyes, but he couldn't see who was so close. When he saw me he rose so suddenly he nearly knocked Rose down. "What?" he yelled out. "Eatkeh?" And then he couldn't believe it. He looked at Rose. As weak as he was, Yasha jumped to his knees and grabbed Rose so hard I was afraid she couldn't breathe. He was laughing and crying, and I thought he was going crazy with happiness. Then they both fell back on the bed, they didn't care, and they hugged and kissed and held each other. And they put their faces together, but they wanted to look at each other, too. So they held each other apart, then came together again, and again moved apart.

When they came to themselves, Rose told him what happened to us. He cried and said he thought we were dead. When he saw the ashes he went crazy. Rose told him to stay calm, and they would see what they could do. Money they didn't have, except Rose had three hundred rubles and they had to pay six hundred for the goods that the goyim took away. "We won't pay them," Yasha said. "They probably think you died."

When the uncle came in, he saw that the tante was very pale. "You heard maybe from Rose and her sister?" he asked. She was afraid to say a word in case he would faint, too, and hurt himself, so she kept quiet. Yasha and Rose were sleeping. I was asleep on the floor and didn't hear anything. Then the uncle went to wash up in the kitchen and the tante made ready the table. When he came back he saw there were two more places. "For who?" he asked. "Yasha can't come to the table, so why more dishes?"

She couldn't hold it in. So quietly she spoke, he couldn't hear. "Am I deaf?" he asked.

"Shah!" she said. "They're sleeping."

"Who?"

"Rose! Eatkeh! They're here!"

Oy, oy, so happy, like at a wedding, like when the sun comes out in winter. He jumped around and hugged her and danced. He was spinning like a top, so happy. Then he quietly opened the door to the bedroom to see us sleeping, Rose and Yasha with their arms wrapped around each other, Rose with her red cheeks so white and her beautiful eyes swollen from crying and no sleep, and me, skinny like a skeleton. I could feel him watching us and I woke up. "Shah, shah," he said, his finger on his lips. "They'll sleep yet." He lifted me off the floor in his arms and carried me to the table. "Oy," he said, "oy, thanks be to God," and I cuddled up to him and cried. I told him I wanted to go home to my parents, and I cried even more.

When Rose heard me crying she got up and came in quickly. She ran over to the uncle, and he put me on a chair so he could hold Rose. And we all cried out of happiness. Then the tante said, "You have to eat. Come, sit, sit, hot cabbage borscht with blintzes, I made special, you'll eat, my God, so skinny you two." It melted in your mouth, we could hardly talk, so nice to eat what's good, and then Yasha came in. The uncle started to bawl him out for getting out of bed, but Rose helped him sit at the table.

"Let him *eat* something," the tante said. "Before he couldn't, now he can."

"I feel good now," Yasha said. "So happy, how can I feel bad? My wonderful wife," and he began kissing her cheeks and her fingers, better than food.

"For what they've been through," the

uncle said, "they don't look so good. But they made it."

Next morning Rose got up first. I heard her talking in the dining room with the uncle. The samovar was standing on the table, and for Rose the uncle poured tea. There was also a big white challeh. Then the tante came in from the kitchen and sat down. Only Yasha was still asleep. I felt very lonesome for my mother as I listened to Rose talking to the uncle. "What can we do now?" she asked. "Yasha can't go to the office. Already they took on another man to be the bookkeeper."

"Don't give up," the uncle said. "We'll think of something."

"With what? Three hundred rubles? And we haven't got anything else."

"Nu, so, my business gets bigger and I have to take on more work to make the bedsprings," the uncle said. "I need a man who will run the books. Yasha can do that."

"Oh, Uncle David, if it weren't for you and tante, we would be lost," Rose said.

"Listen, what does it mean to be an uncle?"

So it was. Rose got three rooms — one for sleeping, one for eating, and one for cooking — from a very nice family. Yasha made seventy rubles a month. The landlady, who came from Warsaw, was very nice. She told Rose that her husband brought material from Warsaw to make clothes, and her husband used to go to the tailors to take their orders. Also, women were buying yard goods on payments and making clothes by themselves, not as good as the tailors but cheaper. One day Rose said to the landlady, "Maybe you can ask the women who buy if I can sew for them." My sister was very handy at everything. She was a man's tailor. So, the landlady asked, and Rose bought a Singer machine and started to sew for the women. They were very happy, and that's how Rose earned even more than Yasha.

On Shabbos, in shul, the uncle was talking. That's how they do it, with the cantor singing so beautifully, and the rabbis praying and singing and the men davening, how they rock themselves back and forth, praying, but all the time talking, too, a little business, a little social, how's by you, what's happening in the family. And the uncle was talking to a tailor. Maybe he needs a good worker. If so, he has a niece by marriage. And the tailor said maybe, why not?

So I went to work for Plotnick, the tailor, and I made ten rubles a month. He had twenty workers — girls from Lethe, boys from Poland and the Ukraine. At the beginning I was shy and I didn't look at the others. But soon we became friends. I was only thirteen, a worker like a grownup, but still a child.

Meanwhile, the girls at the tailor's said that on Shabbos, when we didn't work, we should go to the Tsar's garden. "You'll enjoy," they said. Rose and Yasha said okay, I deserve it. In a big square there were trees and flowers all around and benches, and in the middle was an orchestra, and music was playing and couples danced. If I saw a boy I wanted to meet, I took a pencil and wrote down that I wanted to see him. You gave the letter in an envelope to a child, and for ten kupkes he took it to the boy, and he would come over and dance, and maybe buy you an ice cream cone. That's how I met Heimie. I was thirteen and he was fifteen. Such a happy boy, I'll never forget. Heimie Kaplan, you wouldn't know what he'd do next, maybe pull away the chair so you'd sit on the floor, or rip a piece cloth, so you'd think you tore something. But everybody liked him, and he laughed at everything. To a person like that something bad happens, and Heimie, oy vey, such a young man still, years later, he caught a disease and he couldn't move, only his head. Who knew what would happen? Meanwhile, with my note he came over, and he said, "What is Eatkeh? Is that a fish maybe?" I was blushing, and he grabbed my hand. "We'll see if you can swim," he said, and he pulled me away. We danced! You should see how we danced, so fast that no one could see our feet, like leaves whirling, and we started to laugh so hard we couldn't stop. I thought I would fall to pieces. Finally we sat down and he ran to buy me an ice cream, one kind only they had, vanilla.

"You should go on the stage," he said. "Like a ballerina! Where did you learn to dance so well? In the cow pasture, so you'll watch how you step down?"

So we talked and laughed, and he told me he was also working for a tailor. Then Heimie looked around so no one would hear what he said to me, and he put his lips close to my ear. "You belong to the Russky Zyuse?" he asked me. I never heard of it before. "My God," he said, and he looked at me like he couldn't believe it. "Don't you know?"

"What should I know?" I asked him.

"Everyone belongs, even everyone by Plotnick. Didn't they tell you?"

"What should they tell me?"

So he explained how the Russky Zyuse was helping the workers, they should get paid better and the bosses should treat them like menschen, not like serfs, and that I have to belong also, but secretly, no one should find out because the Tsar didn't like the workers to have a union. He was afraid they'd make a revolution.

So naive, I didn't know. All right, I said, everybody belongs, I'll belong, too. The next week Heimie took me to where he worked, by the poor tailor. He lived in a cellar in a tiny hill with two wooden doors in the dirt. You opened up inside, there was a little room, with the tailor sitting there like a mole, bent up, his skin brown, a few whiskers, and two teeth in front that he couldn't cover with his lips. And even in the summertime he was cold, shivering. A shmatte — an old rag — he wrapped around himself, he couldn't stay warm. When Heimie brought me in, the poor tailor was scared who was I? Like he was chewing a nut in his two teeth, they were making noise, and he looked at me through the top of his glasses. "You bring in strangers?" he asked Heimie. "You know her?" Heimie told him he met me dancing. "Dancers the Tsar has also," the tailor said. "He has them hanging by the rope on the neck." But Heimie said they could trust me with their lives. "Better we should have something else we can trust her with," the tailor said.

Such a room, boards with splinters like fur to keep out the earth, like a grave, and ten boys and girls maybe inside, you could hardly move an arm. In a hole with boards over it they hid a little machine.

You turn the crank and a tiny barrel goes around, and out come papers, leaflets so the people will know what's going on. They started to turn the crank, the tailor couldn't stand still, and he covered his ears so maybe the noise wouldn't go outside. "Shah! Shah!" he yelled in a whisper. "The world can hear you!" What could they do? Finally he said to Heimie, "Send her to watch if someone is coming." So, all right, whatever they told me to do I did it, and I didn't know what I was doing. Heimie told me to sit outside on the ground, and if a policeman should come by, I should start to sing and they'd know.

I was sitting and getting tired after all, and inside the earth they were grinding with the machine and talking. Then I saw two policemen coming. Right away, I started singing at the top of my voice. Going by, walking slowly, they stopped to look at me. Then they came over, and one asked, "Why do you sit on the cold ground?"

I said, "In the house it's hot, so I sit outside to cool off." I was not scared because I made believe nothing was wrong.

He looked at me a long time, his eyes like the hole you put in a dime in a machine, his face like wax. "Where is your passport?" he asked. You had to carry it with you every time you went somewhere. I had it in my apron pocket. He grabbed it from me and held it close. If his nose was longer, he wouldn't be able to see it. I had to hold it in so I wouldn't laugh. He asked, "What are you doing here?"

"I'm sewing. I'm a tailor."

"From where do you come?"

I know that in the passport everything is written down, so why did he ask me? All of a sudden he gave such a kick on the ground with his boot that I had to grab myself with my hand, such a shake I had. "How old are you?" he asked. I said thirteen. Again he said, "From where do you come?" I told him I come from David Horeduck. "What gubernya?" What state? I told him Minsker. "What county?" I told him Moozer.

The other policeman was fat, with a greasy face and a mouth like a pig, a nose on top. Down and up on his toes, like he would float in the sky any minute, a balloon, like he was filled with air. How could he move, floating like a ball on the water. He pulled open the two doors at the same time. Everybody inside, the boys and girls with the tailor, were sitting and standing and drinking tea. I saw they had hidden the machine already, under the boards. The policeman said to them, "She sits outside, so hot, but you drink tea inside. Are you so cold?"

The fat policeman was bouncing on his feet. He made with his nose, sniffing the air. "I smell a stink," he said.

The other one grabbed my arm and pulled me into the room. "It don't smell like the Tsar here."

I said, "We all love the Tsar Nikolai and his whole family."

He said, "Who told you to say that?"

"Nobody told me. By us in the house hangs the Tsar's picture, Nikolai with the Tsarina and their children."

Under his big mustache he was smiling. "What you got in here?"

"We're making clothes," I said. "It's a

tailor, but business is no good. What can we do? We're sitting and waiting, maybe somebody will hire us to make a suit. We make it very cheap." I put his sleeve between my fingers. "You got to have a new suit — look, a hole already by the elbow. Let us fix it for you."

He pulled his arm away and covered the hole with his hand. "Never mind. You don't look at *my* clothes. I look at *your* clothes." With the fat one, they both laughed. Then he said to me, "You don't be afraid. We won't bother *you*. You tell me what all the girls are doing here with the boys."

I said, "We are working, but we don't have what to do today. Our boss pays us when we have work to do and his wife gives us food, and that's all I know."

"What boss?"

I pointed to the poor tailor, who was hiding behind some of the boys and girls. The policeman made with the head, the tailor should come out. Like a schoolboy who did something bad, he came out with his hands held together on his stomach. The policeman said, "That's the boss?

Ha!" and again he and the other one laughed. Then he said to me, "What kind of papers does he make in here?" Papers? "Papers, papers, a lot of papers!"

I said, "We don't have papers. Why would we need papers?"

He said, "The workers give you money so you should keep quiet."

"How could they give me money? They are all poor people. Sometimes I give *them* some money so they can eat something."

"Ha!" he said, and he looked at the boys and girls. "What're you *doing* in here, good-for-nothings!" He said to me, "You watch out, you protect them and they'll use you up."

"I don't know what you want to know. We are workers, we sing, we go to the theaters, and that's all." I hunched up my shoulders, that's all.

The fat policeman was bouncing around. "She is a stupid Jew," he said.

The other one said, "No she isn't. I can see by her black eyes." He came very close to me. I looked down at the floor and started to yawn, while the rest were standing like statues. Then the policemen tried to find something. They were searching in the oven and the bedding, in and under, but they couldn't find anything. They threw everything around, a mess, and they were burning in their skin because they didn't find what they wanted.

Finally, they went out. The first policeman said, "We'll catch you, don't worry." He put two fingers under my chin. "You I'll see again, my little one." Like he would kiss me, so I pulled myself away. He said, "We'll be back!" and he closed the door so hard the whole house was shaking.

I said to everybody, "What is? I don't understand." But Heimie put his finger to his mouth, shah. The tailor went to the little window in front to look out. He made with his head how the policeman hadn't gone away. Finally, after a long time, he made yes, it's all right. And they all cheered and started to kiss me, and they wore me out with their kisses. They told me how I was the smartest girl in the world and I had to be with them to make the leaflets.

But I said, "You are good people, you

want for everybody the best, better for the workers. But I am lonesome for my parents. I haven't seen them for three years already. I am going home to them."

"Don't be foolish, " Heimie said. "You'll stay by us, you'll live here. You won't be able to stand a small town now. Do they have music and a floor for dancing? Can you go to a theater there and see plays? You'll stay, you'll become an actress, so fine you perform! You'll be home, you'll cook and bake and sew and clean — such a life you want? What can you find in your little town you can't find here?"

"My family," I said.

My sister, Rose, also wanted me to stay by her. "Oy," she said, "I'm afraid we won't see each other again."

"I'll come back after a while," I told her. "You are like a second mother to me. I will never leave you."

It is impossible to write it down, the tragedy. Three months later Rose's first son was born. They were happy but their child didn't live long. Time heals every pain and my sister threw herself again into work. Two years later another son was born, God knows, without a roof in his mouth, and he died when he was two weeks old. Then she had another son, very handsome, and Rose hired a Russian girl for three rubles a month. That's the way their life was until the boy was three years old. He was very sick. My sister took him to Kharkov to a big doctor. When she came back, the boy died like a candle. Rose said it was Greesha's mother cursing her. And me? I never went back to Uzefke.

As for Yasha and Rose, years later World War I began and I didn't hear from anyone. Somehow Yasha went to Germany, a prisoner there. Rose stayed in Horeduck. The family put together money and they sent for Yasha to come to America. Rose came three years later. A fortune teller told her to move across the seven seas because she had lost five children and she would have better luck far away.

8

At home life was different. So happy was I to be by my family, don't ask, and they couldn't do enough for me. My mother said she never saw me so skinny, and that they had to build me up. For a long time they didn't want me to do anything. I shouldn't work, I should rest and eat and recover. Eight girls and six boys we were, like a village in our house, but Louis and Meyer were already married, and Hannah and Rose you know, and Abe went to America, maybe he could make something for himself there, and Golde married a nice boy with a clothing goods business. Sometimes she went with him to the big cities when he used to travel.

No one in our town could recognize me, so at first it was lonely. The boys and girls were not refined, and they used to make fun of me for speaking Yiddish like a Gentile almost. On Shabbos I made the samovar with coals on fire underneath, to boil the water, and when the neighbors found out they told everybody that Razzeleh's daughter came back a goyeh — she makes tea on Shabbos. But my father was modern, he was not a fanatic, and he yelled at those stupid women and those common girls who didn't know how people lived in the big cities. And all those foolish boys, they didn't want to be near me. I felt lost in Horeduck, so I told my parents that I wanted to go back. Ma said stay a little longer, I would have enough time to go back, and that's the way time went by.

My mother's brother, Shmuel, had a very very large house near ours, and he was rich. Well, by us he was rich. He made beautiful furniture, also plain furniture, and enough money to buy a house. Two sons he had. The oldest was in America, and the second one, Neeseh, was twenty. He used to help his father, but he wanted to go to America to his brother. Neeseh was always blinking his eyes, some disease he had. And there was Sonia, my cousin, eighteen years old, with two long braids and red cheeks like all the girls in Russia, and not skinny but not fat. The boys couldn't take their eyes off her. She was quiet and shy and already afraid the matchmaker would find a husband for her, already at eighteen an old maid, she couldn't sleep at night, she was so scared. Sonia used to ask me how I was so brave in the big cities, and we became friends, even if I was only fourteen, but with so much experience I was like an older person to her.

Once my aunt, Tante Bernice, Sonia's mother, became sick. She coughed all night, she couldn't stop. By us there was only a felsher, not a real doctor. So they called a good doctor, more expensive, a goy, a Russian doctor who studied in Kiev. The government sent him to make a hospital in our town.

The doctor came in and examined my aunt and told her to stay in bed till she felt better. Sonia stood by her mother, and the doctor was nearby, looking at her. "I don't have a place to stay yet," he said. "I'm by the priest now till I find something. Maybe you know somebody who has a room to rent?"

"Such a big house we got, and my son is in America," Tante Bernice said. "Two empty rooms by us. Maybe the doctor is interested?"

"Yes," he said.

"Sonia," Tante Bernice said.

"Mein Herr Doctor, I will show you the rooms," Sonia said.

They went out of the tante's bedroom, but the doctor didn't take his eyes off Sonia. He was tall, with blond hair and blue eyes, and a very nice smile. But the doctor didn't look at the rooms at all, just at Sonia. He took out forty rubles and put them in her hand, and he said, "I will eat here, too, please." They went back to the tante's bedroom and Sonia gave her mother the money.

"Take out fifty kupkes," the tante said, "and give to the doctor."

"No, no," the doctor said. "For the rooms, with breakfast and supper."

"It's too much," the tante said.

"Keep, keep," the doctor said. "The

government is paying me." Then he put the kupkes in Sonia's hand and said, "You take it." She started to blush and she couldn't look at him. "Soon I will bring my things," the doctor said to Tante Bernice. "You should stay in bed a few days and then you will feel good." He went out after that.

Sonia didn't know what happened to her, everything was falling from her hands, and she didn't see what was in front of her. When the doctor moved in with them, he saw how Neeseh's eyes were blinking from the disease, so he tried to heal the eyes, and he did.

Sonia and I lived like two dear sisters. I was there more than at home. One day in my tante's kitchen I was helping Sonia wash the dishes. I was talking about going back to the big city to my friends, to know what was going on in the world, and here in our town the girls and boys are very common, and they only talk about people and laugh at them. Tears dropped from Sonia's eyes into the dishwater, and her whole body shook. "Sonia, maybe you can move with me," I said. "I'll show you everything, and we can live in my sister Rose's house, and we'll work at sewing and go to the theaters and the dancing. You'll meet nice boys and see how they are doing big things to help the people. I'll show you Heimie, he'll introduce you."

Then Neeseh came from behind and put his head down between us. "The way you wash the dishes, when you're through it'll be time for supper," he said, and he breathed onions on my cheek.

"How can you tell what supper is?" I asked. "The way you nosh, by you all day is supper."

"Skinny," he said to me. "Look who's talking."

"Who's talking? You are talking. Look out." With my shoulder I had to push him. He was standing in my way.

"Oho," he said, "so skinny, so strong. You got a muscle somewhere?" Neeseh grabbed my arm, pinching, so I gave him good in the stomach with my elbow. He was laughing and covering himself. "Help, help! She's making a pogrom on me!" He made at me like he had a Cossack sword in his hand. "Swish, swish! Chopped liver already!"

"Neeseh!" Sonia said. "Leave us alone!"

"Who's bothering?" Again he was bringing his onions close to me.

"I'll call Ma, you'll see who's bothering," she said. He was laughing so much she yelled out, "Ma! Ma!"

"Eatkeh," Sonia said, "we'll finish up quick and we'll have time to go outside."

"Where will you go?" Neeseh asked.

"It isn't your business," she said.

"You shouldn't walk alone on the streets like common girls."

"Look," I said. "Look who's talking." And we laughed, Sonia and me, till we were in stitches. Neeseh was so mad he made dust on the floor when he went out from the kitchen.

So we took a walk, and we held hands like they did in those days in Russia, even the boys when they walked. Where do you go in a small town? You go to the bridge to see the little boat going away, and then you go home. This is the whole entertainment, or the women sit on benches outside their houses and gossip. All of a sudden she held my hand so tight she would break my fingers, and she looked with her mouth wide open, like a ghost was rising out of the ground. And then I saw him, the doctor. He took off his hat to bow to us, so handsome in the uniform of an officer that he wore with shiny boots. "Ladies," he said. "A very beautiful day." He looked at me, too, and he smiled.

Sonia, like a beet, her face was so red, she raised my hand inside her own to give like a little wave to him. "Here is my cousin, Anuta," she said.

"Anuta? Your cousin is a Christian?" the doctor asked. He was smiling at Sonia, and she covered her mouth so she wouldn't laugh too much.

"That's what they called me in the big cities," I said. "In Kiev I was, and nearby Kiev in the big towns. So much I lived through, and more friends I had with Russian boys and girls than with Jewish."

"If you didn't tell me you are Sonia's cousin," the doctor said, "I wouldn't know you're Jewish. You look more like

Spanish to me. You speak very good Russian and you don't dress like the girls here. Very pretty, Anuta.'' Then he looked at Sonia and said, ''Sonia doesn't look like the other girls either.''

Sonia didn't say a word, but all the colors came to her face. I was not afraid because I was through a lot in the big cities. I said to him, ''Honored Doctor, I have a nice little book by Maxim Gorky that I read at night. I like to read stories by Tolstoy also.''

''How do you know so much already?'' he asked.

''In the big cities there were different kinds of educated people, and they used to talk about books and I used to read.''

''And Sonia?'' he said.

She was laughing very softly and raising her head to the sky.

''Don't worry,'' I said. ''I'll give her to read.''

''Would you like me to send some books from my home in Kiev?'' he asked.

''So we can read?'' I said. ''Oh, Herr Doctor, please, yes.''

''My name is Misha Afonsky,'' the

doctor said. "You'll call me Misha?"

So modern he was. We were laughing, Sonia and me. How could we be so familiar? "You have to be Doctor by us, or too many patients will be jealous," I said.

He sighed and said, "So many patients. They sent me, the government, to make a hospital, and I can find only a muzhik's house. I don't have enough room for my patients."

All of a sudden came somebody, rush rush, like a hen at feeding time, with its head going up and down. Cousin Shaneh it was. Such a name, Shaneh in Yiddish means beautiful, but when you stick your nose in like a busybody all the time, how can you be beautiful? She was my age, but short, stubby, always with her eyes looking up at you like from under the ground. So, she came like always, when you didn't want her. She looked and looked and Sonia grabbed my hand, "We have to go now," she said to the doctor, and she pulled me away. I saw him raise his hat and make a little bow, so nice.

Cousin Shaneh the busybody ran to

keep up with us, behind, before, she wouldn't stop. "You talk to the doctor? You have business by the doctor? Somebody is sick?" she kept asking.

I said, "Nobody. Nothing. Don't you know we have to be polite, to say hello to somebody? In the small towns everyone is so common, no one says hello even."

"To a Gentile?" she asked. "A goy? You talk on the street with a man who is not even a Jew?"

"Don't you know he stays at Sonia's house?" I said. "What is he, a stranger, we shouldn't talk?" Then I stopped, I wouldn't go on. I said to Shaneh, "When people don't invite you, you don't go." She looked at me like I wasn't speaking Yiddish to her. "We didn't invite you. Now good-bye, Shaneh," I said. "Go home." I went away quickly with Sonia. Thank God Shaneh didn't come.

"She'll tell everybody we were talking to the doctor," Sonia said. Her whole body was shaking.

"Let her tell. We shouldn't talk to the doctor? He's not a human being?" I asked her. "In this town they don't know what's going on in the world."

With tears in her eyes Sonia said, "Oh, Eatkeh, he likes you very much. If you ask me, he is in love with you."

"Don't be foolish. Don't you see how he looks at you? How can he be in love with me? I am only fourteen, and so skinny. Look how beautiful you are. Is he blind? He wouldn't look at me. He talks nicely to me so he can be with you. You he loves. You, I know it," I told Sonia.

"Don't talk like that," she said, "because I am afraid my parents will hear, and they will kill me and harm you, also."

"I've been through hell and I am still alive. I don't care what happens to me. I am not afraid, and if anything happens to me, I will go right back to the big cities. I don't care. I won't be here long. I am here only for my parents."

"Oy," and she suddenly stopped, like I hurt her. "Eatkeh, Eatkeh, don't go. What, we're more like sisters than cousins, and how could I stand it in this town if I didn't have a person to talk to?"

"You'll have the doctor," I said.

"The doctor!" she said. "You think I can talk to him? What can I say? I feel like a milk cow, only moo I can say to him. I wish I could speak like you, Eatkeh, so nicely it comes out. You're not afraid like me."

How, I don't know, but all of a sudden I had an idea, and I yelled, "Sonia! Sonia! I know what you should do!"

"My God," she said.

"Listen, Sonia, your father has the big house your grandmother left, across from yours. What can he do with such a big house, so old? Do you remember how one day he said he wished it would burn down so he wouldn't have to worry anymore what to do with it? Sonia! He can make it into a hospital! For the doctor!"

"My father wants to make a hospital from his house? How can he make a hospital?" she asked.

"Let me talk with him. You'll see."

So that's how we went to talk with Uncle Shmuel and Tante Bernice. I explained to them how the doctor couldn't find where to make the hospital, and so he had to make it in a peasant home. I said,

"Tante Bernice, you know how he made you well. Such a doctor, and he can't find a place for his patients."

"I don't make my house into a hospital to stink from medicine," Uncle Shmuel said. "So don't bother me."

"The government gives him the money. For the rent you can ask him plenty," I said. "One hundred rubles."

The uncle shook his head back and forth. "One hundred rubles? For one hundred rubles I should make my house into a hospital?"

Then Neeseh said, "Why do you want a goy, a gonif, a thief, to use our house?"

"Two hundred rubles you can ask him," I said.

The uncle was leaning over like in prayer. "Two hundred rubles?" he asked.

"Muzhiks, dirty farmers, goyim — what kind of house will it be?" Neeseh asked.

I looked at him with knives in my eyes. "Jews also get sick," I said to the uncle. "So you'll have a Jewish hospital, you'll have a real doctor, everybody will speak your name, thanks to God."

He looked at Tante Bernice. "So what

do you think?" he asked her.

"They'll call you he-who-heals-the-sick. It'll be a mitzva," I said.

Tante Bernice said, "Yes. How can we say no? Like God tells us, do it."

"Listen," the uncle said to me. "I don't speak good Russian. Maybe you can talk with the doctor, you'll see what he says. Who knows, maybe he wouldn't want to make a hospital here from a Jewish house."

"He wouldn't want, such an anti-Semite," Neeseh said.

"You should bite your tongue," I told him. "He's a good friend to us."

Sonia wouldn't go with me. She was too scared. The doctor came home, he smiled at us and bowed, and he went upstairs to his room. But Neeseh came upstairs behind me and grabbed my arm and gave me such a look. "It's not right you should go into his room by yourself," he said.

"Better I should be in his room by myself than on the street with you." A good push I gave him, and then I knocked on the door. He opened up, the doctor, and when he saw me he smiled.

"Anuta," he said.

Then Neeseh yelled, "It's not nice!"

"To yell in the house is not nice," I said to him, and then I said to the doctor, "Honored Doctor, I want to talk to you."

He made me a little bow and opened the door. I went in and he closed it behind me. Then he asked me to sit down. "Anuta, what can I do for you?"

"I am not sick."

"I see how you are healthy, so pretty."

"You don't have to say."

"Of course I don't have to say. I say because it's true." And then he put his long fingers, soft, gentle, under my chin. "You will be beautiful, Anuta. Already I don't see any girl in Horeduck who is as beautiful."

I would not let him see the tears in my eyes. I looked at the floor. "And Sonia? You forget Sonia so quick?"

He laughed at me. "Sonia is a different beauty. You are like the springtime, fresh and bright, with blossoms all over. Sonia is like the summertime on the steppes, deep and quiet."

"She's deep? I also am deep. When we

are alone, she's not so quiet."

"Anuta," he asked, "what's the matter?"

I wished he would sit down, so close he stood by me. Quickly, I said, "My uncle asked me to tell you that since you don't have a place for your patients, he will rent his house to you."

"His house? For my hospital?"

I nodded my head yes.

"Anuta! Such wonderful news you bring me!" And he grabbed me and gave me a hug, I could feel his buttons. "Come," he said, "I'll go talk to your uncle right away, he shouldn't change his mind."

"Two hundred rubles —"

"Fine, good, I accept," he said, and he was filled with pleasure.

9

Then one day a teacher came from Pinsk. But who could afford? So he gave lessons sometimes to eat, they'll give him meals. Sonia thought maybe she could be more refined and read books like me, the doctor would like her better, she wouldn't be ashamed to talk with him. So she said she would make special meals for the teacher if he would learn her. He wasn't tall, with thick glasses on his eyes and clothes hanging on him. But for a teacher he was good. At noontime she made him a nice meal, he ate up, starving, and then he would teach her.

One day, while sitting with Sonia at the table in the living room, he was reading out loud, pointing to the words. All of a sudden her cheek tickled and something was wet — she couldn't believe he was trying to kiss her! Like she had a bad taste in her mouth, she spit three times so the evil eye shouldn't shine on her, and she stood up. "Sonia," he said, "I can't help myself. So beautiful you are, with cheeks like flowers. What can I do? By me, you are better than wine, Sonia! Oy, I'm sick over it. You've got to come away with me." Then he ran over to the window. "Look outside, how the winter is gone and the rain is all over, and the little flowers are popping up from the earth."

"Shut up," she said. "It's not nice."

He ran back to her. "It's not nice? The most beautiful words, how can they not be nice?" Through his glasses his eyes bulged like the eyes of a frog, and his tongue, like it would stretch out to catch her. Quickly he wrapped his arms around her and poked her cheeks with lips like a fish.

"Oy!" she said to herself, and she pushed him away and ran out of the room. She didn't tell anyone but me. "Eatkeh," she said, "what should I do? I can't tell my parents. My father loves him, a scholar. Every Shabbos he goes with my father to shul, they talk and they look at me. Pa thinks it would be a good match, and he'd have a rabbi in the house for a son-in-law." She cried bitterly and looked around to see if anyone could hear her. "Neeseh also wants I should marry the teacher, so I'll live in misery. He hates me, Neeseh."

Then Neeseh came out with the teacher. They were talking loud, so we could hear. The teacher said, "Yes, it's good, I'm happy here. I can teach so people will know what the books say and how they should live. But your sister, Sonia, she's not like she used to be. Since your cousin, Eatkeh, came from the big city, Sonia doesn't learn well."

"There is something going on I don't know about," Neeseh said. "But I will find out." And then they went out of the room.

"You hear how they talk?" Sonia said.

"Let them say what they want. I won't be here," I told her.

"What should I do?" Sonia cried. "I can't stand to look at him! How can I marry him, such a no-good, a shlepper. And then the doctor — Eatkeh, help me!"

"Do you love him?" I asked.

"Oy, do I love him? I'm scared of my own words."

I said, "If the doctor would love me like he loves you, I wouldn't care what. Let them talk, I wouldn't pay attention. I would go to him and be by him night and day. Let him meet me and kiss me and hold me, that's all. To the end of the world I would go with him, anything." So mad I was at her. So foolish she was, she didn't know what she had. I looked out the window, everything was fresh, so beautiful it tore your heart out.

"I can't get it out of my head that he's a Christian," Sonia said.

I looked at her. "Oy, I could *curse*. A Christian? He's not a good man? He doesn't love you? What do you want, the teacher? If God sends a flood again, the teacher can come on the boat but we tell the doctor no, no you can't, you have to drown because you're a Christian?" Then I stopped to catch my breath, like I was running. Finally, I said, "Listen, if he wants you so badly, he'll turn Jewish."

She started laughing. "Russian men

don't turn Jewish. Only the Jewish girls turn Christian so they can marry Russian men."

"You'll turn Christian?" I asked her.

"My God. I would die first," she said. "Maybe I'll have to die, that's all."

"But the doctor loves you," I said.

Like she would faint, she weaved back and forth. "Oh, Eatkeh, I love him, I love him!" she said. "If he loves me, I'll die!"

"Don't be foolish. You won't die."

"If I don't die, Ma and Pa will kill me if they find out."

"They wouldn't find out. How can they find out?"

"Neeseh."

"Maybe I can talk to him," I said.

"He knows you hate him."

"I don't hate him. I don't love him, but I don't hate him." To make her feel better I said, "Maybe he can learn from me what love means. Your brother doesn't even know how to be with a woman."

"Eatkeh," she said, taking me into her arms.

"How I hate this little town," I said. "I think I will go back to my sister in the big city. I don't feel good here and I miss my friends.''

''Don't go, I beg you,'' she said, holding me so hard I couldn't move. ''Without him I can't live. I'm so mixed up I go around all day and night without a head. I can't eat, I can't sleep, I don't know where I am.''

''You'll be sick.''

''Yes!'' She laughed. ''I'll die and then my head won't hurt anymore!''

So, next day she didn't get out of bed. What's wrong? She didn't feel good. Tante Bernice got scared because Sonia was a picture of health and was never sick a day in her life. She didn't understand, the tante, and she went to the doctor's room. ''Honored Doctor,'' she said, ''my Sonia doesn't feel good.'' He got up so fast that she grabbed her heart.

''Excuse me,'' he said, and they went to Sonia's room. She was lying down, looked pale. When he saw her, the doctor stopped close by her bed and took her hand in his and asked her what was wrong. Sonia opened her big black eyes and looked at him, but she couldn't say a word.

"Sonia!" her mother yelled. "You have to tell the doctor where it hurts you! You want him to help you out, you have to talk!"

The doctor stood up. "Please, madame. It's very hard for me to know what to do when the mother is standing like a bone in the throat."

"Doctor," Sonia said, "I don't know what's the matter with me. Ma, a glass water please, you'll bring me."

The tante went out and the doctor sat on the bed and put his hand on Sonia's face, and then both hands, and he looked closely at her eyes. "Sonia," he whispered, "tell me, please."

With tears in her eyes, her lips trembling, she was shaking all over, like in cold water.

"Sonia," he said, "oh, my Sonia," and he couldn't help himself. Like something pulling him down, he put his lips on her cheek, on her head, on her nose, and finally on her lips.

Like she was drowning, she held onto him. Then she couldn't breathe and she pushed away from him. "Oy," she said,

"Ma will come. She'll come and she'll scream. Oh, God."

"My Sonia." He kissed her hands over and over again.

"Please, please," she said, sobbing, and she turned her head away.

The tante came in with the glass water and the doctor got up quickly. She saw that Sonia's cheeks were red like beets, and my aunt asked, "Honored Doctor, maybe my daughter has a fever?"

He held the glass water to Sonia's lips. Then he ran back to his room to get his medicine. The tante said to Sonia, "You shouldn't worry. He is a beautiful person, a shaneh. He will make you feel better. So why are you crying? You shouldn't be afraid."

The doctor came in and shook powder in a spoon and said to Sonia, "Open up." And he put the medicine in her mouth. A long time he was holding her hand and looking at her.

"She'll be all right?" the tante asked.

Like she woke him up, he came to himself. "Yes. She'll be perfect. She is very strong. A picture of health. I will watch after her day and night. Now she will have a good sleep." He said to Sonia, "Now you'll sleep. When you wake up, everything will be all right. Don't worry."

My aunt thanked him and handed him a half ruble. "I don't take money from the house where I live," he said. Then the doctor made a bow and looked at Sonia and went out of the room.

"Such a fine person," the tante said. "Even a Christian, he doesn't make a difference with us. Everybody says how good he is to the Jews."

But Sonia didn't hear her mother because she was already asleep.

All day I didn't see her. Then I found out she was in bed. When she saw me, she was laughing, with tears on her cheeks. "What is the matter?" I asked. "So mixed up in your head."

"Eatkeh, something happened. Oh, Eatkeh, the doctor —"

I got scared. "What happened? Something by the doctor? Somebody said something?"

"No, oh, no. The doctor kissed me."

Like she hit me on the face. But also,

thank God, he was all right. So I laughed.

"How can you laugh?" she asked. "My mother almost came in when he was kissing me."

"He is a man and he is in love with you. When he sees a chance, he shows how he loves you," I said.

"Oh, do you think? How can it be? God in heaven, let it be!" But then, like a prayer, she held her hands on her chest and, like cold water in her face, she began crying, "No, it should not be! He shouldn't love —"

But Tante Bernice came into the room and said, "Eatkeh, you have nothing to do, you'll help me with the food today. I have to carry to the people who work by us. So, Eatkeh, you'll carry the doctor's meal to him today."

I looked at Sonia. She smiled.

When I took the tray, I set everything up nicely so it would look pretty, and I carried it up and knocked on the door. The doctor told me to come in. "Anuta!" He looked like he was happy to see me. He came over and took the tray and put it on the table. "Come, sit," he said. I was not bashful and so I sat down. "It looks delicious. Did you make it?" I laughed. "So, you carried it. That makes it delicious. Will you share it with me?" No, no, I wouldn't. "Anuta." He looked at me and he was smiling. "Anuta, you are not like the girls here. You are different and you talk such nice Russian because you studied in Kiev." In those days the Jews who had some money used to send their children to Kiev or to Poland to learn.

"I didn't study in Kiev," I said. "When I was very young, I went away from home with my sister. We went to the big cities, to Kiev also, and I learned, I picked up. I learned with my ears." So I told him what happened to me in the big cities. He ate and I talked. Then he asked me how old I was. I said the way I figured it, I would soon be fifteen. In those days you didn't pay attention, you didn't have a birthday like now.

He said, "Your sense is like a young woman's, so nicely you talk. And you dress up clean, nice, elegant. You are a very pretty girl, Anuta."

"Thank you, Herr Doctor," I said, and I stood up to leave.

"Sit a little bit longer and we'll talk," he said.

So again I sat down. I was not afraid.

"It's all right to call you Anuta?"

"Please."

"You are very close to Sonia."

"We are like sisters, better even. We tell each other everything."

"So lucky you are. You should be very happy. No one else has a friend to tell everything to."

"In the big cities I had friends, so many. We could talk all night about books and about what life should be."

"What should be, Anuta?"

"You should be together, people should be close in their hearts so they will know. They should be happy together and live beautifully and talk nicely and enjoy nice things together, with beautiful books and ideas in their heads and they should —" I couldn't look at him anymore. "They should love one another."

"Like sisters and brothers they should love?"

"Also," I said.

I could feel his eyes burning. "Do you think a man should love a woman? Or should the parents decide? Maybe the parents know better how to marry the daughter to someone good?" he asked me.

"When my parents fell in love," I said, "my grandparents didn't like it at first. No one liked it, they made them suffer. But in the end they wouldn't stop, they had the wedding. They live happily now, the best from all the family. People can't get over it, how happy they are."

"But who made such trouble? Your father is Jewish, no? How could it be better?" He wouldn't eat anymore and he pushed the potatoes away with his spoon. "Anuta, would you marry someone who's not a Jew?"

I felt like my face was on fire. "If I love someone, what difference does it make so long as I love him and he loves me?"

"You don't care what your parents will say?" he asked, grabbing my hands so hard my fingers lay together like a bundle.

"They'll say go in good health."

"They wouldn't throw you out?"

"If I marry someone, wouldn't I go where he goes?"

On my hands he patted, patted, patted. He looked at the future, what would be, a dream before his eyes. "Sonia's mother, your aunt, she's your mother's sister? And her father, Sonia's? They are like your parents?" he asked me.

"Tante Bernice? She's got a good heart, but for her to understand is hard. After all, what does she know, in a little town all her life. She is very old-fashioned. And the father, he's good but he's not so good. You take my father, he used to go to the big cities to buy. He's more modern. My mother, God bless, an angel, so good, she can understand in her heart more than the most educated person. You wouldn't worry about her, she suffered enough. She knows what it is to love somebody."

The doctor was smiling. "I wish your parents could be like Sonia's," he said.

Then I stood up and said, "Sonia's parents they are not." Quickly I went to the door.

"Will you tell Sonia for me —" he

started to say.

"I'll tell Sonia you want to see her," I said.

"Every day I see her, but I want to see her alone."

"All right. You'll see her in the woods. No one will know."

He ran over and looked at me. "Maybe it can be, in the woods. By the river the big trees grow close together. Anuta!" So excited, he looked at me. "You'll bring her?"

"You want to see her alone."

"You'll come, too. We need you, Anuta. From myself you'll protect me."

All of a sudden flew open the door. It was Tante Bernice. "How long does it take you to bring a tray food?" she demanded.

The doctor said, "I asked Anuta to keep me company while I was eating."

She saw that he didn't finish everything.

"I had enough," he said. She grabbed the tray to take it back with her. "It was very delicious," he said. "One hundred percent. I thank you."

Like a leaf I went out of the room. The

tante followed me and grabbed me in the hallway. Like actors in the theater when they're whispering, she said, "You should be ashamed, a Jewish girl should have business with a goyisher doctor. It's not nice."

I said, "Tante, don't be afraid. The doctor is very refined and he is alone, so he is lonely. I don't do anything wrong by being friendly or by talking to a man as intelligent as him. He plays very beautifully the guitar."

"Wait, your mother will hear," she said.

"You shouldn't worry. I won't be here anyway. I am going back soon to my sister in the city."

Then I ran quickly away from her and I went to Sonia in her room. She was drinking a glass tea. I told her how I talked with Misha and she wanted to know right away what he said to me. I told her what her mother did and she jumped out of bed. "What she'll do to me, what she'll do to me!" she cried, banging together her fists. "It can't be, she won't allow it, nothing! I don't have any hope!"

When I went back to my own house, my aunt was already there with her gossip. "Now she comes," Tante Bernice said. "I sent her with the meal to the doctor. She didn't come out, so it bothered me."

"So? What do you want from her?" my mother asked.

"You don't care if your daughter sits alone with a Christian in his room?"

"You ask her to take in the meal and now you tell me my daughter sat with the doctor alone. I am telling you not to be afraid of Eatkeh. She is smart. You don't have to watch her. Never again will she bring in the food to the doctor. So, you feel better?"

"Try to do a favor for your own sister, she doesn't appreciate. Do what you want, I don't care. Let her be the talk of the whole town." Out she went from the house, like the wind.

"How can she talk like that?" I asked my mother. "I brought the doctor his meal and I made a visit, we had a conversation, that's all. If you talk to somebody, you have to lie and say you didn't?"

My mother said, "I don't care what visit you make, but by your aunt in her house they sit and think of bad things. I know her, she is my sister. She has been mean since she was a child. Nu, so how is Sonia?"

"The doctor gave her medicine and she feels better."

"To be in the house with Tante Bernice, you could be sick."

Meanwhile, Sonia improved and she did her work in the house, and she also tried to learn. But it didn't come into her head. The teacher didn't understand what was going on in her heart. He told her she wasn't learning well, and he put his arm around her when they were alone. She told him he shouldn't do it, and if he does she'd tell her parents. So, he was angry at her.

Soon the hospital was ready. They put in a lot of beds, and sick people, Russians, were coming from the villages. The doctor began to be very busy, so another young doctor came to help him. The second doctor lived by my sister, Golde, who had a home with three bedrooms.

Misha's office was right across from our house. When he looked out the window he could see me on the porch reading books. So, when he finished with his patients one day he called me to the window with his finger. He said, "Now that Sonia is better, her mother watches her like a hawk, I can't see her. But I have to. Remember you said maybe we can see each other in the woods? Can you bring her?"

"If you want," I said.

"Yes, yes. When?"

"Soon."

"Tonight?"

"Tonight already? I'll see. I'll talk to her," I said.

"Tell her I will wait for her tonight in the woods. Eight o'clock!"

I went back on the porch and again I start to read. A lot of the old gossipers saw me and they start to whisper between them but I didn't pay attention. But my eyes got sleepy and tired, I couldn't read. Finally, I went to see Sonia in her house. With the aunt, I didn't like to go there anymore, but to tell Sonia the doctor wanted to see her, I went in. Sonia grabbed herself like her heart was falling out. "If you are so scared, you shouldn't go," I said.

"I have to see him," she said. "My mother watches, I can't breathe. He goes to his room and out and we make a smile in the hall, but we can't say a word. Eatkeh, you'll go with me? I want you should go with me."

"The doctor already asked me to go with you."

"But how can we? Shaneh is like a spy, such a mouse. She follows me like a shadow."

"You'll see," I said.

I went to my sister, Golde, in her pretty home. She was having tea with the new doctor. She introduced me and he made a nice bow. "I am very pleased to meet you," he said. "My partner in the hospital already told me about you and your beautiful cousin." His name was Shasha. He kept looking at me. I used to dress very nicely, like in the big cities. The women in our town didn't go around very clean except on Shabbos, when everybody got dressed up.

Golde said, "She is very independent. She isn't like other people."

"Like a fire burning in the night," he said.

"A fire burns," I said. "It has to have something to burn. Here is only smoke."

He laughed. "Where there's smoke there's fire."

"A wet log makes a fire?"

Then he put his arms on his knees and leaned toward me. "Misha tells me how smart you are. I have to see more for myself." Then he stood up, he had to go to the hospital. To Golde he made a bow. "I will be happy here. Thank you," he said. She got red in the face. And to me also a bow. "Next time we will talk more."

When he went out, Golde said, "You have to see that the honorable doctor shouldn't fall in love with you."

"The doctor?" I said, feeling hot like the tea. "The honorable doctor is falling in love with Sonia, not with me."

Golde started to laugh. "Why are

you laughing?" I asked her. "It's funny by you?"

She wiped her eyes and said, "No, no, no. It's all right." She was smiling at me. "How can he love Sonia when her parents are so religious? They're not modern like Ma and Pa. By them it wouldn't be so bad. Tante Bernice, she'll find out and she'll kill her. And they'll kill you, too, because you are so close to her."

"It wouldn't matter," I said, and I told her, "Misha wants me and Sonia to meet him in the woods."

"So what do you want from me?" Golde asked.

"We can tell Bernice we are going to visit you to play dominoes in the evening."

"If you go to the woods, everybody will see you," Golde said.

"No one will go over the bridge at night."

By us the lake was in the middle of town. The bridge over the middle of the lake used to rock when we walked on it. Beyond the bridge was a big orchard belonging to Kanage. Past the orchard were a lot of woods where boys and girls used to go walking.

I said, "The doctor wants to go so he can talk to Sonia. What can he do? He can't even say a word to her in the house now. He won't come to have a glass tea anymore with Tante Bernice there also. So nice it could be here, to serve him tea with a little sponge cake. You'll say they were by you tonight? Eight o'clock."

Golde was smiling like she was remembering something. She nodded her head and kissed me, and I ran out, happy to leave.

When I went in the house, my father was sitting with Zaydeh, my grandfather, drinking tea. I kissed my zaydeh on his pink cheek. Like my father he looked, like two brothers in the short coats. I poured tea in the glass and sat next to Zaydeh.

"Nu?" he said. "So, finally, what will you do, my child? Will you stay in the house by your mother? Will we look for a husband?" His nice beard, clean, white, he made smooth with his hand. Little glasses he wore, no rims.

"I am going back pretty soon to the

big cities," I said.

Pa waved his hand at me. "Don't talk. Don't talk."

Zaydeh said, "Listen, she's like you. The same way, you didn't want to be home. It pulled you to go to the big cities."

Pa held his arms out wide. "It pulled me but I am here. So what good did it do me?"

Zaydeh was holding up one finger. "You know from the world what is life. Moses called out the Torah in seventy languages. What is life if you don't know? What can you know? People. You got to know *people.*"

"Here are no people?"

"Ah, my son," he was shaking his head yes and no. "Someday our little town will be a big city also. They will laugh at us, our grandchildren in the generations to come. What did they know? they'll say about us. Even now, what do I know about the world?"

My father patted him on the arm. "You know, Pa, you know."

Getting up, he made noises and oying,

krechtzing. Then he kissed me on the forehead. "Go in good health," he said, and he went to say a prayer first and then take a nap.

My father asked me, "Did you talk to the doctor through the window?"

I sat down and held the glass tea, so hot it burned my hands. "Yes, Pa. Why do you ask me that?" I said.

"Why did you go there?"

"The doctor called me. He asked me how to buy some curtains for the windows." I could hardly say it, such a lie.

"Ah!" he said in disgust. "The gossipers, they are so common, they know how to talk about a person, that's all. They made plenty of trouble for me, too. Right away they see something, they start to talk ugly."

"I won't be here for long anyway," I said.

"My daughter," he said, "you were many years in the big cities and you saw and went through all kinds of things. For your age you are very smart and you understand life. I don't know what to tell

421

you. We only want for you what is best."

Then my dear mother came in with her sweet face and a smile. To him she said, "Dauvidel, did you tell her how they talk?"

I said, "Mamusha, I won't bring you a momzer." That means a bastard, you should forgive the word.

Then I ran quickly to Sonia's house. She was cleaning the doctor's room. "What were you talking about with Misha?" she asked.

"How do you know?"

"The whole street knows you talked to him through the window."

"Let them know," I said.

Sonia was rubbing a table very hard, like she wanted to take away the varnish altogether.

"It's arranged for you. In the woods you'll meet with him. Eight o'clock," I told her.

She stopped rubbing. "How can I meet him? It can't be."

I told her that I had spoken with my sister, Golde. "You shouldn't be afraid. It will be all right," I said. So happy, she grabbed me and squeezed me to her heart.

The time came and Sonia had to bring the supper in from the kitchen. She was so excited everything fell from her hands. Her mother yelled that she would break all the dishes. Sonia had to say something so the tante wouldn't understand what was going on. "Since I'm sick, my hands have been shaking," she said. When she took in the doctor's meal, he smiled at her but he was afraid to say a word. She smiled also and said, "Eat, it will get cold." She went out quickly because always her mother or her brother Neeseh came like dust to spy on her. When she came back to get the empty dishes, the doctor asked, "Did Anuta say something?" Sonia shook her head and went out very nervous. Then she set the table for the working men and her mother told her to bring in the samovar. She went to the kitchen and took down the little brass teapot you put on top the samovar. Inside is coals. It fell down and she burned her hand, such a scream that Misha ran out of his room. "What happened?" he yelled, and then Sonia came out of the kitchen with tears covering her face. The doctor looked at her hand and said, "Come, in my room I have jars of salve. I'll make a bandage."

"A big tumult she makes for nothing," Neeseh said.

"Be quiet," the tante said. "Let him make a bandage. We'll go," she said to the doctor.

"It's all right!" yelled Sonia. "I don't need it!" She ran upstairs to her room and closed the door behind her and had a good cry. When I went in, Sonia told me everything. Everyone was sitting and drinking tea by the table like nothing happened. Sonia said we shouldn't meet with the doctor. "Eatkeh, you see every time something happens to me."

I said, "Do what you want, it doesn't matter to me. I won't be here long anyway. But the time I am here, I would like to enjoy myself. I don't care who I visit with, Gentile or Jew, just so they aren't common. Whoever we go out with, we don't have to marry them."

Sonia looked at me with fright in her eyes. "What will I do? Now it's late. How can we tell him we can't go out tonight?"

"I'll go by the hospital and talk to him."

"The people will see you and they'll say very bad things."

"Let them talk. I'm not afraid," I said.

"Go by the back door so my family won't see you," Sonia said.

"It's better they should see me. Let them see me." I went out of her room and Neeseh was in the hallway, like he was waiting for me. "Why do you have so much to talk about?" he asked me.

I said, "Why don't you go in and listen to what two cousins are saying?"

"I wouldn't be interested."

Outside it was getting dark already. Right away cousin Shaneh, the busybody, came running. "Where are you going?"

"By myself," I said.

"I'll go with you."

"I don't want you."

"Why not?"

"Because you like to gossip and talk about everybody, and that I don't like. When you say what you don't know, that's not very nice."

"So you know everything?" Shaneh said.

"You live very narrish, foolish, and you don't have anyone to learn from. You are a housegirl. You do what your parents tell you."

She raised her chin so she could try to look down on me. "You hold yourself like you are somebody because . . . because you read Russian. I don't want to speak Russian like you. You are a goyeh. You make the samovar on Shabbos and you run after the doctor."

When Shaneh said all that, I slapped her on the cheek. She threw out her hand to hit me but I was very quick. I stepped back and she fell down. Then I went to the hospital to see the doctor. Shaneh ran home right away and told her mother. Her father was my mother's brother. So Tante Pearl ran to our house and told my mother. "Your daughter you should take care of finally. She runs after the Russian doctor and she's there alone now, and she hit Shaneh on the head." So angry she was, she started to spit with her words.

My mother listened, and when Tante Pearl was through, my mother said, "Why do you aggravate yourself with what my

426

daughter is doing? That's none of your business. You should watch your own daughter because she is a gossip and a common person. How many times does she tell on Eatkeh, and how many times did she go to the neighbors and tell their daughters they shouldn't go with Eatkeh? One thing I can tell you, my shvegerin" — sister-in-law — "she is not going to bring you a momzer."

When the doctor saw me, he was very happy, and he showed me all the rooms they made over. Already there were a few patients and I asked them how they felt. Then we went to his office and he said to me, "How can you be so brave to come here?"

I said, "Ponee Doctor, you are angry because I came into the hospital?"

"No, no, please. I am disappointed that Sonia's parents and her brother don't let her out. They watch her like she was a loose girl. She is so pretty and so naive, so quiet. Why do they have to be like that?"

"Mein Doctor," I said. "I don't have to tell you. You are educated, but would you give up your religion to go with a Jewish girl?"

"Why not? If you are in love, that doesn't mean anything."

I said, "By me, you are right. But here, in a little Jewish town, the people are very religious. They wouldn't allow it. They would do something bad to the girl."

"My parents wanted me to be a priest because my father is one. In Kiev, in the gymnasium, I had a friend, Joseph Freedman. We used to carry our books in our hands together. I used to tell him maybe he'll be a doctor and I'll be a priest. And I laughed so hard, Joseph didn't understand. You see, I didn't even want to go with my parents to church. He smiled and said I should laugh, too, because it's almost impossible for a Jew to become a doctor."

Since it was past eight o'clock I said, "Doctor, I have to go home."

He was looking out the window. "In your house it is still light," he said. His window was open and everybody could see what was going on in his office. "And I haven't finished telling you everything about myself and Joseph."

"You'll tell me another time."

Then I got up and held out my hand and the doctor kissed it. "Will I see you tomorrow?" he asked me, and I nodded. "I will talk to Sonia when she brings me my breakfast. It will also give me a chance to see her hand," he said.

When I went out I noticed a tall man run away but I didn't see his face.

Next morning Sonia ran into my room and woke me up. She said Neeseh told her mother I was sitting and talking to the doctor. He was very angry with me and he was saying very dirty things.

I said, "I don't care. I won't be here very long. Do you want to know my plan?"

"What plan?" she asked.

"You have to be calm because everything shows on your face. I will come to your house and say, 'Sonia, come with me for a walk,' and you'll say, 'Why?' and I'll say, 'There is nobody to go with, so let's go together. Maybe we'll stop and see my sister, Golde.' When you bring Misha his supper, you'll tell him quickly we are going so Neeseh won't understand what's going on."

And that's how it was. When Sonia told the doctor our plan, he was very happy and he said he would ride on a horse. And so I went in and asked Sonia to go for a walk, and she asked why all of a sudden, and I said it makes me feel bad to walk around alone. So we went out together. Neeseh looked at me like a spy. When the doctor went out, Neeseh followed him to see where he was going, but he saw the doctor get on a horse and take a different road.

In the night we went carefully, only a little moon in the sky, and we were holding each other tightly by the hand. In those days you could go for a walk at night and no one would bother you on the street. But in the woods, sometimes you don't know who will come, a drunkard maybe. The air in the autumn lay like a cold hand on our heads and we were very afraid, like we weighed two hundred pounds, our feet wouldn't move. When we came to the woods we saw a place under the big tree. Like two cats in front of a fireplace Sonia and I sat close together and we didn't say a word. A whole hour we were sitting and shaking, listening to the noises of the frogs and the crickets and the woods making a noise like a rocking chair. All of a sudden we heard a horse coming and our hearts were pounding. "Sonia," a call like the wind. "Sonia?" It was the doctor.

We were so happy, we both ran right to him and he took us up in his arms. Then he tied the horse to the tree and we walked under his arms a little farther and then we sat down. "Was somebody following you?" he asked. We guaranteed him no, nobody. He took Sonia's hand in his and we sat very quietly. He looked at the river, the tiny moons on the water dancing. He said, "I'm thinking maybe I'll buy a house on the river. There is an empty house I saw with two bedrooms and a living room and a big kitchen. It is still a new house. A writer used to live there but he moved to Pinsk. I'll go tomorrow to see it." He looked at us. "Will you go with me and help me decide?"

"I don't know," Sonia said very quietly.

"If Sonia can't go, then I'll go," I said.

He was playing with her hand. Then he lowered his head and kissed her fingers. He said, very quiet, "Sonia, you are the dearest to me. I love you very much." She pulled away her hand and looked at me. "I'm not afraid of Anuta. She is modern and she understands life very well." Then I took Sonia's hand and put it back in his. I covered her fingers with his fingers and I was holding them like that. "Sonia," he said, "how do you feel?" She tried to say something but only tears came.

"She can't get you out of her mind, day and night," I told him.

"Can you say the words? I love you. Do you love me, too?" he asked her.

"She's so mixed up, she is afraid to say how she feels. She has to hide her love for you. She loves you more than the world. She loves you so much she doesn't know what to do."

"Oh, Sonia!" He kissed our hands and tried to bring her close, to kiss her lips, but she couldn't do it. He said, "Sonia, I'm not religious, even if my father and my brother are priests. I am a free person." That scared her. From his very intelligent words she was shaking. "Don't be afraid," he said. "My liebe Sonia, I understand how by the Jews you don't believe in marrying a Gentile. But I believe when two people love each other, it doesn't matter if I am Gentile and you are Jewish." He spoke with his whole heart. "I'll do anything in the world for you."

Then I pushed her closer to him, and I made her head touch his shoulder. She couldn't say a word, her tears were pouring out from her big black eyes. He took his white handkerchief and wiped her eyes and said, "Don't cry, my dear child. If I didn't love you, I would laugh at you, and I wouldn't ask Anuta to come with you. I know Anuta is not like those girls who want to hurt the others. That's why I always want you to go with her." Then I started to cry myself, I couldn't help it, and he took his white handkerchief and wiped my tears also, and he put my head on his other shoulder and I didn't want to stop.

Finally Sonia said, "My mother will kill me if I come home so late."

"It goes too quickly," he said. He helped lift us up and he took his horse and led the way for us out of the woods. At the end he said, "You'll go with me tomorrow to the house?" Sonia shrugged a shoulder.

"If not Sonia, I'll go," I said.

He shook his head, he understood. Then he leaned toward Sonia and put his lips on hers, not for long because she turned her head. Then he came to me and I held up my face. On the cheek he kissed me, and he climbed up on his horse and rode away.

We came home late, after ten o'clock, and it was a very dark night. I told Sonia she better come to my house. Then Neeseh wouldn't know. In my house Shaneh was sitting. Right away she said, "I know where you were and I know who went with you today."

"Mazel tov. So, with who did we go?" I asked her.

"I know. I know," she said, with her little eyes like a mouse.

"So if you know, say."

Sonia was standing like a ghost was

talking. I said to Shaneh, "Tell us already, spy, who did we go with?" I went up close to her and looked in her eyes.

"Don't you hit me!" she yelled, and she ran out of the house.

"Oy, oy," Sonia said. "She'll tell everyone!"

"She doesn't know. She wants us to pay attention to her. What can she know? Don't worry, she's an ignorant person."

When we started to go into the living room, the door suddenly broke open and Neeseh jumped inside and yelled, "Where were you both so late?"

"Here in the house," I said. "What's the matter?"

"Shaneh told me. It's no use to tell such a lie, liar!"

Then Sonia started to yell at him, "So foolish you are when you talk like that! You look like a big fool and an even bigger one when you curse Eatkeh! So common you are, just like Shaneh, so prost. And you don't have any sense how to live."

Then he pointed his hand at me. "She! She! She teaches you to go out with a

435

goy! She should bring shame to her whole family!"

From the living room came my father. "What's going on?" he asked. "Who makes so much noise?"

"Neeseh," I said. "He went crazy because I won't pay attention to him. So he makes up stories about me."

"Neeseh," my father said. "It's too late at night. Go home already."

"She . . . she . . . she should —"

"To home!" Pa said. "Good night!"

"Uncle David, I am sorry —" Sonia said.

"Don't be sorry," Pa said. "Go, have a good rest. You shouldn't worry your pretty head."

Next day Sonia told me Neeseh didn't say anything to their parents, but she was scared to go see the house Misha wanted to buy. She had to watch herself because of Neeseh and Shaneh. "And you, Eatkeh, you have to watch out. They'll make you big trouble. You shouldn't go with the doctor to see the house."

"I don't care."

"Eatkeh, I'm afraid. Maybe they'll talk

436

about you so much you'll have to leave, and then what could I do by myself? Don't leave me, Eatkeh.''

When I went to the hospital, so many eyes were following me. When Misha saw me he told me to come right in. ''Bad news?'' he asked.

''No bad news and no good news. Sonia is scared to come.''

''I know.'' He sat thinking.

''You want we should go see?''

''Ah.'' He looked at me, such a sad smile. ''Why not? But it's better we don't walk together, you know how people will talk. You go ahead. When I'm finished with the patients, I'll come also.''

Already the cold wind was freezing up the river and the banks, but to me, on my face, like sweet kisses, I felt so good, full of life. I had to run with the wind, like it was carrying me in its arms. Maybe a mile on the other side of the bridge was the house. It was old and no one took care of it. On the windows some shutters were falling off. You could walk inside. Who locked an empty house? The rooms looked nice and cosy — a nice place for the kitchen, a dining room, a living room, and three bedrooms. Here was the bedroom for the master, big, plenty space.

For an hour maybe I was dreaming how to fix up everything in the house to make it beautiful. When the doctor came I ran to the door to welcome him home. So tall, the doctor, with his boots, how he pulled his gloves off his hands and smiled at me. "So," he said, and he looked around and went from one room to another, and I told him what could be, how the furniture could give a nice appearance. "Now it looks dirty, but we can clean it up like new. Such a house will be for a doctor!"

"By myself maybe it's too much for one person," he said.

"Who knows?" I brushed some dust off his arm. "Maybe Sonia could be here."

"Sonia, Sonia, how could she be here? It is impossible!" He stamped on the floor and dust rose like a cloud. "If I changed to Jewish, then she could. But can I change? I could, but my parents, my family, it would kill them. Such whirling in my head!"

"You could live here. Who cares if

you're Gentile or Jewish?"

"Can she live here, Sonia, with a Gentile? In this town?" All of a sudden he grabbed me by the shoulders and I went toward him, but he looked at the wall. "Why here then? We could go away — to the big cities. Oh, God, they would find me everywhere." He looked at me and gently shook me. "Maybe we could go to America? In America they don't care who you are."

"I already have two brothers in America," I said. "They write us how hard it is to make a living, but in America everybody is free."

"Free!" he said. "But how can I go? Here I'm a doctor. There I wouldn't be. I wouldn't even know how to speak in America."

"You'll learn, you'll be!" I said in one big breath. "I'll go with you!"

He looked at me and laughed, happy. "Of course you will!" And he came over to me and took me up in his arms, and I hugged him with all my strength and I wouldn't let go. He had to unwrap himself. Then he looked around the house again. "Ah, this would be nice. Everything I like in this little town. To run away, to jump to a foreign land, to be a nothing there —" He smiled at me. "Maybe Sonia will find courage. But in America she would be even more scared than here." He looked at the walls. "For Sonia, I will buy this house," he said. "I will try."

"And if she can't?"

He looked at me, tears in his eyes. "Then we'll see. We'll see what will happen."

10

It was already winter, before Christmas. The doctor's parents came to visit him in the new house. When they used to go for a walk and the muzhiks saw them, they would fall on their knees because his father was a priest, and they would cross themselves and kiss the hems of their coats. Misha used to laugh. He wasn't like his father and his brother. Then the children of the other priest in the town came home for the holidays. One of them was a girl, pretty with blonde hair and blue eyes, not as pretty as Sonia but more educated and very refined. Her father introduced her to Misha and his parents. The priest from our town said he would make a Christmas party with Jewish music — always the orchestra was made up of Jewish musicians, that's all they had in the town — and they should bring the doctor.

Before Christmas the priest's wife bought fish from us and asked my mother to make gefilte fish. Since Golde was a great berrieh, the cook and the housecleaner, she made the gefilte fish and baked white challeh and stuffed helzel. When we brought it to the priest's wife, in Russian, in a very weak voice, she said how good it smells. I bowed and thanked her. She gave me the money and also candy and nuts and we went away.

The evening came and the doctor went to the priest's for dinner. There were a lot of priests and very nice-looking women from Pinsk and from all the small towns. In the salon was hanging a big blitz lamp. It had a hood with a pot to hold kerosene and a glass to fit over the wick. When you light it, it flashes like lightning. First they danced the polkas and then everything else they knew. They drank vodka and then they danced again. It was very merry. In our little town all the boys and girls, Jewish and Christian, stood beneath the window and watched until they got so cold they had to go home.

442

The doctor danced very nicely with the priest's daughter, Katrina. They were together the whole evening. When he said good night to Katrina and her parents, they asked him to come more often. He said good-bye to everybody and he told his parents he would see them again, and he went out. Katrina's older brother said he would take Misha home because it was daytime now and there was much frost. The brother told the driver he should hook the horses to the carriage, and they got in and covered up their feet with pelts from fur. On the way the brother told Misha he was studying outside of Russia to become a lawyer, but his father would rather have him be a priest. This he didn't want. Misha told him his father wanted him to be a priest also. "So I am a doctor and I love my profession," he said. "I am happy but for one thing. You don't find many educated people here and there is no one to have a conversation with. With women, there is nothing to talk."

The brother said, "I know it. That is why my father sent us out of Russia to learn. My sister is the only girl here who is very educated. She is studying to be a dentist. She is twenty-three and very smart.''

The doctor understood what her brother, Aleksei, was trying to tell him. ''Yes, I spoke to her about different books.''

''You should come over,'' Aleksei said.

And so the doctor did, and he really enjoyed himself. But his heart was with Sonia, and he couldn't understand why it pulled him to her. When he was sitting with Katrina and talking to her, he saw Sonia's face. ''What are you thinking of now?'' she would ask. He jumped like from a dream and said, ''Excuse me.'' She said right away, ''Doctor, I understand, you always have things to think about.'' He thanked her.

So long as his father and brother were there, the doctor had to visit Katrina. Meanwhile, both fathers were talking. Katrina's father said, ''Maybe your son and my daughter should come together.''

Misha's father said, ''That does not depend on you or me, but how the girl and the doctor feel.''

Then Katrina and her mother served tea, but the doctor was very upset. The tea and all the good things were crawling around in his throat.

When he got ready to leave, Katrina didn't want him to go, but he kissed her hand and her mother's hand and then he left. He walked and walked, with the snow whirling around his feet, and he looked at the ground, but he didn't know where he was going.

Finally, he saw he was standing in front of Sonia's house, so he went inside to his room. Sonia was by herself in the dining room ironing his white shirts. She looked so pretty. Her cheeks were red like fire and her black eyes were shining like stars in the heavens. He stood watching her and he couldn't take his eyes off her. She was scared because everybody was sleeping, but she was hoping to see him. All of a sudden he said, "Sonia, Sonia, dearest," and he took the iron from her hand and put his arms around her and gave her such a kiss she almost fainted.

"Misha," she said softly, "no. Go away quickly. Something will happen. Please."

"I love you," he said. "Nobody else. I'll do anything you want, even turn Jewish if your parents will accept me."

"We can't talk here, they'll wake up. Misha!"

He grabbed his shirts in one arm and Sonia in his other arm and, like he was carrying two bundles, he took them upstairs to his room. Sonia was whispering, "No, no, Misha, no," making her fingers dig into his coat. She was hiding her face on his chest. Gently but quickly he took her inside and closed the door.

In the morning Tante Bernice went into Sonia's room and found her sitting all dressed on her bed. "So you're up early," her mother said. "How come?" Sonia didn't say, she just looked at the floor. When her mother went out, Sonia threw herself down on the bed and started to cry. Her mother went to the kitchen to make breakfast, and when everything was ready she called Sonia to help her. Sonia felt like she fell in the water, she didn't hear her mother. Then Tante Bernice yelled again, but this time she went up to the room. She saw Sonia lying in bed with her clothes on and she gave her such a shake that Sonia looked like she didn't know what was going on. The tante started to talk in such a high voice that Sonia said, "Don't yell so loud. It's not nice for the doctor. You'll wake him up."

"What happened to you?"

"I was ironing the clothes almost all night."

"The doctor's clothes? You have to iron all night?"

"Don't worry, I'm up already."

"Who told you to stay up all night to iron the clothes?"

"Nobody told me. Only I couldn't sleep."

"So now you want to sleep, I should do everything myself?"

"I'm coming down. I'm on my way already."

That day I went to the hospital, but the doctor was so busy with his patients that I didn't stay. A lot of boys and girls turned their heads to make believe they didn't see me, but one boy wasn't like them. Osher was his name. He worked for Sonia's father, making furniture. He was twenty years old, not bad-looking, but very bashful.

"Never mind them," he said to me.

"Why should I mind? So ignorant and common they are."

He walked me to Sonia's house, with his eyes on the ground. Finally he said, "I don't mind. You are Sonia's best friend."

"Like sisters," I told him.

Osher was shaking his head like he was sad. When we came to the house and went inside, we saw the teacher running out of the living room, hiding his face with his hand. Then Sonia, with tears on her cheeks and her eyes like fire, yelled "Paskudnyak!" It means a no-good, a bad person.

"What? What?" I said.

"The teacher!"

"What did he do?"

She told us how first she had to wait for him to start the lesson. When he came in, she sat at the table with the book. He wouldn't take his eyes off her. Then he asked her if she prepared the lessons and he started to listen to her and told her right away, "You are not learning well. Your mind is someplace else, not on your book. You better do your lessons or I'll talk with your parents." He was bending over her, a drop fell from his mouth onto the page. Then, like he was hissing, he said, "Neeseh will find out what is going on between you and the doctor. He'll kill you." Sonia grabbed the book and threw it in his face and yelled at him to get out.

Osher said, "I'll go to him, I'll kill *him*."

Sonia put her hand on his arm. "No, Osher, let him go. It would only be bad for you."

His face was blushing, like her hand was on fire on his arm.

"You should stop the lessons," I told her.

"They won't let me," she cried. And then the tears came, her shoulders shaking so much, like she would fall apart. Osher didn't know what to do, he waved his hands but he wouldn't touch her. Finally I said, "It's all right. You can't go out as much for a while. Don't worry, I'll explain." She looked at me to understand

and then she cried some more.

After supper Sonia ran into our kitchen, her face like she had never stopped crying, and she grabbed me but she couldn't talk in front of everybody. So I took her to my bedroom and I closed the door. "Nu? What happened?" I asked her.

"Oy, what didn't happen? The paskudnyak teacher went out to the yard where Neeseh and Pa and all the workers were and he said dirty things about me. He didn't tell the truth but the opposite. So tonight they all came to eat and Pa washed his hands and made the moetze" — the blessing over the bread — "and all sat down to eat, and Neeseh was sitting with his skin burning and nobody said a word. Afterward, Neeseh and Pa stayed, and Pa called me over and said, 'Now we're paying money so you can hit the teacher with a book? We pay him so much money and you insult him? You have to have respect! The teacher is a very refined man. You shouldn't chase him away from you.' I tried to tell how the teacher insulted me but Pa wouldn't listen. He told me I'll have to be good and listen to what the teacher tells me to do. Then Neeseh opened up his big mouth and threw such dirty words at me! Eatkeh, I'm so unhappy! The teacher has talked so badly about me, but, thank God, he didn't say anything about the doctor. I don't know how he knows, and Pa wouldn't let me say a word, and now so much trouble in our house —" I told her that Misha would be all right, they'd see each other after things got better.

So, the next day the teacher came like he owned her and right away he said, "From now on you'll do what I want, not what you want." Sonia didn't say a word. He started to teach her, but when he touched her hand she hit him with the book, and his face got red like fire. That's the way it went for several weeks. Everything was better but Sonia used to see the doctor only when she carried in the meal. So they started to write. Sonia gave me a letter and I gave it to him, and the doctor gave me a letter and I gave it to her. In the notes she asked, are you all right? I can't say how I feel. I wish it could be better. But by him, oy, such beautiful words, such sad words like love for a beautiful flower you pick but it can't stay, like a beautiful flower can't live without water and the flower bends and nobody sees how to give it water. "Why does God put us together if we are both from two separate worlds? Why are we guilty if we are both so much in love? They want to part us. Why can't they understand our nice clean love? But, my dear, don't lose yourself. There will come a good time and we will be together again and no one will interfere. I know how hard it is for you and me not to see one another and to say what is in our hearts. We must have patience."

Meantime, the doctor had to visit Katrina, and they used to treat him very nicely. Katrina used to play the piano, and together they sang Russian songs, love songs also, and together they looked at beautiful books. When the time came for the doctor's brother and father to go back to Kiev, the father came to Misha's office. He told him he should marry Katrina. "She is educated and she will be a good wife for you. Why should you be here alone? The years are going by so fast, and you, my son, are already thirty and Katrina is twenty-three. I think it's a good match for you." Misha's eyes got dark and he swallowed like he was sick and taking a pill. How could he say a word to his dear father whom he loved so much? How could Misha hurt him and say he was in love with a Jewish girl? Then his father asked him why he was making such a sad face. "My son, at least you could tell me how you feel about Katrina."

Misha said, "My dear Papasha, how can I explain to you? I only know Katrina a few months. Only a little have I talked to her, and I don't know what kind of a person she really is. I have to know her more. Should I be tied so quickly with a woman?" The doctor went closer to his father and took him around the shoulders and hugged him. "Don't worry, I'll be all right. I'll see her, I'll talk to her more."

"My son, my son. I am proud of you."

Misha was thinking that when his father goes away with his brother, then he could forget about Katrina. Meanwhile, both fathers shook hands and said their children were almost engaged. By them, the doctor was already a son-in-law. The mother went to the two holy ones and served them a tray with two bottles of vodka. They drank to the health of their children, but they didn't know what was going on. Katrina heard how they laughed and talked. And the doctor, he didn't know either what his father had done.

When the time came for the doctor's father and brother to go away, the priest's wife made a dinner. They ate and drank and said good-bye. Misha took them to the little boat, they left, and then he took Katrina and her parents home. When he was kissing Katrina's hand, she wouldn't let go. "Tomorrow night?" she asked. He said he would see how it was by his patients.

Everything he put in a letter to Sonia, every word. He didn't want to fool her. He wrote how Katrina takes him around, he can't stand it. "I think she must feel that I am cold to her. It is very bad for me. I don't want to be in her company. I don't know how to get out of my web. I feel caught when I am alone with her and

I see your beautiful sad eyes. The way you talk to me with your black eyes, it makes me crazy in my heart. I am so close to you but we are so far apart from each other." He wrote again, "If I can't have you, it's better to die." When Sonia read his letters, she cried so much she started to lose weight and she thought she would have a nervous breakdown.

But the doctor had to keep visiting Katrina, and then the time came when she had to go back to school. Her father said she shouldn't go, she had enough learning already, she doesn't have to study anymore. Misha told her she should finish up and then come back. Her father said, "Misha, what are you saying? Your father and I had a discussion and we drank to your health and Katrina's, you should be married. We made arrangements already. So how can you tell her to go away to study more?" And Katrina was so excited, she fell on Misha's neck and kissed him and cried out of happiness. He was standing like somebody hit him on the head with a hammer.

Misha then wrote to Sonia, "I don't

want to live anymore. I feel like I want to hurt my father for what he did to me. It doesn't matter how it turns out, I won't marry her. I have to do something, but wait, not yet, let it run its course. There's got to be an end.''

Next day he went to his office and found Katrina and her mother there. He held out his hand to her mother and bowed and kissed her hand. Katrina got up and went over to Misha and kissed him, but he didn't feel good.

''Why don't you come to see me?'' Katrina asked. ''Almost three weeks already it's been. How can I wait so long until I see you? Every night in the house I don't know if you'll come.''

''I'm sorry, so busy —'' the doctor said.

''I want to see you Sunday, please.''

''Sunday? If I can catch up —''

''You have to go to church. It's not nice for a priest's son not to pray,'' Katrina said.

''I don't have time. I don't even have enough time to see my patients.''

''Oh, Misha, you give such an excuse?

How can you?"

Then Shasha came and said a man was just carried in. He couldn't walk. And so Misha was glad Shasha called him.

So bitter he got, he stopped thinking about his work. And he began to stay away from the hospital. Finally Misha couldn't stand it any longer. He had to get away. He said, for an excuse, that he had to go to Kiev to find out new things that were going on by the doctors there. Katrina said she would go also, but Misha told her he would be so busy he wouldn't be able to see her. Sonia went around very sad because the doctor was going to pack. She wanted to help him but she couldn't. When he was ready, I went in to his room and gave him my hand and said, "Goodbye, Doctor." He looked at me and wouldn't let go of my hand, and we both understood what we wanted to do. Then he went downstairs. Sonia was sitting, very sad. He couldn't say anything because Tante Bernice was there, and so he was afraid to kiss Sonia's hand. Then he went out of the house.

In Kiev Misha went to his parents'

house. "And how is Katrina?" his mother asked. He nodded his head, she's all right. When his father and two brothers came in, they asked about Katrina also. Misha didn't say a word. He couldn't eat. He was choking. His mother asked him, "Misha, what is it?"

Finally he said, "I don't know."

His mother asked, "You don't know how wonderful Katrina is?"

"No. I don't know."

His father said, "Why don't you know? Is she fine? Is she very learned? We know how she is. What more do you want?"

Misha said, "Papasha, when you don't see a girl very often and you don't go with her very long, how can you know what you feel?"

His father said, "You go to her house and you talk to her for hours. You can find out what you need to know."

"Yes, that's true. But when I didn't see her for a week, two weeks . . . I was very busy in the hospital and she came with her mother and she was angry at me. She talked to me like I was her husband already, and that I don't like. She saw

458

that the hospital was full of patients. She told me she wouldn't let me be in the hospital so long. She comes before the patients. And she told me to come Sunday, early, because they would all go to church."

"She told you such things?"

Did she tell him? Or did he dream it? He put his hand on his head and didn't know what to do. His mother said to him, "So tired, you work too hard. Come, my son, you'll go rest and then we'll talk." She took him by the arm and brought him to the bedroom. Alone, he closed his eyes and saw Sonia, he spoke her name so loud that he got scared himself and jumped up quickly to see if somebody heard. Then he fell asleep, he was so tired and lonesome for Sonia.

Later the maid woke him up when it was time to eat dinner. He washed himself and put on fresh clothes and went into the living room. Who was there? His friends from college. So happy, they grabbed each other and wouldn't part. Then they talked about the old days and they laughed about how they drank vodka together and danced on the tables. Misha asked if they were married already? No one yet, but one friend, Yakob, said he was going with a nurse. "She works with me in the same hospital." Later, when Misha was talking with Yakob alone, Yakob said softly, "I have to tell you she is Jewish."

Misha dropped a piece cheese from his mouth. "What?" he said.

"The nurse in the hospital, she is Jewish. It makes you angry?"

Misha klopped his hand on his back, like Yakob was choking. "Angry? How can I be angry? Tell me, who is she? How did it happen? Do you love her? Will you marry her? What will you do?"

"By you it's all right? If I would marry her, you'll still be my friend?"

"My God, we'll be closer, brothers, blood in blood! Tell me, Yakob! What is she?"

Yakob had to drink more vodka, a big glass, so he wouldn't be ashamed of the tears in his eyes. "Ah," he said, "so pretty, with brown braids, a face like an angel with red cheeks and inside she is full of life and happiness. Her father is in the wood business, and her parents are still young people and not so religious. I go to them, they treat me very nicely. Her name is Olga Coneus. In Jewish it's Cohen.'' Again he poured a glass of vodka down his throat. This time Misha had to klop him on his back. Yakob was choking. ''We are in love very much, but I am afraid of my parents. They don't know about me, that I go with Olga.''

But Misha's father was coming, so they stopped talking. ''You shouldn't separate for so long next time,'' he said. ''Maybe Misha will come here to set up his practice. Maybe with a family he'll need to be near his friends and his parents. Misha, you told Yakob about your girl?''

Like snow Misha's face, but he smiled with his lips and said, ''In the little town where my hospital is there is a girl —''

His father said, ''Her father is my friend, a priest, too. When we went to visit Misha, we stayed by them and they became acquainted, Misha and Katrina. She is a fine girl, very nice. Not so long, you'll dance at Misha's wedding. Ha?'' And he klopped Misha's back with his hand and laughed and poured out more vodka for everyone.

Misha wrote to Sonia. The letters were addressed to me because I used to write to the big cities, to my friends. So she read them in my room, no one should hear. He wrote everything that was going on with his friend, how he has a Jewish girl who is a nurse and she works in the same hospital. He is lonesome for Sonia so much he can't stay away any longer. He will look for furniture, and when he buys he will leave. And he wrote a letter to Katrina, not a love letter, and she wrote and asked him why he didn't say something to her, like he forgot they were engaged. She was very hurt, she said. Misha showed her letter to his parents. "I am not her husband yet and she writes to me and bawls me out." Up and down the room he walked, like in a march, and like a handkerchief he squeezed the letter in his hand.

His mother held out her arms to him. "My son, why should you be so upset? You are right, she is not your wife yet."

"Mamusha!" he yelled, and he grabbed

her in his arms. "Not yet she isn't. Not yet!" And he picked her up and kissed her.

"She will be," his father said.

Misha almost dropped his mother. He looked at his father and then, with his eyes wide, he breathed like he was running, and said, "No, Father, she's not for me."

His father opened his eyes wide. "No? You don't want to marry Katrina?"

"I can't marry her."

"Why not? I talked it over with her father. I gave my word to him. He made the agreement, Misha will marry his daughter. What do you mean you can't marry her?"

"I don't love her."

"Love?" His father turned so pale he couldn't say one word more, and he stood like a stone. The mother went over to him and led him by the arm to a chair.

"It will work out for the best," she said.

Like a furnace catching fire in his chest, the father roared from his seat,

with his fist in the air, "He will marry
her! On my promise I won't turn back!
A holy promise!"

11

So Misha came back to our little town. When he arrived he couldn't talk to Sonia because her parents were watching. He could only look at her and smile. The first night we walked, Sonia and I, like we would visit my sister, Golde, and we ran quickly to the woods. Already it was dark. We saw a tiny red spot by a tree and we heard a voice calling, "Sonia, Sonia, Sonia," and we ran to Misha. They were hugging and kissing and crying for happiness. Sonia couldn't hold it in. I stood and watched and listened.

Misha said to her, "You are my only one, my good one, the most beautiful in the whole world. Why can't you be mine forever? Why has God brought us together if we are of two different religions? Dearest, I will do for you what you want as long as you are mine. I don't want to live without you. I can't marry Katrina, she's not for me. I can't stand to be in her company. I will tell her that on Sunday. She doesn't know I am here yet. We must do something. I can't live this way without you."

We were sitting on the grass and listening to his love talk. He told us about Kiev and his friend, who was also going with a Jewish girl. All of a sudden I realized it was late and that we had to go home. But Misha couldn't pull himself away from Sonia. Then he took a little box from his pocket. He opened it and took out a gold locket and put it around Sonia's neck. She held him around and kissed him for the present and he kissed her and said she was worth the whole world. Then he took out another little box and opened it and said, "Anuta, for you." A tiny pin with a red stone. Still it shows the light today. Then I didn't care. I threw my arms around his neck and gave him such a kiss.

He took us out of the woods, not walking but running, so late it was, and he went home while we went to my house. Inside the door we looked at our presents. "How can I put on the locket? My parents will ask me where I got such a thing," Sonia said.

"I will tell them Golde's husband brought them from Kiev. He got them special from a good customer," I said.

Sonia clutched the locket to her heart and tears poured down her red cheeks. "Oh, Anuta," she said, "you could go crazy not to love such a wonderful man like Misha."

"Maybe I will go crazy," I told her. "What should I do? I will never marry a goy. My parents would kill me, and they would kill Misha. I can't!"

I said, "I don't know what I should tell you to do. Now we have to go to bed."

Sunday Misha went to see Katrina. When he came in, she ran like a bird and fell on his neck and kissed him. He was like a statue and he didn't move, his arms hanging down. She pulled herself away from his and yelled, "Papasha, Mamusha, come in! Misha is here!" The parents came in and gave him their hands, they were happy to see him. The father asked how's by Misha's father, the mother asked if he bought the furniture, when will it come, because Katrina didn't want to go back and study. She wanted only to marry, to make a home right away. Why should they wait? Misha was so tsetummelt, so mixed up in the head, he didn't know what he should say to them. The mother said he would eat with them, they wanted to ask him about everything.

"You are very kind," he said. "I came as soon as I could, so many patients I have, you know, so long I was away. It's full in the office, they're dying."

Katrina said, "How could you go away, you didn't write me, and now you can't stay for supper? Come, come, you'll sit, you'll eat good things — look how skinny! — you'll tell us what is happening in Kiev. You heard maybe something about the Tsar? Take hold of my arm like a good boy, Misha. Mamusha, did you tell the cook already?"

"Excuse me. I can't, I have patients —" Misha said.

"They didn't die when you were in

Kiev, so they won't die while you're eating supper. You're the only doctor in the hospital? You don't have Shasha? Let him take care of the patients and give you a chance so you can have a minute by your family."

"Shasha can't stand on his feet, he's so tired from work. I have to be there."

"It's more important you should be there, you'll leave the bride in the house alone? I haven't seen you for a month, you can't stay two minutes?"

He grabbed his hat and his cane and he bowed to the parents. "Excuse me. I'm sorry."

Katrina ran after him into the street. "Misha! Misha!" she cried. But he bent his head like in a storm and he went away fast.

And that's the way it was. When it got dark, he sat in his office without any light. I was sitting and looking out the window, and I saw it was dark by the doctor. Then I saw Neeseh go and look at the hospital, and I went outside to the porch. "Why are you looking at the hospital?" I asked him.

Neeseh jumped and then he looked toward me. "Where is Sonia?"

"How do I know? I am not a spy."

"I never saw Sonia go out without you."

"Is she blind? Is she a cripple?"

Then he came closer so he could see me. He put his hands in his pockets. "I don't hate you," he started to say. He was bending closer, to see me. "I only watch for your own good. All right, who cares what Sonia is doing by the doctor? Let her ruin her life. You have to ruin your life also?"

"So who cares?"

All of a sudden somebody was coming toward us. "Arrh!" Neeseh said.

Shaneh it was. "Neeseh? It's you?" she said. He wouldn't answer. She said, "Did you see —" but she saw I was there, so she stopped.

Finally she asked, "Did you see them?"

"Who?" Neeseh said.

"Sonia. The doctor."

"Did *you* see them?" he asked.

"I didn't see them but they are both gone."

"Gone? Where could they go?"

"Into the woods."

Neeseh waved his hands in the dark. "Liar! You always tell lies!" Like he was in a hurry, he went quickly to his house. Then Shaneh started to cry.

"Why do you always tell lies?" I asked her.

With her hand on her face to wipe away the tears, she said, "You are always going together, you and Sonia."

"So? You have to tell lies then? You go all the time to see Neeseh and you tell him lies. I want to know why. It doesn't bother me if you talk about me because you know I won't be here long and my parents don't listen to you. But you talk about Sonia, that's too much. Why do you always run to Neeseh? Do you think he loves you?"

Oy, she cried like I was hitting her. "I can tell you he hates you for your lies," I said.

Like she was swallowing the words, Shaneh said, "He hates me. He loves you, that's why. That's why I follow, to see where you go."

"Don't follow me and don't tell lies to Neeseh. Maybe he could love you also. You should be nice, then people will love you. When you'll be mean, they'll be mean to you."

Then someone came out of the hospital, and I said to Shaneh, "Go home now. Go leave people alone, they won't bother you. Go, quick!" She ran away to her house. Who was coming? The doctor? I couldn't see, it was so dark. Finally I could see it was Sonia coming out of the doctor's office.

"Sonia?" I said.

Like I was shooting a bullet at her, she held her heart, and then she came toward me. "Please!" she whispered. "All the world can hear you!"

"You think no one watches where you go?"

"Oy, somebody was watching? Who? Neeseh? Shaneh? Did they see?"

"You shouldn't go alone, it's not safe."

"Oh, Eatkeh, I couldn't help it. He came by on the street, I saw him, so unhappy. He had to talk, to see me, so what could we do? We went into his office."

"You talked in the dark?"

"We didn't know the time."

"Couldn't you see how dark everything is?"

Sonia yelled out, "Don't ask me!" and like a ghost she was running away, her scarf waving behind her. What did she want from me? I had to help her get in more trouble? What could I do? Let them talk in the dark in his office. Didn't they know people were spying on them? I had to be like a soldier outside on guard? Anyway, I was busy. I made up my mind I would write to my brother Velvel — William — in America. He ran away to America because he didn't want to be in the Tsar's army. For twenty-five years you had to be in and they tried to make you a Christian. We had four brothers who had gone to America, and now they were sending us money to come also. Pa and Ma didn't want to. How could they leave their home? In the end some went, some didn't, God keep them. But now I had it in my heart to go. If Velvel could help me, I would go.

That's the way it went one week, and I didn't see the doctor or very much of Sonia. The doctor started to fix up his house nicely, his furniture came on the wagon, and he was very busy. He saw that he could move away from Sonia's house; but he couldn't find a woman to cook for him. So, in the shtetl lived the Kanage's son. He used to have what they call here in America a ranch, and he wasn't married yet, very good-looking, and he had butlers and he used to go to Warsaw, where he got a cook. She was short and fat. Her name was Hilda. She used to come to us to buy fish, cheese, butter and milk, and she used to talk with my mother, always crying because she was alone. My mother had a good heart and she used to listen.

My mother told her, "If you'll go to the Russian doctor to cook, then you can be your own boss." And that appealed to her.

One day, while I was sitting on the porch reading a book, I heard Misha call my name from his window. I went right over to his office and sat down with him. First he asked me how Sonia is, he was worried. "When I lived there, I saw her more. Now I see her only once a week maybe, I can't stand it. I can't sleep or eat. Anuta, listen. I have a friend in Kiev. He is coming to visit me. He is an officer. We went to college together. I want he should see how beautiful and educated Sonia is. He'll tell my parents, maybe they'll understand better if something should happen. I want to make a party for him on Sunday evening. I'll invite Shasha, with the nurse in the hospital, and you'll come with Sonia. I can play the guitar very nicely and Shasha can play the balalaika. We will enjoy and be safe, nothing will happen. Anuta, it will be all right." He looked at me, his eyes like in a fever. "Can you? Can she? Will you help me out?" he begged.

"I could even tell my parents," I said. "I'm not afraid. But with Sonia, what can we do? All her life she will be the same."

"You can arrange it," he said. "She can visit you or your sister Golde, like always."

"Golde doesn't like to lie for us anymore. She is angry with Shasha and she wants him to move to another house now."

Misha got up, his fists pressing against his head, and he walked back and forth across the room. "What to do? Such a town, where people are so fanatic!"

I said, "I will talk it over with Golde. We'll see how it comes out."

Misha grabbed both my hands and kissed them. "Anuta! I know I can leave it to you."

When I went out the old women sitting there saw me and started to run like poisoned mice. This time like they couldn't stop, such yelling and running and raising their hands to the sky. All of a sudden they were in front of my house and they started to pound on the door, such a tumult, and everybody came out to the street to see what was going on. When my parents came out, the women without the teeth and with hairs growing on their warts started to yell, and they pointed their crooked fingers at me, a thing of bad luck, how I wasn't a decent girl, how I went to the doctor's office, I was an embarrassment to all the Jewish girls, they had to chase me out of our shtetl, or our daughters will be old maids.

And then my mother waved her arms and yelled at the women, "What do you want from the doctor? If it wasn't for the doctor you would be dead a long time already! Does he ask money from you when you don't pay him? You want for a doctor an anti-Semite? You should get down on your knees and thank God that the doctor does so much for the Jews! You talk, you raise a tumult for the whole town, it's a shame for the goyim!"

The doctor was outside, too, but he couldn't understand one word because everybody was yelling in Yiddish. Sonia looked at him with her big black eyes and he didn't take his eyes off her face until everybody went away.

In the evening Sonia came to sit in my room. I told her Misha wants her and me to come to his house so he can introduce us to his friend. Sonia raised up her face. "Oy, vey!" With tears she tried to see me. "How could I go? It can't be!" she cried. "You went through such a scandal today, the whole town was going on wheels."

I said, "If you don't want to go, you don't have to."

"How can I go? You'll pull out all my teeth? I should die, then you'll take my body to his house?"

"A way we'll find, a plan."

"What can we do? Golde won't help now. I don't blame her. Always we want her to tell lies for us."

"You'll talk to Osher," I said.

"Osher?"

"He can't take his eyes off you," I told her.

"He's a nice boy, Osher. But how can he —"

"You'll go out with him."

"With Osher?"

"You'll talk to him and he'll take you for a walk. Maybe you'll visit his aunt. Come Sunday in the evening, you'll go out with him, everybody will see, and he'll go to his aunt. And we'll go on to the party."

"Oy, oy." Like in her face no blood was showing. "Osher? Why will Osher do such a thing?"

"You appeal to him. Maybe he loves you even."

"How can I ask him to do such a thing?"

"You ask."

"I can't. My bones shake inside."

"I'm not scared. If everything goes the way we plan, then everything will be smooth."

"Poor Osher."

"Poor Osher? For Osher it'll be a blessing, like the Torah on his shoulder. For you it will be a mitzva, a good thing."

So, when she carried dinner to the table, Sonia smiled at Osher. He looked behind himself. He thought she smiled at somebody else. And every time he came in from work, she spoke very nicely to him, and Neeseh watched the whole thing. Finally she said to Osher, "A nice day. Will you take a walk?" It hurt her so much to ask him, but what could she do if she didn't have another way? So they walked, everybody could see, it was all right. Another day they walked. Came Friday she told him they should go see his aunt. Her husband was a tailor, very poor, and Osher went there for Shabbos.

The aunt and the uncle made tea and listened to Sonia, how she talked nicely, and they looked at Osher, maybe he would make a good match finally. On the way back to her house, Sonia said to him, "Will you take me again to your aunt's?" He made with his head yes. "Sunday in the evening?" He couldn't understand what happened all of a sudden, but he said yes, yes, yes, he would. "Please, you'll dress very nicely?" she asked him.

Came Sunday. When Sonia changed her dress after supper, Neeseh said, "Where are you going tonight you should get so dolled up?" She didn't answer him. Then Neeseh yelled at her, "You think you'll go out with Eatkeh somewhere, to see somebody? Over my dead body you'll go!" Still she didn't answer him, and so he ran to their mother, in the living room, and he screamed she lets Sonia go out with me.

Tante Bernice said, "She's not going with Eatkeh. She goes with Osher to his aunt. He appeals to her. So? A nice quiet boy. It won't hurt her. So I told her to go ahead."

Neeseh couldn't find anything to say, so he went out of the house.

When Osher came in with his white shirt and his wrinkled coat, he didn't look at Sonia but down at the floor. "You look very nice," she told him. A fire broke out on his face. Then Sonia asked her mother, "It's all right we'll come back in a few hours?"

Tante Bernice said, "So long as I know where you are, it's all right."

It was dark already. Everybody was watching Sonia go out with Osher. He walked so he wouldn't touch her and he looked at the ground. What could he say? Not a word came out. Sonia said, "Osher, will there be snow?" He shook his head no, no, there wouldn't be any snow. "Maybe the moon will be a good light for us." He looked up at the sky. You couldn't see the moon yet. They walked, Sonia like she was running a long time. She took little breaths and little clouds came out of her mouth.

"Osher, I want to ask you something," Sonia said. "But nobody has to know it. If you swear you won't tell a person —"

He looked at her. She felt so bad, like a cold sweat was upon her. "Osher —" She took him by the hand. She could feel him start to shake in her fingers. How could she make a plan with him? Maybe she would hurt him.

"Nu?" he said.

Sonia shook her head no, nothing. Pieces of white fell from the sky and made little cold spots on their cheeks. Sonia raised her face — oy, she made a wish — take out the worries which set like stones on her head. Never mind, she would go to Osher's aunt and have a cup tea. And Misha, let *him* worry. He would think she didn't care, she wouldn't come to him. And Eatkeh, so easy for her to go live her own life. What to do? Marry the teacher? Better to be dead. Maybe she'll marry Osher, why not? At least she wouldn't have such pains in every part of her body.

Then she squeezed his hand and stopped walking. She looked at his eyes. "Osher," she said, "I appeal to you a little bit?"

Like she grabbed his throat, he couldn't talk.

"Do you like me, Osher?" she asked him.

He made a nod with his head.

"If you swear you won't tell a person, I will love you," she said.

So terrible she felt. She saw his mouth open up, but she didn't hear a word. It moved, his mouth finally. "What?" he said. But like she was deaf to the world. Like in a bad dream, the whole sky was swimming and the ground made black and white patches, an animal, a cow maybe, maybe a bird, a crow was calling, ah, ah, "What? What?" It was Osher. She jumped inside herself. "What?" he said.

From a dream she heard how she talked. "Osher? You'll swear by God?"

"You want I should swear, I'll swear."

"Swear to me by God. Then I will tell you what I want from you."

"I swear to you by God."

"You know my cousin Eatkeh?" she asked.

"How could I not know Eatkeh?"

"They don't say nice things about her."

"What do they know?"

"I love my cousin. She is going back to

the big cities. I want to see her but my parents and my brother don't like it. Tonight she wants to tell me what she'll do and what plans she makes for her future. How can I see her without my parents and Neeseh knowing? If they find out they'll make trouble for her."

"So," Osher said, "we can go together to see her."

"No!" She jumped. "We can't! I mean, she doesn't want — she has to see me by myself. Oy, vey, it's no good, it's no good!" She began to cry like she would cry her heart out.

My God, my God, he didn't know what to do, he couldn't put a finger on her. "Shah, shah, it'll be all right," Osher said softly. "Don't cry. Listen, you'll go to her without me. Why not? No one will know. I'll tell them we paid a visit to my aunt. I'll make by myself. Who talks to my aunt? No one. What for? You'll go see your cousin and I'll wait by my aunt. When you come there, we'll go back to your house like we were together all evening at my aunt's."

"Osher!" she said. "So good you are!

Osher! So we'll be good friends and I will give you good things to eat every time and you will have a ruble in your pocket."

Even in the dark, with the moon coming, he was blushing. He smiled all over his face, so pleased he was. "I won't tell anybody," he said. And so, together they walked to his aunt's house, and Sonia touched his arm and smiled at him, and he went inside. Sonia started to run like a child.

By the doctor's house I was waiting already. The house was surrounded by a lot of trees, and it shined in the blue water like the trees were standing in the lake. The house had red shutters and the sheet-iron roof was painted green. And there was a white fence. Everything looked beautiful and rich. The doctor kept his house like they do in Kiev.

I was waiting until Sonia came. A long time, hours I thought, maybe she got too scared, maybe Neeseh spied on her. Finally, I went up the door to knock. "Wait!" someone said. It was Sonia. She couldn't catch her breath. "Eatkeh! Eatkeh, we'll go home. Please. Osher is waiting by his aunt. Go with me."

"What're you saying?" I asked. "Here we are. How can we go?"

"My parents will kill me. Neeseh will kill me."

"You saw somebody follow you?"

"No, but —"

"So who will know?" I asked, and I knocked.

Hilda, the doctor's cook, opened the door. When she saw us she couldn't believe it. Sonia covered her mouth with her hand. Hilda was standing like a dog by the door.

Then Misha came and said, "Let in my best friends." And he came over and held us both. Like she was mad, Hilda went to the kitchen. "I was upset because you hadn't come yet. Thank God now," Misha said. He couldn't wait, he took us into the living room. An officer was standing, tall, and dressed in a white uniform, and he gave his hand to Sonia. He didn't take his eyes off her. On the couch was sitting the nurse. She was over thirty, tall and with yellow hair. Next to her was Shasha.

Misha, meanwhile, poured wine. Sonia

got very red on her cheeks, and her black eyes sparkled like two diamonds. The officer told Misha in Russian that he never saw such beautiful girls.

In Russian I said, "Thank you for your nice compliments."

"You are Russian?" he asked me.

"No, I learned Russian in the big cities," I said.

Then Hilda put out all the food, the good fish from my mother, the baked things. Misha said, "Sonia makes marvelous things."

But Sonia looked at Hilda and said, "I think Hilda does better than me. Such tasty things she makes."

So pleased was Hilda, but she kept looking at Sonia, who didn't feel good because Hilda's eyes were looking right through her. But then Hilda finally went into the kitchen.

Misha went up to Sonia and said, "What is the matter, Dearest?" She felt she was going to cry from his loving words. Then he gave her a glass water and put in some powder. Sonia drank it and felt better, and so did Misha.

We were all talking but I didn't feel comfortable, like something wasn't right. I heard somebody close a door. Who could it be? I peeked into the kitchen but I couldn't see Hilda. Where did she go? Maybe to bring in more wood for the fire. I didn't want to scare anyone, so I didn't say a word.

Candles burned in every room. The clock with a long chain hung in the front room. Here, it is the "grandpa's clock." Soon the doctor closed all the shutters so no one could see what was going on in his house. So happy he was, he kissed everybody and even started to dance. We all went to the table to eat, delicious it smelled, the cooked geese and the fish. Sonia ate only the fish. Red roses were on the table. Misha took one and put it in Sonia's hair. It was so pretty on her that his friend said very quietly, "I never saw such a beautiful girl." You almost couldn't hear him.

So we were eating and drinking, and then both doctors took out balalaikas and played them, and everybody was singing. Misha sang beautiful songs, always with his eyes on Sonia. Then the officer jumped out of his chair and yelled, "Doctor, my tovarish, play a waltz!" Both the doctors played Viennese waltzes, and the officer went over to Sonia to dance. She looked at Misha. He nodded that she could dance with his best friend. She raised herself up and turned around like a bird and forgot all her troubles. She couldn't see anyone except her beautiful Misha, like she was flying with him through the sky, and she began to sing, "How beautiful is the sky, with the beautiful shiny stars, and how quiet is the night and calm. How two souls are flying together and how the shiny stars light up their love path. No one follows them, no one is shouting. How nice and quiet, so it is in the skies." She kept singing: "God watch me with my life, the way I am in love. It is good to be in love and to be loved, such a pure clean love like mine." And, like she was in a dream, she jumped awake, her face burning. Misha stopped playing. He went over to her and kissed her hands.

Then I heard the clock pound twelve

times. I yelled out, "Sonia! Do you hear?"

Everybody stopped to listen. In the kitchen the door was closing.

"It's all right," Misha said.

Sonia said, "I'm afraid for Osher. He'll worry, he'll go to my house to see if I'm safe. My life will be finished!"

Misha was scared. He got our coats and everybody started to say good-bye to Misha's friend. Misha didn't want us to go so fast, but we couldn't help it. On the porch he said to Sonia, "Life won't be right. You are my love." And he couldn't stop, he kissed her on her lips and she put her arms around him. Then, in the light of the doorway, something was rising like a bear. I saw the teeth and I heard a noise come from its mouth, and like a long arm something came down, with a tooth in the middle, right on Sonia's back. Sonia fell and let out a scream, and Neeseh was bending over her with a big board in his hands, a two-by-four, an old piece of wood with nails in it. Me, I didn't know how, but I was hitting Neeseh and kicking him, and he started to pull me by my two braids and he hit me so hard I screamed and fell to the floor. Then Shasha gave Neeseh such a hit on the face that he turned dark in the eyes and blood ran out of his mouth. Misha was yelling "Help me!" and he pulled out the wood with the nails. From Sonia's back came a lot of blood. The officer would have killed Neeseh but Misha said, "I need something to bandage," and he took Sonia in his arms. The officer pulled the tablecloth from the table and tore it into long pieces. Misha raised Sonia's blouse and wrapped the cloth around her.

"Now I'll go kill that man," the officer said.

Misha said, "No. He's her brother."

Like I was dreaming, with Shasha and the nurse holding me, I yelled at Neeseh, "You killed her! You killed her! God will punish you!" He stood like a stone, he couldn't talk. I yelled at him, "Dreck! Chozzer!" I tried to hit him and he fell down in the snow, on his knees, and then like a dog on the ice he tried to go, slipping and slipping, and then he went away into the dark.

The officer ran to bring the three horses and hook them up to the sleigh, like a droshky but with skis to run on the snow. Like babies in blankets, they carried us, bundled up in the sleigh. The officer yelled at the horses and we went so fast I couldn't see, the snow went inside my eyes. Misha held Sonia close, and he kissed her and whispered in her ear.

In the hospital Misha put her in the best room. My face was black from the hit Neeseh gave me. Whenever I lifted my head, I fell back into Shasha's arms. "We'll make a bed for you, too," he said.

When I heard him I got up and said, "I feel better. I want to go home. My parents don't know what happened to me. It's better I should go home."

Shasha said, "I'll go with you. If I see that boy, I'll cut his hands so he'll never hit again."

We walked a little bit and I fell, so Shasha took me in his arms and carried me to our house. Everybody was sleeping. But my mother heard me tell Shasha how badly my head hurts. She ran out in her nightgown and screamed, "What happened? What is with my child?'' She held me and started to cry very quietly so my father wouldn't hear. They took me to my room and put me in bed. My mother asked Shasha what happened and he told her everything. My mother thanked him and Shasha went out. It was three o'clock in the morning.

Next day my mother came to look at me. She didn't tell my father anything. In the shtetl they said that Sonia's father caught her with the doctor. Everybody added to it and said she was going to have a baby by the doctor. She lay in the hospital for three weeks and Misha didn't leave her for a minute. My uncle and aunt were afraid to go see her because Misha said he wouldn't allow it and that he would shoot Neeseh.

Meanwhile, my mother went to her sister and asked, "Where is Neeseh?"

"Why do you want Neeseh?" my aunt said.

"How come you don't know that your son almost killed Eatkeh?"

"What're you saying?"

"I'll arrest him. I have a good witness,

the doctor carried her home in his arms. She is so beaten up you can't see her face."

"She shouldn't go at night to the doctor's house to visit, she won't be in trouble. Don't you know how everybody speaks very badly about her? She doesn't conduct herself right."

Then my mother gave such a yell that my aunt was scared. "You watch your daughter, not my daughter! My daughter won't bring a momzer to me! We know who she visits, she doesn't hide from us! I want to teach your son how to be a mensch, not to go in and beat people up before he knows anything. Everybody talks about *him*, and they talk badly about you and your husband! You are bitter people and you don't even know how to live with others. You are my sister but you are common, like an animal, you and your husband are so stupid, and your mean son, no one wants to look at him!" Then my mother spit in her sister's face and went out of the house. She gave such a slam with the door that the glass fell out of the window and everybody ran in from their rooms to ask my aunt what was going on.

And then Neeseh came in with a black eye and a swollen face. He couldn't go out of the house and he couldn't go to the doctor. His mother cried, "Why did you beat up Eatkeh? The tante will arrest you and the whole town will know and they'll talk about you! It'll be so bad you won't find a place in the shtetl! For what, for what?"

Meanwhile, Misha didn't go to see Katrina. He forgot all about her. She couldn't wait so long for him, so she talked with her mother and they both went to see him. When they came in, Shasha went into Sonia's room to tell Misha that Katrina and her mother were waiting in the office. Misha stayed with Sonia and she kept quiet and didn't take her eyes off him. They looked at one another like they knew what was going on, but they didn't talk. Finally, he let go of her hand.

"A minute. Then I'll be back," he said.

In the hall Shasha was saying, "By the Jewish people, the children have to marry who the parents want."

Said Misha, "It looks like that."

So he went into the office and bowed and kissed the mother's hand. Katrina got up and went to him and kissed his cheek. Shasha went out to his own office.

"Why don't you come to see me? Almost three weeks again," Katrina said. "How can you be like that?"

"I'll come," he said. "I am sorry. Forgive me, I have to see my patients now."

"Shasha can't see them?" Katrina asked. "He sits in his office. Let him take care of them."

"He has to write the reports. He is very busy also. Excuse me."

"One minute more you can talk to me."

"More than a minute already. Excuse me. A doctor is a doctor. What can I do?" And he went out and she yelled at him he should stay. But he didn't stop. He was walking away and thinking how she could talk to him like that. I'm not her husband yet and she's telling me what to do. She's not like Sonia, with her sweet smile and good soul. Why should it happen to Sonia? She has to take so much for her foolish parents. They want to dray her head — it means to bother her — with the teacher whom she can't stand.

Then he came into Sonia's room and talked over with her what the priest's wife and Katrina had said. "Katrina thinks I am her husband already. She has made a big mistake. I'll never marry her." Sonia started to cry and he told her, "My dearest, everything will work out the way we want it. First we have to see you are in good health."

Next day Misha said to Hilda, "Here are your wages. Now take your clothes and leave and never come back." She didn't know where she was and couldn't say a word. Finally, she packed up her things and came to us. When she saw my mother, she fell on her shoulder and started to cry. My mother said right away, "Nu, it's your own fault. Because of you, Neeseh beat up my daughter. Why did you do it? You lost your job, and it was such a good one for you. Why, Hilda, why did you do it? Sonia and Eatkeh were so good to you."

Hilda was crying, she didn't know

herself why. She said, "I was jealous of Sonia. The doctor always used to talk about her cooking. I went to her parents to tell on her and I saw Neeseh. Now I don't know what to do."

After two days I could get up, so I went to see Sonia in the hospital. We kissed each other and cried. Sonia spoke to me: "How good you are, you do so much for me. What can I do? Maybe there is only one way for me — to die and end such a life. Why me? To have such parents and such a stupid brother."

"You shouldn't talk," I said.

"But I go crazy, I can't do anything."

I said, "Listen. All the time my brothers in America write we should come. They say for the girls it isn't good to go to America if they can't do anything. Me, I can sew and make clothes. You can cook and bake and make clothes. You and Misha could go with me to America and there Misha can be a Jew."

She cried, all over her face were tears. "Oh, God," she said, "how can I?" She was shaking her head no. "Something won't let me do it, to get married to a

Christian. Even if he will be a Jew. Still he wouldn't be. I'm afraid of God." After all, she was from a small town, so how could she think differently?

I said, "Do what is best for you. I'll write you how things are in America."

She was crying but I ran outside. All of a sudden it came to me — I would go to America! Why not? It came to me on the street and I yelled out of happiness, "I'm going to America! I'm going to America!"

Then I ran back inside the hospital to see Misha. I told him my plan. "And why not? You can bring Sonia, you'll be free in America, no one will bother you."

"Free?" He put his hand on his chin. "What can I do in America?"

"Do? You'll be a doctor like here."

"In America I'll be nothing. First, I don't know how to talk there. Second, I can't be a doctor in America, they don't allow foreigners. In the next place, I couldn't even make a living. What can I do, ride a horse? In America they have plenty of horse riders."

"You'll go, you'll find out. Don't you want to be with Sonia?"

"More than my life. But will she go?"

I raised my shoulder. "You know better than me."

"All right! I don't care, let me work with the shovel, we'll go. We'll go!" he said, and he grabbed my hands and pulled me toward him. "You'll talk to Sonia. Make her see it'll be all right, we'll be together. You have to!"

I ran to Sonia and told her what Misha said. "He'll do what he can, any work. And he'll turn Jewish, don't worry. He's got money now, he'll take with him enough for both."

"I can't," she said.

"You don't love him?" I asked her.

"I love him so much I'll do anything for him. But not go to America."

"So you'll hide yourself with him the rest of your life in this town? I won't be here. Who's going to help you?"

"Don't hurt me, Eatkeh! Help me! I'm lost! I'm afraid!"

"I'll help you. You'll come to America with me and Misha. You'll be with us. Why do you have to worry?"

She was crying. "I can't go."

"Why? Excuses you give, so bad I never heard. Misha won't be Jewish, you can't marry a Christian. *Misha* you'll marry. In America no one will bother you with such foolishness."

"I won't make him throw away his life."

"Why are you so scared? Listen." I put my face close to hers. "If you love him, you'll go!"

"I'll kill myself!" she said.

"Why?"

"I have inside me a baby!"

Oy, why couldn't I see? Like my hand in front of my face, like her face on mine. "All right. Now it's not a problem, you have to marry," I said.

She was shaking her head no, she wouldn't. "He'll lose his job here and in America he wouldn't find another. I'll bring him nothing but tsuris," she said. Miseries she would bring.

"Now he'll marry you right away, no question."

"No! Eatkeh!" She grabbed my face, my cheeks, pinching. "If you tell him, I'll — I'll kill myself. Let God hear me, I swear to God, I will kill myself if you say a word," Sonia cried.

Such a swear, like a curse on me, like I would die also if something came out of my mouth about her. I said, "May God fall on my head if I say one word."

Then she lay there like she didn't have blood in her body. "I want to die," she said. "How can I live without him? But with him I can't live either."

"Wait," I said. "You'll see. Something will happen and you'll be so happy you won't believe it. I promise." For a long time after she cried in my arms.

12

Finally, Misha couldn't keep Sonia in the hospital any longer. She had to go home. So she lay in her bed and I went to see her, and I brought her letters from Misha. Her parents wouldn't allow him to come in. One week later he wrote that he had to go to Kiev to see his parents. His father wasn't so young, he didn't feel good, and he wanted to see his son. Misha wrote to Sonia: "My dearest, it will be very hard for me to leave you here. I'll be so lonesome. How can I leave you? It lays heavy on my chest. I can't talk. I feel like my life is going down, and it is hard for me to part from you. I can't go on with my profession. I can't be good to my patients. Nothing lays in my head, only you, my dear Sonia."

It hurt me that they were from two

different worlds, and it was a tragedy to look at his face and see how he was fading from her, and on her face how she was dying for him. She couldn't make up her mind what to do. So Misha kept going around without a head. I decided to ask my mother if she would let Misha see Sonia in our house to say good-bye. Why not? So I told them both they should come, no one will know. And if they know, then let them. My parents would protect them. My mother put out a white tablecloth in my room and she carried in food for Sonia and Misha. It was Sunday and my mother brought all the good things left from Shabbos. She put out some wine and said, "Come." Misha took Sonia's hand and led her to the table and, like a gentleman, helped her sit down. Then he helped me, too. We started to eat but Sonia and I couldn't. My face was swollen still.

The whole afternoon Sonia and Misha sat. He tried to talk her into going to America with me. "If I can't have you, I will never get married," Misha told her. "Without you, my world is dark like the night, like the world is dead for me. I know your beautiful love is for me, but we are from two separate worlds. Why did God put us together if we can't enjoy our nice clean love? I saw beautiful women, educated, and I never loved them, but when I saw you I went out of my mind. With my work I can't go on. My head spins. I am getting crazy. My dearest, give me advice. Only you can help me. Let's go to America, where no one will know what we are, Jew or Christian. Sonia, please, save my life and yours. I will talk to your parents —"

Sonia cried like he was sticking a knife in her. "Don't talk! They'll kill me!" she sobbed. "Oy, I wish I could die!"

"They won't kill you," Misha said. "It takes only for you to love me. Then we can be together forever."

"My God, my God, I can't live without you!" Sonia fell into his arms and couldn't stop, like her lungs would come out through her mouth.

"So, if you love me," Misha said, "I am blessed."

And then she looked into his eyes.

"From me you'll die!" she said.

Misha didn't understand. "How can I die from you? From you I'll *live.*"

"They won't allow it, Misha," she said. "You have to leave me!"

He looked puzzled but he smiled at her. "They learned their lesson, dear. They are good and sorry for what they did to you. And Neeseh? He won't show his face."

"They'll send him to kill you."

"For what? Why? Ah, Dearest, you shouldn't worry."

Then Sonia grabbed his shirt. "I am not pure! I will give birth to a momzer!"

"Holy Mother Mary," Misha said. He was bending this way, that way, like he drank a full glass vodka and it made him shiver down and up, shaking him, like in a convulsion. He tried to stand up, but he sat right down again and put his hands around Sonia's face. "Tomorrow I'll go to the priest. He'll marry us," Misha said.

I yelled at him. "The priest? The priest will marry you?"

He didn't know where his mind was. "No. No. We'll go to the rabbi," he said.

"The rabbi?" I yelled. "The rabbi

won't marry you!'' Then I yelled at Sonia, "You had to tell him! You couldn't keep a secret!"

Misha spoke like a drunkard, like a man already dead. "We'll go to Kiev."

"What for?" I asked. "Who'll take you? Where will she be? In a house? You'll give parties with her? She'll have a child and no father?"

Then, at me all of a sudden, he yelled, "Shut up! Don't stick your nose in!"

Oy! Better he should cut my throat with a doctor's sharp knife. Sonia was crying like a baby and Misha buried his face in his hands. I couldn't take it anymore, and so I ran out of the room. I wouldn't let them see me cry. Let them go to Kiev. Let them go to the priest, to the rabbi. Let them go to America, I wouldn't stick my nose in. Such a life in the shtetl! I couldn't stand it anymore.

Outside I saw Neeseh. Like an old man, he was standing all worn out, his hand shaking in the wind. "Nu?" he said.

Like he was drowning in a lake and reaching up for me. "Anuta!" he said. I stopped to look at him. It was the first time he called me by my Russian name. "Where are you going?" he asked me.

"To America!"

He grabbed me with both his hands. "In America they need furniture also. A person can open a factory in America and make furniture."

"So, open," I told him.

He couldn't speak. Nothing would come out. A noise he made, whispering. All over his face he was sweating, his whole body was like a leaf. Finally, like a hoe moving in the dirt, he said, "You'll go with me."

"Go with you? Where will I go with you?" I asked him.

"America."

"America?"

Only with his head could he say yes.

"Don't be a shmegegge," I said, and I walked away from him.

He was yelling after me, "I can make a good life for you in America! A good life we can have! Anuta!"

Oy, God, I had to get out. I had to save myself, to make a life. What could I see in this world? I went right to my mother to tell her, and I got out my passport and ran to the man who made them, Moishe Tivel his name, and I said please make me a new one because mine was old. And he told me in two weeks I would get the new passport.

My mother cried and said, "Oy, vey, how hard it was for me to raise children. And where do they go now? They fly away like the birds for the winter, and when summer comes they fly back, but my children will never see their parents again."

Two weeks passed, and all of a sudden came two Russian policemen to our house. Like bears in the springtime, they blinked at us.

"You have a daughter, Anuta?" one of the Russians asked my father.

"There she is," my father said, pointing at me.

Right away they spoke to me and said I had to go to the police station. "Why? What do you want from her?" my father asked. But they just said I had to go. So I went and my parents came with me. Everybody in the shtetl saw them take me and they started to say that I am not a nice person and that they caught me with a Christian. When I went into the police station, they took me to another room and wouldn't let my parents in. There was a tall man in a uniform, with a big mustache. "Where is your passport?" he yelled. I didn't know what to say. "You better tell the truth!" he shouted.

I said gently, in Russian, "Your Honor, I took it to have a new passport made. My old one is expiring."

"You talk nice Russian," he said.

"Thank you."

"It looks like you aren't afraid like the other girls who go to America."

How did he know I was going. "I am not scared," I said.

"Why do you need to go to America, such a strange land? Isn't it good for you here?"

I said, "By us we have a lot of children, especially girls. We are eight sisters and six brothers, so it is very hard for our parents to give us all to eat. We have to work and I have to go to America to make money to send back. It'll be good for Russia."

He made a little laugh. "How old are you?"

I told him I was going to be fifteen.

"You already know too much for your years," he told me.

"I was in the big cities many years."

"So, why don't you go back there?"

I said, "Inspector, sir, if I go back, I'll need a new passport."

"Make a new passport and go back to the big cities then."

I made a bow with my head, all right.

"Who did you give your passport to?" he demanded.

I said his name was Moishe Tivel.

"How much money did you give him?"

"I don't know how much he will charge me. He told me he had to send it to the police."

"Who told you to talk like that?"

"I know myself because it isn't the first time my passport was expiring and I had to get a new one."

"Do you know where Moishe Tivel is?"

"He must be in his house."

"Do you know where he is?"

"No, mein Herr."

Finally, he opened the door and my mother went white like a sheet because I was so long in coming out. My father said to the officer, "Why are you so long with my child?"

His eyebrows, like a mustache, came down on his eyes and he yelled, "Get out! I don't want to see you! Your daughter is smarter than you! She knows how to talk, but don't you interrupt me." So he took me back inside the room. For three hours he kept me. It was very hard for me to tell him what he wanted. Then he asked me a question: "Do you hate the Tsar?"

I said, "How could you ask me such a question? He is our father and he gives everyone land and food and work, and so we love him. In our house hangs a picture of the Tsar and his family."

He started to smile underneath his blond mustache. I was not afraid, because they taught me in the big cities what to say if I should fall into the hands of the police. Then he said I couldn't get the new passport because they were looking for Moishe Tivel.

I felt very bad but I said, "If I can't

have a passport I'd have to stay home. It's not good for Russia like that."

He was rubbing his chin. Many girls, when they ask them, don't know the answers. In the end he said, "Such a smart one. I hope you won't be too smart for yourself. Go away now, and we'll see what's what. Don't let me catch you with something false."

I ran out of the room and we went home quick. Next day I went to Moishe Tivel when it was dark so no one would see. His wife cried that somebody squealed on her husband. So he ran away at night, but she didn't know about passports. I came back home and told my father. He said, "I understand what's going on. The police were looking for him and they couldn't find him, so now they dropped it altogether."

I said, "Pa, what will I do? I can't live here anymore. I have to go or I'll die in my head."

He said, "My child, I will do what I can. There comes an agent from Pinsk sometimes. He takes people who want to go to America, but he has to be quiet so no one should know."

"When will he come?" I asked him.

"He'll come, he'll come, you'll see."

Every day I asked again. Finally, after four days, comes in the house a little man like a peddlar, with a dirty beard, and his eyes wouldn't stay still. He told my parents he could deliver me right now from our little town to Detroit for two hundred rubles. I said right away that I want to go, I don't want to stay here. "It's not good for me because in the house there are still five sisters," I said.

"If you go, you'll have to steal across the border because you don't have a passport," my father reminded me.

The agent, like he had a cold, his nose dripping, said, "She won't be by herself. There are seven more girls in shtetls who will go." And then he waved a finger at me. "You aren't supposed to tell anyone you are going to America. First you have to get the passport. I could lose my life, but by me my people come first. For two hundred rubles I don't make a penny. It's a bargain."

So that's how it was. I didn't see Sonia

very much. One day, when I was running by the hospital, I saw Misha. How could I leave and not tell him? So I went into the hospital and he hugged me and asked, "Where do you hide? I don't see you. We worry all the time."

"I'm going to America."

He was smiling at me. "Yes, we'll convince Sonia finally."

"I'm going tomorrow."

Like I hit him in his eyes. "Tomorrow? How can it be tomorrow?"

"I couldn't tell, we could lose our lives. Tomorrow with seven more girls I'm going. We'll sneak over the border and then go to America."

"You'll leave us alone?" Misha asked me.

"I told Sonia she should go with me. You can go with me."

He was shaking his head, "I can't go now."

"You'll listen to Sonia? She's scared, you have to force her."

"How can I force her? She won't go."

"So you'll die here, too!" And I couldn't help it. I started to cry. He put his arm around me but it made me mad. I wouldn't allow it. Finally, I should be a woman, I thought. The tears wanted to jump out from my eyes. But I yelled at him. "You don't want to go! You want to do nothing! She makes you scared!"

"Anuta —"

"Don't touch me! Stay here and throw away your life!" I would have run out of the hospital but he grabbed me. Under my breath I made a curse on him and I cried on his chest. I could hear his heart pounding.

He said softly, "Anuta, maybe I can be free also. Meantime, you have to be free for our sake. For my sake, Anuta." He raised my chin in his hand to look at me. Then he took from his neck a chain with a tiny cross on it and he placed it in my hand. "I know you can't wear it around your neck, but I want you to remember me. Keep it with you. Maybe someday you'll need it," he said.

Over the years, many, many times I needed it.

In the evening Sonia came to say good-bye. I showed her the chain with the cross, and she looked at it. "How can he give you such a thing?" she asked. "He can't forget he's a Christian."

I said, "See, Sonia, how good he is to me. Because he loves you. Then he loves everybody. How can anybody hate such a wonderful person like Misha? How he suffers from you, and from your parents and Neeseh. Why can't you go with him to America?"

She made no with her head, sad, like she gave up. Then she smiled and grabbed me and we both cried.

So I said good-bye. With my parents like I would never see them again, the whole night we cried. Came the sun, I took my bundle in my hand and I kissed everyone, even Osher. I didn't say good-bye to Sonia's parents or to Neeseh, but I could see him looking out a window.

We were eight girls going to Warsaw on the train. The agent brought us to a hotel, stinking from the street from fish, like a barracks where soldiers stay. At night we slept on the floor and the mice bit our feet. Food? We couldn't eat. It was like garbage. Three weeks we suffered before the agent came back. He told us now to go on the train, but it was far from the city. We had to walk with our heavy bundles almost a whole day until we came to the train. Then it took us away, and it stopped in a little town. The agent said we had to go to a small house far away from the town. Oy, we walked nearly a whole day again. We had to wait till night the next day, sitting on the floor and sleeping, eating only bread and tea. Night came. It was very dark, and we were eighty people and some little children. One woman was going to her husband, with a one-year-old child. When he went to America, she was pregnant.

Finally, after two days, the agent came and led us out in the dark. On the way there were Russian soldiers. The agent paid them not to look at us. We would lie on the grass in a lot of hay, and then the agent would take us from one soldier to the next. We went that way for fifteen miles. We had no more strength and we all dropped to the ground. If they caught us, we would get shot or they would kill the soldiers. So no one said a word. Then it started to rain. Near me was a woman with a child in her arms, crying. A soldier ran quickly to her and told her she had to keep the baby quiet. But the rain got worse and the baby cried harder. The soldier said, "If you don't keep the baby quiet, I'll have to kill you, or else everybody will be killed."

When I heard that, I was like a dead person, and I told her to give me the child. I rocked the baby and sang a nice song. "Shah, shah," I said softly, and the baby fell asleep. Then I told the mother I couldn't carry the baby anymore, I was so tired. So the mother took the baby again, but it cried. The mother covered its mouth to keep it quiet and she prayed, "God, oy, God, don't let my child die." She wrapped up the baby so tight no one could hear if it cried.

Then a river came and we had to cross up to our waists. One soldier saw that I was going to fall, and he took me on his back. I weighed ninety pounds then. I thanked him and he carried me until daylight. When we came out of the river, wet and without strength, and no sleep or food, we were over the border, but we thought we had still more to go.

Then we saw big wagons with a lot of straw, each one with four horses. By every wagon a man was standing, and we were all scared. It rained so hard we couldn't walk. I felt sick and I cried from the cold. All of a sudden two soldiers came onto the road. The laughed at how we were standing, wet and shaking. The agent whispered quickly we should put together kupkes, like quarters, and give to them. We did and they went away. Then he told us to get into the wagons. "Now you're in Germany," he said. "Go in good health." Him we never saw again.

We traveled a half day till we came to a little town where they took us into a big house with one big room for women and children, and a separate one for men. We waited for them to take us by train to Berlin and then to Bremen, where the ship was. Three weeks we waited. I had brought a little bit to eat, my mother had put it in. But it was all gone. One week they didn't give us food. By me was sewn in my coat fifty rubles. When you came to

America, you had to show money. That's the way it was then. I was scared to take out some rubles to buy food. After two days without eating, I took out five rubles.

Finally, like we were dead, they took us out of the house and we went by train to Berlin. There, they put one thousand immigrants in a big place with a lot of bunks for sleeping. One man was standing with a whip whirling over his head like you drive cattle. He hurt me with the whip and it got dark in my eyes, and I cried. A young man ran over and hit him in the face and yelled at him, "We are people!" And everybody started to yell, "We are people!"

In Bremen we had to stay two more weeks till the boat left. I didn't have what to eat. In the bunk near me was a Polish woman. "Come with me and we'll eat together," she said. But I couldn't, I didn't have any more money. I didn't want to write home because if they sent money, it wouldn't come in time. And that's the way we both lay and talked. She told me she was there for five weeks, from

Warsaw she came. She said she had some money and that she would buy me every day a bowl soup. That's the way I ate. The Polish woman said when we get to America we would see each other and I would pay her. She couldn't go yet because she had to heal her eyes. I never saw her again.

Finally came the time we should go and we went to the boat. A little boat we took to get to the big boat. *Bremen* they called it. It was in the Russian war with Turkey, a very old ship. It danced on the water like a ballerina. Everybody got sick right away. The bread was so hard we used to throw it in the ocean. We lay in the bottom of the boat and rats jumped over us as we screamed. There was a big storm and the boat was crying like an old woman, oy, in her bones, and everybody was yelling that pretty soon the boat was going to break, and the sailors were running up and down, and water came in through the bottom.

That's the way it was on the ocean for thirty-two days. We arrived in America on Sunday. Everybody was standing on one side of the boat, so they told us we had to move around or the boat would tip over. Like a hand held toward us, America was waving. Everybody was waving back. Hello, hello, here we are.

13

What happened with Misha and Sonia?
Don't ask. In Detroit my brothers took
me in and I went to work in a dress
factory. I wrote to everybody, but for a
long time came nothing. I thought my
heart would stop. Was there a pogrom, a
fanatic, a disease? Finally, Golde wrote
for all of them. The Tsar was taking into
the army whoever they could lay their
hands on. People were hiding and
running. In the family, we had to send
money so they could come to America.
For Sonia, my God, in the end Misha
couldn't stand it anymore. He had to go
in the army and he took her away with
him. No one knew where. Maybe to Kiev,
maybe to Warsaw, like they disappeared
in the air. My bones hurt, Misha and
Sonia should be safe.

Soon we brought my parents and the children, but Golde stayed with her husband in the shtetl. In the war we didn't hear, and we thought we lost her. But she went to Palestine, to Israel, and she lives now in a kibbutz. Every month I send money to her.

Only sixteen, and my family got together with my husband's family to marry us. What could I do? A young girl, like I was lost in Detroit. Everything so fast like I was blind. And he wanted, they wanted, I didn't know what to do — a whole other story. My life went by, I had children, and we were poor, with my husband and his little junkyard this time bankrupt, that time bankrupt — the life I didn't dream about. I wouldn't give up for the world my children and my grandchildren, God bless them. They are my life.

Came one day, like a dead person from the grave, Shaneh. An old woman already. She couldn't believe how young I looked. I fix myself up. Why should I want to look like an old woman? Shaneh, she was fat and had wrinkles, she didn't care. She told me how finally the families put up together, they married her to Neeseh. Two children they had. One night the police came and took Neeseh to Siberia, they never heard from him again. Shaneh used to go at night with the children to steal potatoes. It all went to the Communisten. How they got out of Russia, it's a whole story.

Finally, she was looking at me like somebody would hear, and she put her finger up to her mouth. She said, like a secret, "I saw in Chicago, you wouldn't believe. Sonia."

My God! Soon I saved up some money my husband gave me. Even if he got mad I didn't care. I went to Chicago. I found in a very poor neighborhood an old house. When I came in and saw Sonia, we fell on each other and cried and couldn't tear ourselves apart. Sonia was thin and her beautiful dark eyes were sunk inside and her cheeks were yellow. Not the same Sonia. She showed me pictures of her seven children, and then in the evening came home her husband. Osher. Now he was old and had a big beard.

We didn't sleep the whole night. Sonia and me, we talked and talked about what we both lived through. What happened? She and Misha were running to Kiev, where they lived like poor students. She couldn't marry, he wasn't a Jew. And he couldn't marry, she wasn't a Christian. They had to keep secret they weren't married. One month before the baby came, Misha had to go to war. And there he was killed.

Like my own heart would stop. Misha. At least he would be young always.

We cried and cried, Sonia and me. When the news came he was killed, she said, she didn't want to live any longer. In the end, she cried so much her baby came out dead. Then she didn't care, let them do to her what they wanted. But she sent home a letter, could they help her out? Next week Osher came. He told her that in her family she was dead, they wouldn't speak her name. Now she didn't know what to do, Osher wouldn't leave her alone, she married him. Like me, she worked by sewing. Osher, he shoveled snow, he fixed furniture, he delivered

527

pamphlets for the students. One night the police came and they sent Osher and Sonia to Siberia. She didn't know what happened to her family because they couldn't send letters and, anyhow, they wouldn't write. It was good she was in Siberia. If not, they wouldn't be here today. When it ended with the Nazis, everybody was free. Osher came out an old man, and she was also broken and old, but with seven children, six daughters and one son. They went to Germany for a long time and then their children came to America, and afterwards they brought the parents.

Sonia wears around her neck the locket with Misha's picture inside. She never takes it off. There were times when she didn't have what to eat, but she wouldn't sell it. When I am with her she can talk the whole day about how good it was with Misha, how she married without love, and how she can never forget him.

My chain with the little cross I keep in my dresser drawer.